TEACHING

GONG YOGA

To Meher Prem Kaur,

Open the Heart
and Let your
Divine Love
Touch All,

Mehtab

Meher Prem Kaur

TEACHING
GONG YOGA

THEORY AND PRACTICE

MEHTAB BENTON

Bookshelf Press

Teaching Gong Yoga: Theory and Practice
Copyright © 2014 by Michael Benton

Foreign publication rights available from the publisher.

Bookshelf Press books may be ordered by contacting:

Bookshelf Press
PO Box 50028
Austin, TX 78763
www.bookshelfpress.com
orders@bookshelfpress.com

You should not undertake any exercise or therapeutic regimen recommended in this book before consulting your personal physician. Neither the author nor the publisher shall be responsible or liable for any loss or damage allegedly arising as a consequence of your use or application of any information or suggestions contained in this book.

Cover and interior art by Brandi November Lyons (hari-and-avatar.com).

ISBN: 978-1-939239-04-4 (pbk)

Library of Congress Control Number: 2014908882
Printed in the United States of America

The mallet is the will of the infinite,

The gong, the creation,

And the sound is the spirit song,

The heartbeat of the soul.

Yogi Bhajan

Contents

Introduction

All yoga is based upon sound. The sound of the breath, the sound of a mantra, and even the unheard sounds realized only in the deepest state of meditation, all these sounds represent the essence of yoga, the vibrations and frequencies that take us from the gross to the subtle, from the finite to the infinite.

And of all the sounds, it is the Sound of the Gong that most closely represents what Yoga sounds like.

Within the Gong are all the sounds of the universe. Its holistic resonance brings us to a one-pointed centeredness, a welcomed integration of disparate consciousness into a single moment of wholeness where all possibilities exist. Its sound envelope creates a unified field of consciousness that is the purpose of all yoga practices.

And while Yoga can certainly be experienced without the Gong, why would you?

Yogi Bhajan the master of Kundalini Yoga who brought the Gong to the practice of yoga in the Western world said, "The sound of the Gong is the first sound in the universe, the sound that created this universe. It is the primal whisper of the soul, and its sound is the echo of the Original Word that created the world, the sound within all sounds."

For all of its power to enhance and accelerate the practices of yoga, the use of the Gong is often relegated to the end of the yoga class as a pleasant way to relax. Yet the gong can also be a powerful accompaniment to the practices of asana, pranayama, mantra, mudra and meditation, if the yoga teacher understands the theory and techniques of playing the gong in such a manner.

In my previous work, *Gong Yoga*, I expressed my hope that it would be seen as a pioneering effort to encourage the use of the gong in the practice of yoga. In this book, my intention is to show you how this can be done.

The Gong

is the first and last instrument

of the Human Mind.

Yogi Bhajan

What Is Gong Yoga?

Gong Yoga uses the sound of the Gong with the practices of Yoga to energize and facilitate the movement of prana to heal the body, clear the mind and elevate the consciousness. It is an integration of Nada Yoga (yoga of sound) and Laya Yoga (yoga of absorption) with the practices of Hatha Yoga and Kundalini Yoga.

The practice of Gong Yoga uses the techniques of asana, mudra, bandha, pranayama, and mantra to prepare the body and mind to optimally receive and interact with the sound of the gong so that an extended state of spontaneous meditation and therapeutic relaxation occurs.

Unlike other yoga disciplines that can be done as an individual practice, Gong Yoga requires a teacher to play the gong while the practice is done. It is best experienced when the yoga teacher is also a skilled gong player, and when the students can give themselves fully and freely to the sound of the gong.

Origins of Gong Yoga

The association of the sound of the gong and the practice of yoga is mentioned as early as the 14th century by Yogi Swatmarama in the *Hatha Yoga Pradipika*, one of the seminal works on the practice of hatha yoga.

In the final chapter of the *Pradipika* there is a discussion of the stages the yogi passes through on his journey to enlightenment. One of the distinguishing landmarks is the experience of hearing the internal sounds produced by the awakening of the Kundalini energy of awareness. These inner sounds progress in subtlety as awareness increases. The first stages of sound are heard as the sound of the ocean itself. From this roaring wave-like sound, the yogi then hears the sound of various drums that are refined into "the sound of the conch, the gong (bronze kettledrum), and the horn." Indeed, another ancient text notes that when the Kundalini energy awakens the heart center, the listener experiences an internal silent sound like "a gong exploding at the center of the sun." Gradually the crashing sound of the gong dissolves until the yogi hears only a humming like that of the honeybee and becomes completely absorbed.

These inner sounds heard by the yogis in deep meditation, brought about by the inner practices of yoga such as pratyahara, dhyana, and dharana, were externalized by students and followers through instruments and music in a form of Nada Yoga that were then used in the external practices of yoga such as asana, mudra and pranayama.

Different regions of India favored particular instruments for their meditation practices, including flutes and drums, but it was in the areas of the world now known as Pakistan, Afghanistan, Tibet and northern India that the gong became the instrument of the yogi.

Gong Yoga in the Twentieth Century

The explicit use of the gong to facilitate yoga and meditation in modern times can be traced to Northern India in the late nineteenth century when Kundalini Yoga masters played the gongs to awaken the intuitive faculties and create a transcendent consciousness in themselves and their students. One such yoga master was Sant Hazara Singh, a great Sikh mystic and Kundalini yogi of the early twentieth century. Hazara Singh lived in Gujaranwala, India (which is now Pakistan) and in 1937, he accepted an 8-year old boy as his student and taught him Kundalini Yoga, Gatka (a sword-based martial art), and gong meditation.

In 1945, Hazara Singh pronounced the boy at the age of 16 to be a Kundalini Yoga master. Twenty-four years later in 1969, the boy, now a man by the name of Yogi Bhajan, was teaching Kundalini Yoga in the back of a furniture store in Los Angeles. Soon a community of hippies turned yogis were studying with the teacher who shared his knowledge of yoga, meditation, and the gong.

Yogi Bhajan originally introduced the gong in his yoga classes to rehabilitate the nervous systems of the young drug users now turned yoga students. By the 1970s and 1980s, the gong was turning up throughout the United States and around the world in the Kundalini Yoga ashrams he had inspired. In 1990 Yogi Bhajan taught an instructional class in how to play the gong that inspired a monograph a few years later by Gurucharan Singh Khalsa called *The Art of the Gong*. The first book to formalize the practice of yoga with the gong, *Gong Yoga*, was originally written in 1997 and published in 2008.

Gong Yoga Today

Along with the publication of *Gong Yoga*, the use of the gong in the practice of yoga grew beyond its almost exclusive use by Kundalini Yoga teachers as yoga teachers from other traditions experimented with the gong in their classes. Gong players also began adding yoga practices into their gong trainings and workshops, creating an innovative if highly varied approach to using the powerful sound of the gong with the transformational practices of yoga.

As with any emerging style of yoga, there is often experimentation and interpretation by the early practitioners and teachers that create a vital expression of the practice but sometimes at the expense of consistency, particular if the underlying structure of the practice is not explicitly understood.

And indeed, there is an underlying structure to practicing and teaching Gong Yoga that goes beyond simply playing the gong while yoga is done. This structure is based upon one of the oldest models in yoga, the concept of the five bodies of existence, the Panchamaya Koshas, and when this model is employed with specific gong playing techniques that complement the authentic yoga practices of asana, pranayama, mantra and meditation, then the full power of Gong Yoga, in both its theory and practice, can be realized.

By sustained practice

of all the components of yoga,

The impurities dwindle away,

And wisdom's radiant light shines forth

with discriminative knowledge.

Yoga Sutras (II:28)

Mehtab Benton

Gong Yoga: Five Levels of Existence

The experience of practicing and teaching Gong Yoga is more easily understood by using one of the oldest contextual models that explains how yoga works. This model helps us appreciate the multi-level nature of yoga and its practices, as well as how various yoga techniques, when combined with the sound of the gong, take the practitioner of Gong Yoga through increasingly subtle layers of existence until the ultimate goal of yoga is reached, union and merger into the Infinite Self.

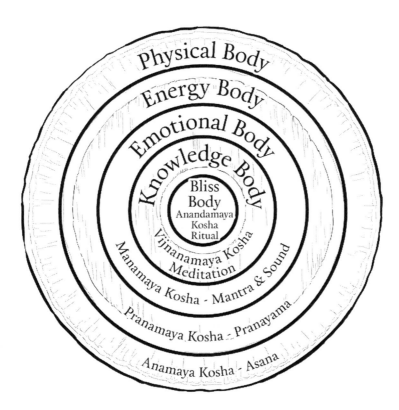

The Yogic Model and the Gong

The model that explains how the gong works in the practice of yoga first appears in one of the earliest yogic texts, the Taittiriya Upanishad (circa 6th century BCE) and is referred to as the Panchamaya Kosha model, or the five (*pancha*) layers (*koshas*) of the mutually coexisting energies of the human experience. The koshas are identified in the Upanishads, and later in the Advaita Vedenta, as five successive layers, or bodies, of objectification that hide the nature (*maya*) of the True Self (*atman*), much like wrappers that hide our eternal essence. Through the practice of yoga, we are able to pierce these veils of illusory separateness and achieve the realization of Oneness.

The Physical Body and the Anamaya Kosha

The outer wrapper, or first kosha, is called the Anamaya Kosha and represents the physical body, the most completely objectified representation of self. The word *ana* means food as this layer of existence, or sheath of illusion, feeds our strongest sense of individuated self. Also, the anamaya kosha, or physical body, is known as **Sthula Sharira**, or "the body that decays" without food.

The next three layers of self make up what is known as the subtle body in yoga, or **Sukshma Sharira**, and consist of the Pranamaya

Kosha, or energy body, the Manamaya Kosha, or the feeling mind body, and the Vijnanamaya Kosha, the discerning knowledge body.

The Energy Body and the Pranamaya Kosha

The Pranamaya Kosha is the life energy (*prana*) sheath of our existence and regulates the movement of physical and mental energies through the subtle channels (*nadis*) and energy centers of the body (*chakras*). This kosha is most associated with the breath, the next subtle level of existence after the physical body. The Pranamaya Kosha is intimately associated with the Anamaya Kosha, just as the breath is with the physical body, and both are dependent on each other and coexist almost as a one-to-one mapping.

The Emotional Body and the Manamaya Kosha

The Manamaya Kosha, the third layer of existence, is the mental (*mana* means mind) or emotional body that holds the physical and pranic body together through the passage of time and organizes our sensory sensations and feelings. This is also the aspect of self that controls sequential thought process and a continuing sense of identity or individuation.

The Knowledge Body and the Vijnanamaya Kosha

The Vijnanamaya Kosha, the fourth layer of existence, is the knowledge (*vijnana*) body or higher discerning intelligence that contains wisdom and the witnessing consciousness that allows us to realize the eternal truths. This is the most refined layer of the **Sukshma Sharira**, or the subtle body, where the experience of ordinary existence through time and space ends.

The Bliss Body and the Anandamaya Kosha

The Ananadamaya Kosha, the final layer of existence that hides the True Self, makes up the causal body in yoga, or the **Karana Sharira**, that exists beyond time and space and is the deepest essence of our being. This kosha is also known as the bliss (*ananda*) body for it contains everlasting happiness, love, and ecstasy that transcends the limiting human experience and brings us to the state of union.

The primary purpose of yoga is to gain full awareness and control over these five bodies or layers of energy, ranging from the gross machinations of the physical body with muscles, organs, and senses to the increasingly subtle realms of prana, feelings, thoughts, and eventually pure light.

The Koshas and the Practices of Yoga

Through all the practices of yoga, from the gross to the subtle, the five koshas of the self are affected by various yogic techniques. Practicing **asanas**, or yoga postures, strengthen the physical body (anamaya kosha) while the practice of **pranayama** or breath control works on the pranic body (pranamaya kosha). The emotional body (manamaya kosha) that processes our mundane thoughts and feelings is accessed through **mantra** and sacred sound. The knowledge body (vijnanamaya kosha) is essentially affected through **meditation** and practices such as mudras that direct prana to the highest centers. The bliss body (anandamaya kosha) is experienced through **ritual** and a transcendent state of relaxation and integration that dissolves the illusion (maya) of all five koshas.

For each kosha, and the yoga techniques that accompany them, one can trace the effects that the sound of the gong produces. When used with asana, pranayama, mantra, sound, meditation, ritual and relaxation, the gong accelerates the progress of the yogi in integrating the five koshas that make up the human experience and enables us to realize our eternal nature.

Understanding how the gong can be played with the various techniques of yoga to affect the physical, subtle and causal body is first step of our journey in practicing and teaching Gong Yoga.

The Yoga Teacher as Gong Player

All yoga is fundamentally about cultivating, storing, directing, and transforming prana, the vital life force energy of the universe that is instrumental in the elevation of consciousness. All asana, pranayama, mantra, mudra, bandha, and meditation are essentially about controlling and maximizing the flow of prana through the physical and subtle bodies in order to reconnect to the causal body, the eternal soul within each individuated consciousness, or *atman.*

With the usual practices of yoga, this prana is under the control of the individual practitioner and the role of the teacher is to instruct, guide and inspire the student to use the techniques of yoga in the most effective way to access and use this prana.

In the practice of Gong Yoga, the gong itself is an instrument of prana in that its sound both creates and directs the flow of the prana in the listener and practitioner. As such, the gong becomes the intermediary between the yoga teacher and the student and provides a method by which the teacher can support and guide the student in the utilization of the prana or vital life force that yoga works with.

To do this, the yoga teacher must attain a degree of skill in playing the gong before teaching Gong Yoga. This skill requires familiarity with gong playing techniques, as well as understanding the unique requirements of playing the gong while teaching yoga. More importantly, this skill also requires that the gong player or yoga teacher understand the basic nature, instrumentality and methodology of using the gong to affect the yoga practice.

In essence, the yoga teacher needs a familiarity of how the gong moves prana through different playing techniques and the various playing areas of the gong. We need to see the gong not only as a tool in the practice of yoga but also as a **map** to access the physical, emotional, and energy bodies of the practitioner.

The Gong As Map of the Body

The practice of yoga begins with the physical body as we move from the gross to the subtle through a refinement of practices and consciousness. The Gong itself can be used as a map of the physical body, and by playing various areas of the gong, the teacher can aid in directing prana to different regions of the body.

Body Map and the Gong

Ancient Indian philosophy, and many Western wisdom traditions, has as fundamental principle that the human body is the microcosm of the Universe, or the greater macrocosm. The principle that the divine is present in every object, cell and atom is the basis of many esoteric teachings and was popularized by the Hermetic writers during the Western renaissance with the phrases, "As above, so below,' and "As without, so within." This divine immanence means that the physical body itself is a map of the universal body, the One.

In Yoga, we see this principle illumined even in the name of Hatha Yoga that literally means Sun-Moon, a reference to the Sun energy and the Moon energy that exists both without and within the body. The third eye, for example, is where this Sun and Moon energy unite to bring enlightenment to the yoga practitioner. The spine, the central energy channel of the body in yoga where the Kundalini energy is channeled, is referred to in yogic texts as Meru-dandu, a reference to Mount Meru, a mountain considered to be the axis of the earth, and the energy channels (*nadis*) in the body are referred to as rivers while the five basic yogic energies of the body (*vayus*) are called winds. And in all evolutionary processes, there is an understanding that evolution proceeds from the bottom to the top, much like the Kundalini energy rises in the body from the base of the body up to the crown.

In a similar manner, the gong can provide a bridge between cosmology and biology when it is used as a map of the physical body. To do this, consider the gong as a representation of the human body. At the bottom of the gong is the base of the body, from the feet to the tip of the spine. At the top of the gong is the top of the body, the head and crown. In the center of the gong, or its heart, is the heart of the human body.

When the gong is played in the lower area, the lower areas of the body are affected. When the gong is played in the upper area, the organs and glands in the upper body are affected.

Furthermore when the gong is played with a downward movement, it corresponds to a downward movement of the body, and a similar correspondence for upward movements. By visualizing the human body superimposed over the gong face, the gong teacher can use different playing areas of the gong to direct the movement of prana through the body of the practitioner.

The Gong Playing Areas

From the discussion of the Gong as a map of the human body, we gain an appreciation of how different playing areas of the gong can be used by the Gong Yoga teacher. The nature, quality and the effect of the sound produced by the gong depend upon where the gong is struck or played.

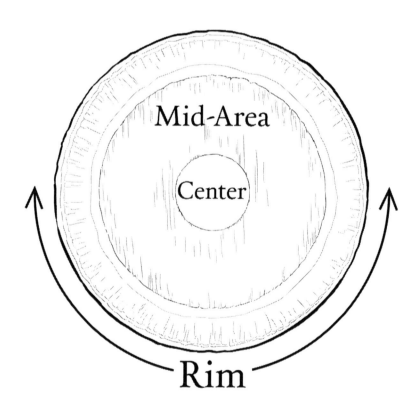

The Three Major Areas

The surface of the gong may be divided into three striking areas: Center area, Mid-area, and Rim area. On some gongs, you can see these areas clearly delimited by the finish on the surface. The center area appears to be like a small sun with a diameter about one-quarter the size of the entire gong. The rim area is slightly rough and extends in a few inches from the edge. The mid-area between the rim and the center is the largest playing area, sometimes colored between the darker rim and the brighter center. Each playing area produces a different quality of sound when struck.

Striking the gong near the center area gives a rich, enduring and carrying sound–almost like a strong fundamental note. Striking in the mid-area between the center and rim produces a deep, complete and swelling sound–rich and complex in tone coloring. Striking in the rim area gives an airy, sparkling and roaring sound–partial tones that transcend any specific pitch.

The Percussion Points

In addition to the three major areas, there are 14 discrete playing areas on the gong called percussion points. Think of the gong as a clock face divided into 12 areas, one for each hour. The 12 o'clock position is at the top of the gong (or more precisely in the top of the mid-area of the gong below the rim). The 6 o'clock position is at the bottom, again above the rim area. The other clock positions go around the outer mid-area of gong so there are 12 points or localized areas that can be struck. In the middle of the gong, there is a zero position so that the upper center area (before the mid-area begins) is known as "Up 0" and the lower center area is known as "Down 0." So we now have 14 total percussion points on the gong (including the two center "0" points) where the vast majority of the mallet strikes will occur.

Each percussion point produces a distinctive sound, and can be played in various sequences with other points to create a specific effect. For example, playing the percussion points 3, 6, 9, and 12 in repeated sequences distribute energy equally around the body.

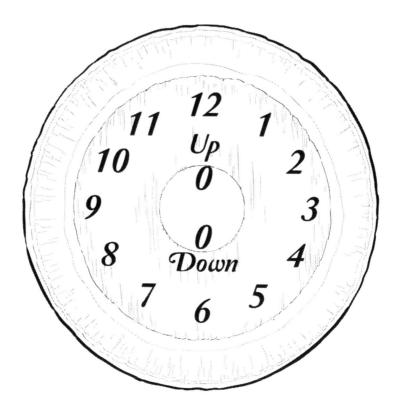

The Gong: Rhythm and Volume

In addition to the playing areas of the gong, the Gong Yoga teacher uses the techniques of rhythm and volume to create, cultivate, and direct the prana during a yoga practice. The effects of increasing or decreasing the rhythm and volume when playing the gong are discussed in the sections on the various yoga techniques (asanas, pranayamas, etc.). In general, a faster rhythm or louder volume increases the movement of prana while a slower rhythm or softer volume consolidates the movement of prana. The playing areas struck and the intention of the player further modifies the effects of the rhythm and volume.

The Gong Basic Skills and Equipment

The book assumes that the yoga teacher has acquired a basic level of playing skills as outlined in the book *Gong Yoga* or the DVD course, *How To Play the Gong*. There should be familiarity with the playing areas, mallet strikes, and creating sequences of sound through playing the percussion points. While the gong itself is a good teacher and intuitive playing does develop through your own yoga practice and playing practice, familiarity with the basic playing techniques is essential to teach Gong Yoga. If you do not have the basic playing skills yet, then an experienced gong player can accompany you as you teach until you do so.

In addition to playing skills, a suitable gong is also required to teach gong yoga. While passionate arguments can be made for different sizes, types, and brands of gong, there are general guidelines that may be helpful.

First, the gong must be a suitable size to create a sound that can have a significant effect on the practitioner. If undersized, the gong will have more of a musical than a pranic impact. If oversized, the gong can overwhelm the practice and the practitioner. Personal opinions and experiences vary widely, but in general a preferred gong size for a Gong Yoga class is between 24 inches and 38 inches. A 30 to 34 inch gong is highly recommended for versatility.

There are roughly two major categories of gongs: Symphonic Gongs and Tuned Gongs. While the tuned gongs (such as the Planetary Gongs tuned to orbital frequencies) produce beautiful sounds and have a potent uniqueness, their limited range is best used for specific purposes. The symphonic gongs produce complex overtones and a strong fundamental note that give a wider range of playing options, especially for meditation and relaxation. Every Gong Yoga teacher should have at least one symphonic gong and may add tuned gongs as desired.

As far as manufacturing brands go, this is what gong players argue about! If you can play them or hear them played, that is the best way to select your gong.

Gong Equipment for the Gong Yoga Teacher

Here is a suggested list of the equipment needed to teach Gong Yoga, from basics to more advanced teaching.

Basic Set

- Gong – 24 inch to 36-inch Symphonic Gong
- Mallet – One mallet, sized appropriately for the gong
- Stand – Portable floor stand for playing while sitting

Intermediate Set

- Gongs – 30 inch to 36-inch Symphonic Gong
       Smaller Symphonic Gong or Tuned Gong
- Mallets – Two mallets, sized appropriately for both gongs
       One mallet the next size smaller.
- Stands – Portable floor stand
       Large upright stand for playing while standing

Advanced Set

- Gongs – 30 inch to 36-inch Symphonic Gong
       Smaller (or larger) Symphonic Gong
       Hand-held Gong
       Tuned Gongs, one or more
- Mallets –Mallets, sized appropriately for each gong
       Smaller pair(s) of mallets
       Rubbing mallet(s)
- Stands – Portable floor stand
       Large upright stand for playing while standing
       Stand for multiple gongs

Asana and the Gong: Playing for the Physical Body

The asanas, or postures, of yoga work directly on the physical body to improve muscular and skeletal functioning and benefit the organs and glandular system. In yoga philosophy, the physical body is akin to the Anamaya Kosha, or the sheath or level of existence that requires the taking of food to exist in the incarnated realm. It is the grossest level of existence, and it is most readily accessed through the technique of asana.

The gong affects the anamaya kosha, or physical body, in several ways. First, the gong produces a sound wave that is almost tangible, which stimulates the physical body by influencing the surface of the skin. The sonic touch of the gong can be a healing touch as its sound stimulates the body's dermatomes.

Dermatomes are surface areas of skin extending from the spine throughout the body. Through a network of nerves, these skin areas are connected to different organs in the body and with corresponding segments of the spinal cord. These skin areas can be stimulated by sound waves, much like a massage, and produce effects on corresponding organs and other areas of the body.

Secondly, when used with asanas, the sonic massage of the gong and its stimulation of the dermatomes bring additional benefits to the yoga practitioner, particularly in the area of pain relief. The sound of the gong has been found to be helpful in reducing pain associated with neck pain, headaches, cramping, muscle strains, and neurological pain (see *Gong Yoga: Healing and Enlightenment Through Sound*).

On a more subtle level, the sound of the gong has proven to be an excellent way to deepen the focus of the asana practitioner, allowing a deeper connection to the flow of energy or prana that is produced and released through the asana practice. On a practical level, the gong can be used to orchestrate and direct the movement of the yoga practitioner through the sequences of an asana practice.

Classification of Yoga Asanas

Most yoga practices in the Western world are based on the postures, or asanas, of Hatha Yoga and are a good introduction to understanding how the gong can be used in the practice and teaching of yoga.

The origins of the classical asanas in Hatha Yoga are shrouded in mystery and myth, going back to the god Shiva who is said to initially have taught 8,400,000 postures representing the 8,400,000 life forms the soul travels through to achieve enlightenment. (Depending upon interpretations, this number has also been represented as 840,000 and 84,000). Of these, 84 asanas were said to be primary in covering all aspects of the human existence.

Even so, there are still hundreds of asanas commonly taught in yoga. By putting them in general categories, we can more easily interact with the different types of postures, regardless of the specific asana, through the sound of the gong.

A classical approach to categorizing asanas is borrowed from the Vedic science of Ayurveda that uses yoga postures for healing and therapy. Asanas are primarily classified as being Brimhana or Langhana in nature by the effects they have on the body.

Langhana Asanas	Brimhana Asanas
Cool	Warm
Relax	Activate
Release energy	Build energy
Promote elimination	Promote strengthening
Aid parasympathetic nervous system	Aid sympathetic nervous system
Increase sensory activity	Increase motor activity
Aid in treatment of tension, stress, insomnia, constipation, headaches, chronic pain, irritability, arthritis, stroke, allergies, inflammation.	Aid in treatment of fatigue, low vitality, lethargy, diarrhea, poor circulation, depression, asthma, chronic fatigue, apathy, weakness.

When we use the traditional categorization of asanas according to body position or movement, we can create the following chart that relates the asana category to its ability to producing a Langhana or Brimhana effect, with the strongest producing Langhana and Brimhana asanas at the top of the chart and least producing at the bottom of the chart, as follows:

Langhana Asana Categories	Brimhana Asana Categories
Supine	Handstands, Arm Balances
Sitting	Back Bend
Twisting	Abdominal
Forward Bend	Standing
Inversions	Inversions

The supine postures are the most Langhana in nature, with the sitting postures next, followed by the twisting asanas and then the forward bending asanas. Handstands and arm balancing asanas produce the strongest Brimhana effect, followed in descending order by back bends, abdominal and finally standing postures. Notice that inversions (such as headstand and shoulderstand) have an equal effect of producing Langhana and Brimhana energy and are balancing in effect.

Playing the Gong for Langhana and Brimhana

The gong player can also create Langhana and Brimhana effects by controlling the rhythm, modulating the volume, or by striking different playing areas of the gong. In this way, the Gong Yoga teacher can enhance the effects that the various asanas have on the practitioner. In the simplest application, the gong can be played in a Langhana manner when Langhana postures are done and in a Brimhana manner when Brimhana postures are done.

How Gong Rhythm Affects Asana

As the rhythm, or rate, of striking the gong increases, the quality of Brimhana also increases. Similarly as the rhythm is slowed, the quality of Langhana increases. This would mean that for supine postures (Langhana), the gong is played slowly and for handstands the gong is played rapidly (Brimhana).

The rhythm ranges from slow to fast (using the baseline tempo of the individual gong player) according to the type of asana performed. Notice a moderate and equal rhythm corresponds to the inverted postures as they create a balance between Langhana and Brimhana.

Asana Categories	Rhythm Rate
Supine	Very Slow
Sitting	Slow
Twisting	Somewhat Slow
Forward Bend	Slightly slow
Inversions	Moderate equal rhythm
Standing	Slightly fast
Abdominal	Somewhat Fast
Back Bend	Fast
Handstands, Arm Balances	Very fast

The gong player also has the ability to moderate the effects of a Langhana or Brimhana asana by playing in contrast. For example, the Gong Yoga teacher can modify the Brimhana effects of a back bending posture by playing the gong slowly. Such an approach may be useful to create a specific response in the yoga practitioner, as for example when it is desired to cool or slow down a practice as a back bend is performed.

How Gong Volume Affects Asana

As the volume or intensity of striking the gong increases, the Brimhana quality also increases. Conversely, as the volume decreases, the quality of Langhana increases. For example, for supine postures the gong is played softly and for handstands the gong is played loudly.

The volume ranges from soft to loud according to the type of asana performed. Notice that a moderate volume (balanced) corresponds to the inverted postures that are balancing in effect.

Asana Categories	Volume Level
Supine	Very Soft
Sitting	Soft
Twisting	Somewhat Soft
Forward Bend	Slightly soft
Inversions	Moderate volume
Standing	Slightly loud
Abdominal	Somewhat loud
Back Bend	Loud
Handstands, Arm Balances	Very loud

As with rhythm, the gong player has the ability to moderate the effects of an asana by playing in contrast, such as playing softly for a back bend in order to reduce a tendency to over extend the posture.

Using Rhythm and Volume for Transitions and Sequencing

As students move from asana to asana, rhythm and volume can be combined to sequence the flow of energy and to set expectations for transitions between one group of postures and the next. Here are general guidelines to follow:

When moving from a posture that increases Brimhana, keep the volume the same but **increase the rhythm**, such as:.
- Forward Bend to Back Bend – Volume remains slightly soft but rhythm gradually increases from moderately slow to fast.
- Sitting Posture to Standing Posture – Volume remains soft but rhythm gradually increases from slow to slightly fast.

When moving from a posture that increases Langhana, keep the rhythm the same but **decrease the volume**, such as:.
- Back Bend to Forward Bend – Rhythm remains fast but volume gradually decreases from loud to slightly soft.
- Standing Posture to Sitting Posture – Rhythm remains slightly fast but volume decreases from slightly loud to soft.

Once the transition occurs, volume and rhythm can be matched appropriately to the asana being performed. Notice that rhythm and volume are relative according to the individual's own playing style.

How Gong Playing Areas Affects Asana

The gong player can also increase or decrease the Langhana and Brimhana effects of an asana by striking different areas of the gong. Here are general guidelines for each category of asana:

Asana Categories	Gong Playing Area(s)
Supine	Bottom of gong; Side closest to player
Sitting	Near bottom of gong; Side closest to player
Twisting	Bottom mid-area; Middle from player
Forward Bend	Below center; Side farthest from player
Inversions	Alternate above and below center
Standing	Above center; Side closest to player
Abdominal	Top mid-area of gong; Middle from player
Back Bend	Near top of gong; Side farthest from player
Handstands, Arm Balances	Top of gong; Side farthest from player

Rhythm and volume may be integrated into these playing areas of the gong to maximize or moderate the Langhana and Brimhana effects of the asanas. For example, for a challenging arm balance, such as Scorpion pose, the gong can be played loudly and quickly at the top of the gong. For a handstand that is supported against the wall (and requires less effort), the gong can be played slower or softer at the top of the gong. Both asanas are high in Brimhana, yet the experience of the practitioner is different in the execution of the two postures. This difference in the effort required by the postures can be acknowledged by moderating the volume and rhythm.

Langhana and Brimhana Playing in Summary

While you may create various combinations of rhythm, volume and playing areas to match the Langhana and Brimhana qualities of various asanas, here are general guidelines for these playing techniques:

1. Faster rhythm supports Brimhana. Slower rhythm supports Langhana.

2. Louder volume supports Brimhana. Softer volume supports Langhana.

3. Playing upper half of the gong supports Brimhana. Playing lower half of the gong supports Langhana.

4. Playing the area farthest from the player supports Brimhana. Playing the area closest to the player supports Langhana.

Timing Asanas with the Gong

Asanas are typically held for a number of breaths, a number of repetitions, or for a prescribed length of time. The gong can serve as a timer or counter when working with asanas by creating a signal to move into or release from one posture to the next.

For example, in the practice of Ashtanga yoga the practitioner often holds a posture for a count of five or five breaths. The gong in this case may be struck rhythmically five times to signal the holding period for the asana. After the fifth gong strike, the practitioner moves into the next asana in the sequence and continues. In this way, an Ashtanga class could be conducted without words by using the gong to direct the flow of the class if the practitioner knows the prescribed sequence.

Alternatively, the gong can be struck only at the end of the holding period of an asana, signifying a time to release and move into the next posture. When the gong is struck, the practitioner inhales and then releases the posture on the exhale.

If the practitioner can hold a posture for an extended period of time, the gong can be played in various ways to release blocked energy and move prana along the energy lines of the asana, such as increasing the rhythm and the volume as the posture is held.

Teaching Considerations in Using the Gong with Asanas

If the asana practice requires much verbal instruction or visual demonstration, it may be necessary to have both a yoga teacher and a gong player working together. The gong player will have to be aware of creating space for verbal instructions by occasionally muffling or quieting the gong so the teacher can be heard.

As a posture is held, the gong may be played appropriately to enhance the energy of the asana. For example, an extended warrior pose could be accompanied by a steady almost martial tempo that is fiery and focused. A long forward bend, on the other hand, would be enhanced by a slow, watery beat that encourages release and letting go.

Again, the player must be skillful and cognizant of the asana practice itself to understand what is needed from the gong. Simply playing the gong while asanas are being done is not enough to make it an appropriate yogic tool.

In general, these guidelines may be followed when playing the gong with asanas:

- Upward moving postures receive upward strikes of the gong.
- Downward moving postures receive downward strikes of the gong.
- Centering or neutral movements receive strikes near the center of the gong.
- Challenging postures receive faster strikes. Releasing postures receive slower strikes.

Sun Salutations and the Gong

The most common Hatha asana practice is the classical Sun Salutation (Surya Namaskara). While there are many versions of Sun Salutations, modified by teachers over the last 100 years to suit their particular practice or lineage, the classical version consists of 12 postures or positions:

1. Pranamasana (Prayer pose)
2. Hasta Utthanasana (Raised arm pose)
3. Padahastasana (Hand to foot pose)
4. Ashwa Sanchalanasana (Equestrian pose)
5. Parvatasana (Mountain pose; also Downward Dog)
6. Ashtanga Namaskara (Eight Point Bowing; also Plank)
7. Bhujangasana (Cobra pose; also Upward Dog)
8. Parvatasana (Mountain pose; also Downward Dog)
9. Ashwa Sanchalanasana (Equestrian pose)
10. Padahastasana (Hand to foot pose)
11. Hasta Utthanasana (Raised arm pose)
12. Pranamasana (Prayer pose)

These 12 positions are practiced twice to complete one round, changing sides (right leg, left leg) during Ashwa Sanchalanasana.

While there are variations (Upward Dog instead of Cobra, or Plank Pose instead of Eight Point Bowing), the general orientation (forward bend, backbend) of the sun salutation is fairly consistent.

A simple way to use the gong with sun salutations is to play one stroke of the gong for each posture. The rhythm of the strokes is equal, and may be slowed or increased depending upon how fast the sun salutation is to be done. While there are many ways to play these strokes, here is one simple and intuitive approach:

The postures in the salutation that have an upward movement or backbend take an upward strike on the top half of the gong. Postures that move downward or forward receive a downward strike on the bottom half of the gong. Postures that are centering or neutral in nature receive a strike near the center of the gong. Here are the gong strikes associated with the 12 asanas or postures that comprise a sun salutation:

Sun Salutation Asana	Gong Playing Technique
Pranamasana (Prayer pose)	Center Strike
Hasta Utthanasana (Raised arm pose)	Upward Strike
Padahastasana (Hand to foot pose)	Downward Strike
Ashwa Sanchalanasana (Equestrian pose)	Upward Strike
Parvatasana (Mountain pose; also Downward Dog)	Downward Strike
Ashtanga Namaskara (8-Point Bowing; or Plank)	Center Strike
Bhujangasana (Cobra pose; also Upward Dog)	Upward Strike
Parvatasana (Mountain pose; also Downward Dog)	Downward Strike
Ashwa Sanchalanasana (Equestrian pose)	Upward Strike
Padahastasana (Hand to foot pose)	Downward Strike
Hasta Utthanasana (Raised arm pose)	Upward Strike
Pranamasana (Prayer pose)	Center Strike

Surya Namaskara

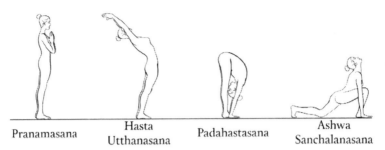

Pranamasana   Hasta Utthanasana   Padahastasana   Ashwa Sanchalanasana

Parvatasana   Ashtanga Namaskara

Bhujangasana   Parvatasana

Ashwa Sanchalanasana   Padahastasana   Hasta Utthanasana   Pranamasana

Asana Sequences with the Gong

The following asana sequences from different styles of yoga may be practiced with the gong according to the movement and nature of each posture. The asana sequence is first given and then a way of playing the gong is specified for each posture.

Note that the gong does not need to be played with every posture in a sequence, and the gong playing guidelines may be adjusted as needed by the teacher.

Hatha Yoga Sequence with the Gong

The following sequence takes 35 to 50 minutes and is a beginner-friendly approach to a Hatha-based asana practice using the gong.

1. Sukhasana (Easy Pose)
2. Adho Mukha Svanasana (Downward Dog)
3. Surya Namaskar: (Sun Salutations)
4. Vrksasana (Tree)
5. Utthita Trikonasana (Extended Triangle)
6. Utthita Parsvakonasana (Extended Side Angle)
7. Dandasana (Staff)
8. Paschimottanasana (Seated Forward Bend)
9. Baddha Konasana (Bound Angle)
10. Upavistha Konasana (Wide Angle)
11. Navasana (Boat)
12. Salabhasana (Locust)
13. Setu Bandha Sarvangasana (Supported Bridge)
14. Viparita Karani (Half Shoulderstand or Legs-Up-the-Wall)
15. Supta Matsyendrasana (Reclining Twist)
16. Savasana (Corpse)

Suggested Gong Techniques for Hatha Yoga Sequence

Asana	Gong Playing Technique(s)
Sukhasana (Easy Pose)	Three slow medium-soft strikes near center
Adho Mukha Svanasana (Downward Dog)	Three slow medium-soft strikes, downward bottom half of gong
Surya Namaskar (Sun Salutation)	Same as previously described for 2-4 complete rounds
Vrksasana (Tree)	Three to five medium strikes, slightly below top rim
Utthita Trikonasana (Extended Triangle)	Strike diagonally, medium rhythm and volume each side
Utthita Parsvakonasana (Extended Side Angle)	Strike diagonally, increased rhythm and volume each side
Dandasana (Staff)	Three slow medium-soft strikes, downward bottom half of gong
Paschimottanasana (Seated Forward Bend)	Three slow soft strikes, downward bottom half of gong
Baddha Konasana (Bound Angle)	Three medium strikes, downward bottom half of gong
Upavistha Konasana (Wide Angle)	Three medium-loud downward strikes, bottom half of gong
Navasana (Boat)	Fast loud strikes right below center of gong
Salabhasana (Locust)	Medium fast and medium loud upward strikes top half of gong
Setu Bandha Sarvangasana (Supported Bridge)	Fast and medium loud upward strikes top half of gong
Viparita Karani (Supported Half Shoulderstand)	Alternate soft to medium slow strikes above and below center
Supta Matsyendrasana (Reclining Twist)	Medium to medium fast and medium loud bottom mid area
Savasana (Corpse)	As desired for relaxation

Easy

Downward

Extended Triangle

Tree

Extended Side Triangle

Seated Forward Bend

Staff

Bound Angle

Wide Angle

Boat

Locust

Supported Bridge

Reclining Twist

Supported Shoulder Stand

Corpse

Vinyasa Flow Yoga Sequence with the Gong

The following sequence moves with the breath and incorporates vinyasa transitions between the postures on both sides while using the gong.

1. Tadasana (Mountain)

2. Surya Namaskar (Sun Salutations): 5 Rounds

3. Adho Mukha Svanasana (Downward Dog): 10 Breaths

4. Vinyasa to Virabhadrasana I (Warrior 1), right and left: 5 Rounds, 5 Breaths

5. Vinyasa to Virabhadrasana II (Warrior 2), right and left: 5 Rounds, 5 Breaths

6. Vinyasa to Virabhadrasana III (Warrior 3), right and left side: 5 Rounds, 5 breaths

7. Vrksasana (Tree), right and left: 5 Breaths

8. Natarajasana (Dancer), right and left: 5 Breaths

9. Garudasana (Eagle), right and left: 5 Breaths

10. Tadasana (Mountain)

The vinyasa transitions may be orchestrated by using the gong to signal the movement with the breath.

Suggested Gong Techniques for Vinyasa Flow Sequence

Asana	Gong Playing Technique(s)
Tadasana (Mountain) 5 breaths	Five slow medium-soft strikes near center
Surya Namaskar (Sun Salutations)	Same as previously described for five complete rounds
Adho Mukha Svanasana (Downward Dog) 10 breaths	Ten slow medium-soft strikes, downward bottom
Virabhadrasana I (Warrior 1) 5 breaths each side, 5 rounds	Above center, medium to fast, medium to loud
Virabhadrasana II (Warrior 2) 5 breaths each side, 5 rounds	Above center, fast, loud
Virabhadrasana III (Warrior 3) 5 breaths each side, 5 rounds	Above center, faster and louder
Vrksasana (Tree) 5 breaths each side	Medium strikes, slightly below top rim
Natarajasana (Dancer) 5 breaths each side	Medium-soft slower strikes, alternate above below center
Garudasana (Eagle) 5 breaths each side	Harder strikes, alternate above below center
Tadasana (Mountain) 10 breaths	Ten slow soft strikes near center

Mehtab Benton

Mountain

Downward

Warrior 2

Warrior 1

Warrior 3

Tree

Dancer

Eagle

Mountain

Kundalini Yoga Sequence with the Gong

Kundalini Yoga as taught by Yogi Bhajan is practiced in **kriyas**, or formalized sequences of postures, breathing techniques, mudras, meditations and mantras that are not altered or changed by the teacher except for modifying the length of time the exercise is done. While most Kundalini kriyas do not specify the explicit use of the gong for an exercise, the gong can be played with them, much in the same way that Kundalini music or mantras are used to accompany a kriya.

The following sequence of Kundalini postures (indicated by English names first, in keeping with the protocol of Kundalini Yoga) has been called the Magnificent Seven asanas for women to practice. Notice that the Breath of Fire (Agni Pran), the signature breath of Kundalini Yoga, is used with the second posture.

1. Cat Stretch, Knee Drops, or the Reclining Twist (Supta Matsyendrasana)

2. Stretch Pose (Uttanapadasana)

3. Cobra Pose (Bhujangasana)

4. Cat/Cow (Marjariasana)

5. Seated Forward Bend (Paschimottanasana)

6. Reclining Rock Pose (Supta Virasana)

7. Half-Shoulderstand (Ardha Sarvangasana; Vipariti Karani)

8. Corpse (Savasana)

Suggested Gong Techniques for Kundalini Sequence

Asana	Gong Playing Technique(s)
Cat Stretch or Reclining Twist (Supta Matsyendrasana) 5 times each side	Slow medium-soft strike for each movement, 5 rounds
Stretch Pose (Uttanapadasana) with Breath of Fire (Agni Pran) 1 minute	Fast, medium-loud below center
Cobra Pose (Bhujangasana) with Breath of Fire (Agni Pran) 1 minute	Fast, loud near top
Cat/Cow (Marjariasana) 3 minutes	Medium strike, above and below center on inhale/exhale
Seated Forward Bend (Paschimottanasana) 3 minutes	Soft, slow bottom half
Reclining Rock Pose (Supta Virasana)	Soft-medium, slightly faster bottom half
Half-Shoulderstand (Ardha Sarvangasana or Vipariti Karani)	Soft to medium slow strikes alternate above/below center
Savasana (Corpse)	As desired for relaxation

Cat Stretch

Stretch Pose

Cobra Pose

Cat/Cow

Mehtab Benton

Seated Forward Bend

Reclining Rock Pose

Half-Shoulderstand

Corpse Pose

The Gong Yoga Teacher's Practice: Asana

The Gong Yoga teacher also practices asana when playing the gong by following the directive given by the sage Patanjali in the *Yoga Sutras* (2:46): "Asana is performed with steadiness and ease." When playing the gong, the teacher assumes a position and posture in relation to the gong that is stable and relaxed that allows the sound to be fully produced.

If the gong is played while sitting on the floor, the gong teacher may use any major seated asana, such as Sukhasana (Easy Pose) or Padmasana (Lotus Pose). One of the most effective seated asanas for playing the gong is on the heels (Virasana, Hero or Rock Pose) for easy access to the playing surface of the gong.

If the gong is played while standing, the gong teacher assumes a modified Tadasana or Mountain pose in which the feet are hip width apart with the pelvis in a neutral, balanced position and the navel point pulled slightly in. An inner alignment of the spine is maintained from the base to the crown of the head.

In either seated or standing position, the shoulders are relaxed and the heart remains open. The movement of the arms initiates from the heart, moves through the shoulders and then into the wrists. In yoga, the arms and hands are considered to be the work organs of the heart chakra and take its energy into the outside world.

To maximize the energy transfer from the heart into the playing of the gong, the shoulders and the wrists are opened and made flexible by various yoga asanas such as Gomukhasana (Cow Pose), Garudasana (Eagle Pose), Urdhava Baddha Anguilasana (interlaced hands, arms over the hand with palms inverted).

Asana Sequence for Playing the Gong

Playing the gong effectively requires that there be no energy blocks in the shoulders, elbows and wrists of the gong player that prevent the fluid transfer of prana from the heart into the gong. According to yogic thought and Ayurvedic principles, the blocks in the major joints of the body can be released through a series of exercises known as *pavanmuktasana*, or asanas that free the movement of prana.

While there are several dozen asanas in the pavanmuktasana series, the following sequence of eight exercises systematically address the major areas of the body affected by playing the gong: hands, wrists, elbows, shoulders and chest.

Hands To Fists

Sitting or standing, extend the hands out in front of the body, horizontal to the shoulders. Stretch and tense the fingers of both hands. Then close the fingers over the thumbs to make tight fists. Repeat 10 times.

Wrist Bends

Sitting or standing, repeat the above arm position. Now bend the wrists so the fingers point up, and then bend the wrists so the fingers point down. Repeat 10 times.

Wrist Rotations

Sitting or standing, repeat the above arm position. Make a fist of the right hand around the thumb and rotate 10 times in one direction. Then reverse the direction and rotate again 10 times. Repeat with the left hand. Now repeat with both fists at the same time.

Elbow Forward Bends

Sitting or standing, bring both arms straight out in front with the palms up. Bend both arms at the elbows and touch the fingers to the shoulders. Then straighten the arms again. Repeat 10 times.

Elbow Side Bends

Sitting or standing, bring the arms out from the shoulders, parallel to the ground with palms up. Bend the elbows and touch fingers to the shoulders. Then straighten the arms out again. Repeat 10 times.

Shoulder Rotations

Sitting or standing, bring the fingers to the top of the shoulders. Keep the hands on the shoulders and circle the shoulders forward 10 times. Then circle backwards 10 times. Make the circles so the elbows touch in front of the chest as you rotate the shoulders.

Shoulder Lifts

Sitting with the legs stretched out, make fists of the hands and move the arms from the shoulders, keeping the elbows straight, up to a 60 degree angle and back down to a 60 degree angle. Alternate the arms so the right arm is up and the left arm is down and so on. You can inhale up and exhale as the arms come down. Repeat 20 times.

Heart Pumps

Standing, or ideally squatting on the floor, interlace the fingers and clasp the hands together and raise the arms straight over the head, elbows straight, and then sweep the arms down. Move in a pumping motion, inhaling up and exhaling down. Repeat 20 times.

Mehtab Benton

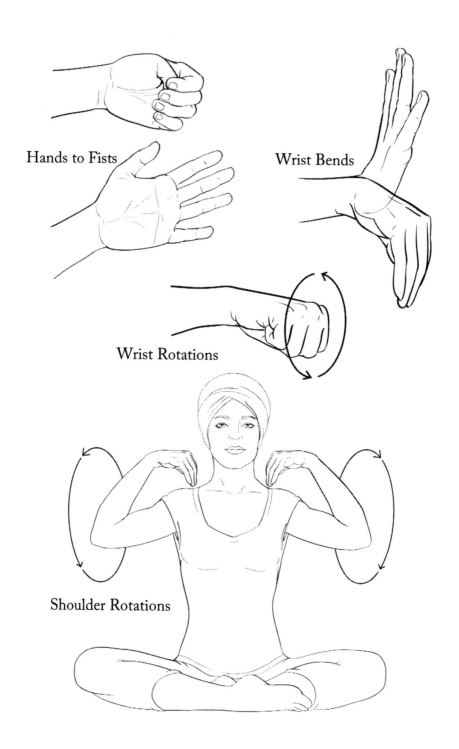

Hands to Fists

Wrist Bends

Wrist Rotations

Shoulder Rotations

Elbow Forward Bends   Elbow Side Bends

Heart Pumps

Shoulder Lifts

With every breath,

The sound of love surrounds us.

Rumi

Pranayama and the Gong: Playing for the Energy Body

The relationship between the sound of the gong and the energy body exists because all sound is essentially the expression of prana, the vital energy of the universe. The primal sound in yoga, the sound of OM, is the highest level of sound vibration that created the universe of time, space, and form.

This original cosmic sound came into existence through the force of prana (*prana shakti*), and so it is sound that is the original instrumentality of the expression of all prana, the energy that causes every atom to move and every breath to be taken. It is sound that is the powerful and original vehicle for prana (energy and consciousness), and so it is sound that we work with to master the energy body or pranamaya kosha.

As Swami Satchidananda said, "Physical sound can lead you to the inner vibrations of prana. Prana is the cause of all sound, and sound is the expression of prana." The intrinsic relationship between prana (vital life force) and sound underlies all creation, and is fundamental in playing the gong for all yoga practices and especially the practice of pranayama.

The relationship between sound and prana extends throughout the energy body and affects all aspects of yogic anatomy, including the elements (tattvas), the five basic energies (vayus), the energy channels (nadis), and the energy centers (chakras).

Sound, Prana and the Five Tattvas

The five *tattvas*, or elements, of the material world are earth, water, fire, air and ether (space). Prana is transferred through the five tattvas and is made available to the living organism through one of the five senses associated with that element.

For example, prana is transferred through the element of earth and the sense of smell in the food we eat. Some foods, such as leafy greens, are high in prana while other foods, such as decaying meat, are low in prana.

Prana is transferred through the element of water and the sense of taste by the fluids we drink. Some fluids are high in prana, such as mountain streams, while others are low, such as stagnant water.

Prana comes to us through the element of fire and the sense of sight through light and heat, such as the prana present in sunlight. Environments full of light, such as deserts, are high in prana while areas low in natural light, such as confined spaces, are low in prana.

Prana is transferred through the element of air and the sense of touch through the air we breathe and feel of wind on the skin. Again, environments that are airy invite circulation and are high in prana while places with poor air quality are low in prana.

Finally prana is transferred through the element of space, or ether, and assimilated through the sense of hearing. Sounds that expand and move freely through space in harmony are higher in prana than sounds that are discordant, damped or muffled.

In the same way the five elements or tattvas move from the grossest (earth) to the subtlest (ether), so does prana become more refined as we move from the fundamental sense of smell to the developed sense of hearing, and similarly from the grossest carrier of prana, food, to the subtlest carrier of prana, sound.

Sound carried through the element of ether and perceived by the sense of hearing, as well as the unheard sound (*anahata*) that transcends the physical senses, is the most subtle and ethereal component of the pranamaya kosha. It is through using sound with breath control and awareness (*pranayama*) that we can strengthen, balance, and expand our energy body.

The Energy Body and Yogic Anatomy

The energy body or pranamaya kosha has a structure much the same way that the physical body has its anatomy of organs, glands and bones. The three major components of the energy body anatomy are the vayus (primary energies that move through the pranamaya kosha), the nadis (the subtle energy channels that carry the prana or vital life force), and the chakras (the energy centers that transform prana). The gong may be used in relation to all these components of yogic anatomy to create healing and transformation.

The Five Vayus and the Gong

Within the pranamaya kosha, or the body of the breath, reside five primal energies or **vayus** called the *pancha pranas*. These five vayus, were described hundreds of years ago in the *Chandogya Upanishad* (II.13.6) as the gate keepers to the heavenly world. They represent the five basic types and movements of energy within the body and, when they are mastered, they open the gateway to enlightenment as well as insuring radiant health and well-being.

The five vayus are primarily affected by the breath and emotions and may also be influenced through sound and playing the gong. Whenever the gong is played, one or more of the vayus or primal energies is affected and can be strengthened or balanced depending upon how the gong is played.

The five vayus were originally named and described as follows:

- **Prana Vayu** (that which goes everywhere)
  Responsible for reception or taking in, including breath, food, and sensory input. Prana Vayu is distinguished from universal Prana or *maha prana* in the practice of pranayama.

- **Apana Vayu** (that which takes away)
  Responsible for elimination: what should (or should not) be eliminated, and when to eliminate or release.

- **Samana Vayu** (that which takes what is required to where it is needed)

Responsible for distribution of nourishment and assimilation throughout the body

- **Udana Vayu** (that which leads up)
  Responsible for speaking, movement of the body and for elevation of energy.

- **Vyana Vayu** (that which makes things distinct)
  Responsible for sensation, as well as lifting, grasping, throwing.

Prana Vayu

Prana vayu is the incoming energy as represented by the inhalation of the breath. It is initiating, propulsive, and activating in nature. It is localized at the area of the heart, between the larynx and the diaphragm. The element of prana vayu is fire, the ability to move and transform. The prana vayu is associated with perception, everything that comes into the body, be it seeing, eating or otherwise bringing in, and fulfills the subtle function of mental energization. It affects the heart, lungs and brain and gives energy and vitality. When unbalanced or deficient, it creates addictive behavior, misdirected actions and attempts to find wholeness outside of the self.

Prana Vayu and the Gong

Prana vayu is activated by the initiating strike on the gong. It is the energy that brings the sound of the gong into being. It begins as we make the strike toward the gong and is released with initial sound of the gong. It is the birthing of the sound of the gong that activates the prana vayu in the listener. When the prana vayu is present in the sound of the gong, it brings us into time and starts the journey within. The primary playing area of the gong that contains the prana vayu is the upper half of the gong, between the center and below the rim, as well as to the far side of the player.

Apana Vayu

Apana vayu is the downward energy as represented by the exhalation of the breath. It is releasing, relieving, and relaxing in nature. It is localized below the navel and in the lower half of the body. The element of apana vayu is earth, the ability to ground and stabilize. The apana vayu is associated with elimination; everything that must leave the body or mind, be it bodily wastes, reproductive fluids, the birth of a child, as well as old ideas, beliefs, and experiences, and it fulfills the subtle function of mental elimination. It affects the reproduction and elimination systems and gives detachment and dispassion. When unbalanced or deficient, it creates fear, depression and stagnation of the self.

Apana Vayu and the Gong

Apana vayu is activated by the decaying sound of the gong after the strike. It is the energy that takes the sound of the gong away as it fades. Apana vayu begins as we release the contact of the mallet from the gong and allow our own energy to release into the sound of the gong. It is the lessening and declining of the sound of the gong that activates the apana vayu in the listener. When the apana vayu is present in the sound of the gong, it brings us into the relationship of time as it decays and comes to an end. The primary playing area of the gong that contains apana vayu is the lower half, between the center and the rim, as well as to the inside area near the player.

Samana Vayu

Samana vayu is the balancing moving energy as represented by the retention of the breath. It is circular, digestive, and distributive in nature. It is localized at the area of the navel, around the stomach and intestines. The element of samana vayu is water, the ability to transport and assimilate. The samana vayu is associated with digestion and assimilation of everything that comes into the body be it food, knowledge or experiences, and fulfills the subtle function of mental absorption. It affects the digestive organs and gives balance and concentration. When unbalanced or deficient, it creates attachment and greed, and a tendency to hold onto beliefs and emotions that do not serve us.

Samana Vayu and the Gong

Samana vayu is activated by the circular striking of the gong. It is the energy that smoothly assimilates and distributes the integrated sound of the gong. It expresses itself as we strike the gong in a balanced and coordinated manner, moving energy and sound around and around the center of the gong. It is the gentle roaring of the gong that creates a balanced and continuous sound in the listener. When the samana vayu is present in the sound of the gong, it brings a state of fullness and richness where all that is needed is present. The primary playing area of the gong that contains the samana vayu is the area around the center of the gong.

Udana Vayu

Udana vayu is the upward moving energy as represented by the exhalation of the breath after retention. It is positive, transformational, and expressive in nature. It is localized in the upper chest and throat and moving up into the head and beyond. The element of udana vayu is air, the ability to move and flow. The udana vayu is associated with speech upon exhalation and everything that comes up and out of the body, be it spoken words or any forms of self-expression or self-elevation. It fulfills the subtle function of mental expansion and raising the consciousness. It affects the sensory organs in the head area and gives enthusiasm and joy. When unbalanced or deficient, it creates pride and scattered thinking, and an inability to awaken spiritual potentiality.

Udana Vayu and the Gong

Udana vayu is activated by the upward striking of the gong. It is the energy that lifts and raises the sound and rhythm of the gong. It expresses itself as we strike the gong in an elevating and energetic manner, sending energy and sound higher and higher. It is the sparkling sound of the gong that creates a sense of joy and excitement in the listener. When the udana vayu is present in the sound of the gong, it brings a state of high spirits and positive thoughts and an experience of being larger than we are. The primary playing area of the gong that contains the udana vayu is the area near the top of the gong and below the rim.

Vyana Vayu

Vyana vayu is the outward moving energy as represented by the suspension of the breath after inhalation. It is expansive, migratory, and peripheral in nature. It is localized in the limbs of the body and moves the vital energy of the heart (blood) and lungs (breath) to all areas of the body. As such, the vyana vayu is responsible for the experience of all sensation. The element of vyana vayu is ether, the ability to create and enter into space. The vyana vayu is associated with movement and circulation and everything that moves through the body and mind, be it fluids, nerve impulses, feelings or ideas. It fulfills the subtle function of mental circulation and creates a healthy exchange and balance throughout the individual. It affects muscular and nervous movement and gives agility and flexibility. When unbalanced or deficient, it creates separation, dissipation, alienation and disintegration, and an inability to unite with others and to create a connection with the world outside.

Vyana Vayu and the Gong

Vyana vayu is activated by the outward striking of the gong. It is the energy that takes the sound of the gong out and away. It expresses itself as we strike the gong from the center to edge, sending energy and sound farther and farther away. It is the expanding sound of the gong that creates a sense of boundless space in the listener. When the vyana vayu is present in the sound of the gong, it brings us into union and dissolves the boundaries between the listener and the sound. The primary playing area of the gong that contains the vyana vayu is the right below and all around the rim of the gong.

Balancing the Vayus: Point-to-Point Breathing

A simple yoga practice to balance the vayus with the gong is to breathe consciously from point to point in the body during a guided relaxation as the gong is played. The practice begins by inhaling from the feet up to the crown of the head, and then exhaling from the crown of the head back down to the feet. The inhale-exhale cycle is repeated 2-3 times.

Then the breath is inhaled from the ankles to the crown of the head and exhaled back down to the ankles 2-3 times. The breath sequence continues moving upward from point to point through the body (ankles, knees, base of spine, etc.) until the third eye point is reached, at which time the sequence reverses as the breath is exhaled downward from point to point (throat, heart, navel point, etc.).

The gong is played in such a way to mimic and connect the movement of breath through the different areas of the body, almost as if the human body were superimposed on the gong surface with the head near the top rim and the feet near the bottom rim.

Point-to-Point Breathing Relaxation Practice

Begin by having students relax on their backs and connect to the breath as the diaphragm rises and falls. Guide the students to inhale from a specific point in their body up to the crown of their head and then exhale down from the crown back to that point. The inhale and exhale are measured by the strike of the gong as the breath is moved up and down the body.

Repeat each breathing point once or twice and then move to the next point in the body as described in the routine. The gong is struck in different areas as specified to balance the different areas of the body, the chakras and the vayus.

- Inhale, visualizing the breath entering the **bottom of the feet** as the gong is struck in an *upward* direction *above rim at the bottom of the gong*. Continue inhaling with the sound as the breath is drawn up to the crown of the head.

Point To Point Breathing

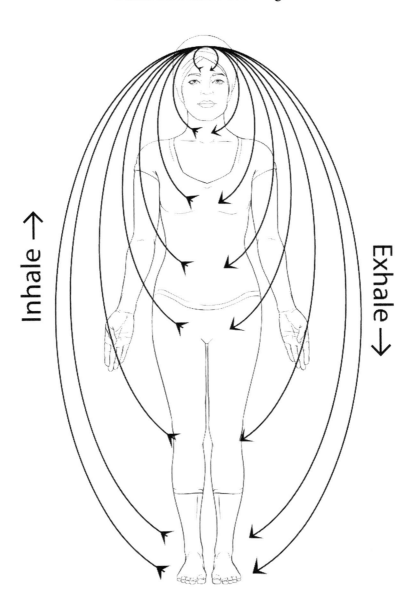

Inhale →

Exhale →

Mehtab Benton

- From the crown, exhale the breath slowly out as the gong is struck in a *downward* direction *below the rim at the top of the gong*. Continue exhaling with the sound as the breath is pressed back down to the **bottom of the feet**.
- Repeat the breath and visualization with the gong.

- Inhale, visualizing the breath entering the **ankles** as the gong is struck in an *upward* direction *slightly higher than the bottom of the gong*. Continue inhaling with the sound of the gong as the breath is drawn up to the crown of the head.
- From the crown, exhale the breath slowly out as the gong is struck in a *downward* direction *below the rim at the top of the gong*. Continue exhaling with the sound as the breath is pressed back down to the **ankles**.
- Repeat the breath and visualization with the gong.

- Inhale, visualizing the breath entering the **knees** as the gong is struck in an *upward* direction *slightly higher than at the bottom of the gong*. Continue inhaling with the sound as the breath is drawn up to the crown of the head.
- From the crown, exhale the breath slowly out as the gong is struck in a *downward* direction *below the rim at the top of the gong*. Continue exhaling with the sound as the breath is pressed back down to the **knees**.
- Repeat the breath and visualization with the gong.

- Inhale, visualizing the breath entering the **base of the spine** as the gong is struck in an *upward* direction *slightly higher than and below the center of the gong*. Continue inhaling with the sound as the breath is drawn up to the crown of the head.
- From the crown, exhale the breath slowly out as the gong is struck in a *downward* direction *below the rim at the top of*

the gong. Continue exhaling with the sound as the breath is pressed back down to the **base of the spine**.

- Repeat the breath and visualization with the gong.

- Inhale, visualizing the breath entering the **navel point** as the gong is struck in an *upward* direction *slightly below the center of the gong.* Continue inhaling with the sound as the breath is drawn up to the crown of the head.
- From the crown, exhale the breath slowly out as the gong is struck in a *downward* direction *below the rim at the top of the gong.* Continue exhaling with the sound as the breath is pressed back down to the **navel point**.
- Repeat the breath and visualization with the gong.

- Inhale, visualizing the breath entering the **heart** as the gong is struck in an *upward* direction *slightly above the center of the gong.* Continue inhaling with the sound as the breath is drawn up to the crown of the head.
- From the crown, exhale the breath slowly out as the gong is struck in a *downward* direction *below the rim at the top of the gong.* Continue exhaling with the sound as the breath is pressed back down to the **heart**.
- Repeat the breath and visualization with the gong.

- Inhale, visualizing the breath entering the **throat** as the gong is struck in an *upward* direction *higher than and above the center of the gong.* Continue inhaling with the sound as the breath is drawn up to the crown of the head.
- From the crown, exhale the breath slowly out as the gong is struck in a *downward* direction *below the rim at the top of the gong.* Continue exhaling with the sound as the breath is pressed back down to the **throat**.
- Repeat the breath and visualization with the gong.

- Inhale, visualizing the breath entering the **third eye** as the gong is struck in an *upward* direction *higher than and above the center of the gong.* Continue inhaling with the sound as the breath is drawn up to the crown of the head.
- From the crown, exhale the breath slowly out as the gong is struck in a *downward* direction *below the rim at the top of the gong.* Continue exhaling with the sound as the breath is pressed back down to the **third eye**.
- Repeat the breath and visualization with the gong.

Now reverse the journey by directing the exhale to move systematically back down through the different body points: third eye, throat, heart, navel point, base of spine, knees, ankles, and bottoms of feet. To end, let the breath relax and enjoy the balance created in the body.

The Three Major Nadis and the Gong

Within the energy body or pranamaya kosha, is a network of energy channels called **nadis**. In yogic anatomy, the nadis are rivers of energy that flow through the energetic or subtle body, much like the concept of meridians that carry *chi* in Eastern medicine. These energy channels carry prana or vital life force and play a key role in the awakening of the Kundalini energy of spiritual awareness. When the gong is played, these nadis can be cleared and the listener experiences an increased energy flow into previously blocked areas.

This increased flow of prana through the nadis and the resulting increase in vital energy is one way the gong serves as a healing instrument. In addition, the movement of prana through the nadis awakens, balances, and strengthens the energy of the chakra system. The functioning of the nadis is enhanced by breathing practices (pranayama), cleansing disciplines (shatkarmas), dietary regimens, and the sound of the gong.

Occasionally the sound of the gong produces tingling sensations or movement of energy in the body. These sensations often occur as the sound of the gong clears blockages in the nadis that may have existed since birth or resulted from traumas.

Most yogic texts say there are 72,000 nadis that carry prana through the physical body as well as the subtle or energy body. Of the 72,000 energy channels, there are 14 major nadis used in the practice of Ayurveda and yoga therapy. Of these, three nadis play an important role in the pranamaya practices associated with the energy body: the Ida, the Pingala, and the Sushmna.

Ida: The Lunar Energy Channel

The Ida Nadi is associated with the right hemisphere of the brain and the left side of the body or the feminine or lunar polarity. In pranayama practices, breathing through the left nostril is said to increase the flow of prana through the Ida Nadi that creates a receptive, intuitive, and subjective state of consciousness that favors mental activities. The Ida Nadi brings coolness to the mind and body and makes the parasympathetic nervous system dominant.

Pingala: The Solar Energy Channel

The Pingala Nadi is associated with the left hemisphere of the brain and the right side of the body and the masculine or solar polarity. In pranayama practices, breathing through the right nostril is said to increase the flow of prana through the Pingala Nadi that creates a projective, analytical, and objective state of consciousness that favors physical activities. The Ida Nadi brings warmth to the mind and body and makes the sympathetic nervous system dominant.

Sushmna: The Central Energy Channel

The Sushmna Nadi is associated with the integrated whole brain and the transcendence of polarities. In pranayama practices, breathing equally through both nostrils is said to increase the flow of prana through the Sushmna Nadi to create a neutral, balanced, and centered state of consciousness that favors spiritual activities. The Sushmna Nadi brings equanimity and awareness and is associated with the central nervous system.

Swara Yoga, The Flow of Prana and the Gong

The human body follows a natural rhythm in which the flow of prana alternates between the Ida Nadi and the Pingala Nada every hour to 2 ½ hours, depending upon the individual's biorhythms. When the left nostril is more open and more breath flows through the left side, the Ida Nadi is active. When the right nostril is more open and more breath flows through the right nostril, the Pingala Nadi is dominant.

While the breath pattern changes from right to left and left to right naturally, we can use pranayama techniques as well as applying pressure points to control which nostril the breath is primarily flowing through and thus control which side of the brain is most active during a Gong Yoga class or meditation.

One simple way to control the flow of breath while the gong is being played during relaxation is to lie on one side of the body to open the opposite nostril (lying on the left side opens right nostril;

lying on the right side opens left nostril).

Another way to activate the Ida or Pingala Nadi during a gong relaxation is to make the sound of the gong dominant in the right ear to activate the Pingala Nadi or in the left war to activate the Ida Nadi. This can be done by closing close off sound in the right ear and open the flow of prana through the Ida Nadi, or lying on the left side to close off sound in the left ear and open the flow of prana through the Pingala Nadi. More subtly, the gong can be played on the right side of the room in relation to the students to work on the Pingala Nadi or played on the left side of the students to activate the Ida Nadi.

To Open the Flow of the Ida Nadi with the Gong

Block the right nostril and inhale through the left nostril. Then block the left nostril and exhale through the right nostril. Strike the gong at percussion point 10 on the inhale and at percussion point 4 on the exhale. This can be done for 3-7 minutes to fully open the flow of prana to activate the Ida Nadi.

To Open the Flow of the Pingala Nadi with the Gong

Block the left nostril and inhale through the right nostril. Then block the right nostril and exhale through the left nostril. Strike the gong at percussion point 2 on the inhale and at percussion point 8 on the exhale. This can be done for 3-7 minutes to fully open the flow of prana to activate the Pingala Nadi

To Open the Flow of the Sushumna Nadi with the Gong

Practice the previous exercise for the Ida Nadi for 3 minutes. Then practice the previous exercise for the Pingala Nadi for 3 minutes. Play the gong as specified for both exercises. Then begin breathing through both nostrils. On the inhale play up the vertical axis of the gong with short multiple strikes, starting at percussion point 6 and ending at percussion point 12 at the top of the inhale. On the exhale, make one strong strike to percussion point 0 (down). Repeat this breathing and gong pattern for 3 minutes.

The Seven Chakras and the Gong

Within the energy body or pranamaya kosha, are a series of transformational energy centers known as the chakras. Most yoga traditions postulate seven major chakras that align along the Sushumna, or the major central energy channel. The chakras serve as transformers for the prana moving through the Ida and the Pingala nadis, changing and altering the energy to create different frequencies and vortices of power that affect all the levels (koshas) of existence, including the physical body (organs, nerve plexuses, endocrine glands, etc.), the emotional body (psychological states, mental attitudes), the knowledge body (levels of consciousness), and the bliss body (samskaras and tendencies from previous lives).

The chakras hold the keys to achieving the ultimate goal of yoga, integration, union and transcendence, and all the practices of yoga are involved in the balancing and aligning the energies of the chakras, including the use of mantra and sound.

There are many mantras and sounds that resonate with the different energy centers, and this resonance holds a particular frequency for each chakra.

Because of this intimate relationship between sound frequencies and chakras, the gong is a powerful instrument for opening and balancing the flow of energy through them. As the gong is played with its wide range of complex frequency patterns, the chakras come into a natural resonance. It is as if there were a million notes being played simultaneously until the perfect melody is struck for each specific chakra.

The chakras make up one of the richest conceptual frameworks in yoga, and through working with the chakras with various yoga practices and the sound of the gong, we can affect and transform the three bodies - Physical, Subtle, and Causal - as well as all the attendant domains of these bodies, including the organs, glands, physical conditions, psychological states, sensory experiences, and karmic lessons.

Chakras and the Physical Body

Chakra	Physical Body (1) Location (2) Nervous Plexus (3) Endocrine Gland (4) Body Associations (5) Physical Ailments
First Muladhara	1. Perineum, base of spine 2. Coccygeal Plexus 3. Adrenals 4. Bones, feet, leg, immune system, colon, rectum 5. Constipation, hemorrhoids, obesity, sciatica
Second Svadhisthana	1. Sacral spine 2. Sacral Plexus 3. Gonads 4. Bladder, genitals, kidney, prostrate, uterus 5. Pelvic or low back pain. Urinary, sexual problems
Third Manipura	1. Navel 2. Solar Plexus 3. Pancreas 4. Digestive system, liver, muscles 5. Diabetes, hepatitis, indigestion, ulcers
Fourth Anahata	1. Center of chest 2. Heart Plexus 3. Thymus 4. Arms, hands, heart, lungs 5. Asthma, circulatory system, heart
Fifth Vishuddha	1. Throat 2. Pharyngeal Plexus 3. Thyroid, parathyroid 4. Neck, shoulders 5. Ear, nose and throat problems
Sixth Ajna	1. Center of head, brow point, root of nose 2. Hypothalamus, Autonomic Nervous System 3. Pituitary (Pineal) 4. Eyes 5. Eye problems, headaches, sinusitis
Seventh Sahasrara	1. Center of head, anterior fontanel 2. Cerebral Cortex, Central Nervous System 3. Pineal (Pituitary) 4. Brain, Nervous System 5. Symptoms without physical cause

Chakras and the Subtle Body

Chakra	Subtle Body (1) Kosha (2) Vayu (3) Tattva (element) (4) Tanmatra (sensory expression)
First Muladhara	1. Anamaya Kosha 2. Apana Vayu 3. Prithvi Tattva (Earth) 4. Smell
Second Svadhisthana	1. Pranamaya Kosha 2. Apana Vayu / Vyana Vayu 3. Apas Tattva (Water) 4. Taste
Third Manipura	1. Pranamaya Kosha 2. Samana Vayu 3. Agni Tattva (Fire) 4. Sight
Fourth Anahata	1. Manomaya Kosha 2. Prana Vayu / Vyana Vayu 3. Vayu Tattva (Air) 4. Touch
Fifth Vishuddha	1. Vijnanamaya Kosha 2. Udana Vayu 3. Akasha Tattva (Ether) 4. Hearing
Sixth Ajna	1. Vijnanamaya Kosha 2. Five Vayus (Prana, Apana, Udana, Vyana, Udana) 3. Manas (Mind) / Light 4. Thought
Seventh Sahasrara	1. Anandamaya Kosha 2. Transcendent 3. Transcendent 4. Transcendent

Mehtab Benton

Chakras and the Causal Body

Chakra	Causal Body (1) Goals (2) Karmic Lessons (3) Needs
First Muladhara	1. Survival, security, stability, grounding, prosperity, physical health, family 2. Living in the material world 3. To be present, to feel
Second Svadhisthana	1. Sexuality, creativity, fluidity, pleasure, bonding, relaxation, worthiness, emotional connection 2. Creatively manifesting through relationship 3. To let go, to be sexual, to create, to live
Third Manipura	1. Manifestation, strength of will, purpose, power, accomplishment, vitality, taking action, energy 2. Empowerment through self-acceptance 3. To act, to move, to commit
Fourth Anahata	1. Neutrality, balance, compassion, integration, appropriate boundaries 2. Trusting in the benevolence of the universe 3. To give, to receive, to forgive, to love
Fifth Vishuddha	1. Self-expression, truth, communication, resonance, harmony 2. Speaking and living the Truth 3. To express, to listen, to empathize
Sixth Ajna	1. Intuition, perception, visualization, imagination, focus, insight, understanding 2. Seeing the One beyond dualities 3. To know the truth, to see the unseen, to live in an expanded state of reality
Seventh Sahasrara	1. Consciousness, enlightenment, surrender, union, merger, transcendence 2. Connecting to the infinite 3. To be at One, to align with the divine

Mehtab Benton

Playing the Gong for the Chakras

When playing the gong to affect the chakras, there are five considerations for the Gong Yoga teacher:

- The nature of the gong
- The playing areas of the gong
- The rhythm of the gong playing
- The intention of the player
- The state of the listener

Nature of the Gong and the Chakras

Each gong carries a frequency and vibration. Some gongs are tuned to a specific frequency, such as the Paiste Planetary gongs, while others produce a wide range of tones. The chakras have also been associated with various frequencies and musical notes, yet it must be noted that in the original practices of yoga, these sound frequencies were never specified. As a result, much of what has been speculated about chakras having specific tone frequencies cannot be verified through the teachings of yoga. Indeed, when the chakras were first discussed in the Upanishads, the Western musical scale was not even known. Yet the chakras do have a frequency of vibration. The question is: Can a gong be tuned to a specific frequency whereby it affects a specific chakra in everyone?

While there is little doubt that the size, composition and tuning of a gong will have specific effects on the chakra system, it is an oversimplification to say that Gong A will balance the fourth chakra or Gong C will balance the sixth chakra. In reality, as we will see later, any gong is capable of balancing any chakra. Yet there is always a Western fascination about obtaining a dedicated tool to accomplish a specific task, such as having a set of seven gongs to take care of the seven chakras.

For the sake of discussion (and future research), the following table is one of the many postulations that have made about how certain gongs vibrate to the frequencies of specific chakras. However, caution is advised that there is no universal acceptance about the chakras and their tuned frequencies. The closest frequency of the chakras approximated by one of the tuned Paiste Planetary Gongs is also given for comparison and experimentation.

Chakra	Frequency	Paiste Planetary Gong
First (Root)	194.18 Hz	Sidereal Day (194.71 Hz)
Second (Sacral)	210.42 Hz	Synodic Moon (210.42 Hz)
Third (Solar Plexus)	126.22 Hz	Sun (126.27 Hz)
Fourth (Heart)	136.10 Hz	Earth (136.10 Hz)
Fifth (Throat)	141.27 Hz	Mercury (141.27 Hz)
Sixth (Third Eye)	221.23 Hz	Venus (221.23 Hz)
Seventh (Crown)	172.06 Hz	Platonic Year (172.06 Hz)

Another way to associate the planetary gongs with the chakras is to use the traditional association of the seven visible planets with the chakras according to Jyotish, or Indian Astrology, as follows. Notice that the only consistent association between this and the previous approach is Mercury Planetary Gong for the fifth chakra,

Chakra	Paiste Planetary Gong
First (Root)	Saturn
Second (Sacral)	Jupiter
Third (Solar Plexus)	Mars
Fourth (Heart)	Venus
Fifth (Throat)	Mercury
Sixth (Third Eye)	Moon
Seventh (Crown)	Sun

Playing Areas of the Gong and the Chakras

The area of the gong that is struck also affects the different chakras. According to Yogi Bhajan, master of Kundalini Yoga and the gong, the seven major chakras may be accessed through the gong playing area by superimposing a map of the chakra system as it aligns up within the body, moving from bottom to top.

In this manner, the first chakra would be located at the bottom of the gong, directly above the rim area. The second chakra would be right above the first chakra and the third chakra right below the bottom center of the gong. The fourth chakra would be around the center of the gong and the fifth chakra above the top of the center of the gong. The sixth chakra is closer to the top of the gong and the seventh or crown chakra is right beneath the top rim of the gong. The aura that surrounds the energy body and the seven chakras is associated with the rim area around the gong face.

This mapping of the chakras over the face of the gong corresponds to the ancient astrological mapping of the areas of the body to the signs of the zodiac, or the Cosmic Man, with the first sign (Aries) corresponding to the head and so on down to the last sign (Pisces) associated with the feet.

This follows one of the major teachings of esoteric philosophy that the subtle or etheric body aligns with the physical body, which is one of the reasons for the medical condition known as *phantom limb* in which a person seems to feel an arm or leg long after it has been amputated.

The playing areas of the gong allow the Gong Yoga teacher to access individual chakras as well as working with the energetic paring of the chakras. The following chakras are often associated as working together through their higher and lower frequencies, and both of these chakras may be balanced by alternating strikes between their respective areas: Chakras 1 and 7; Chakras 2 and 6; Chakras 3 and 5; Chakras 4 and 8 (aura area around the rim).

Chakras and the Playing Areas of the Gong

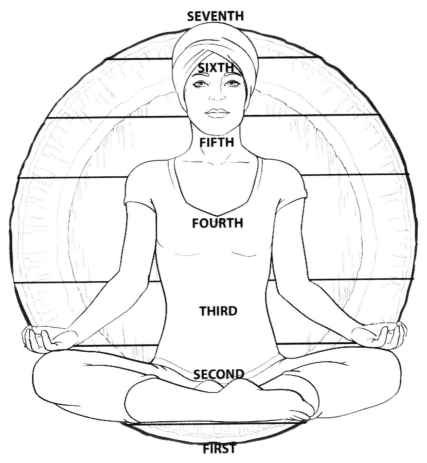

SEVENTH

SIXTH

FIFTH

FOURTH

THIRD

SECOND

FIRST

Playing Rhythms and the Chakras

One of the more consistent and observable effects of the gong on the chakras follows this basic rule: The faster the rhythm, the higher the chakra affected. A slow rhythm resonates with the lower chakras while a fast rhythm moves energy to the higher chakras.

The relationship between a slow rhythm and a fast rhythm is dependent upon the player's individual baseline rhythm, but it does follow a ratio of 3:5:7. In other words, a slow rhythm has a value of "3" and a medium rhythm would be "5" (or about 1.67 times as fast as a slow rhythm). A fast rhythm would be "7" (or proportionately about 2.33 times as fast as a slow rhythm or 1.4 times faster than the medium rhythm).

Again, these proportions are relative to the individual rhythm of the player and not an absolute measurement. Most simply, the more the rhythm is increased, the higher the chakra that is affected.

Playing Intention and the Chakras

Like all sound produced, the intention behind the production of the sound is paramount. An angry and unfeeling gong player will have little success in working with the heart chakra regardless of the frequency of the gong, the area of the gong that is struck, or the rhythm of the playing.

An effective way to play the gong for a specific chakra is to play in a manner that is in accordance with the major keyword of each chakra, such as the following table shows.

Chakra	Intention Keyword
First (Root)	Security
Second (Sacral)	Connection
Third (Solar Plexus)	Manifestation
Fourth (Heart)	Compassion
Fifth (Throat)	Expression
Sixth (Third Eye)	Perception
Seventh (Crown)	Unity

For example when playing the gong for the fifth chakra, the intention of the player is to express and create with a desire to communicate. When playing for the second chakra, the intention is to connect the listener to the sound and create a relationship between the player and the gong, and so on.

Condition of the Listener and the Chakras

The condition of the listener is perhaps the paramount factor in how the gong affects the chakras. This condition to a large degree is based upon the karmas of the listener, the life experiences, and whether there is a deficiency or sufficiency of prana in the various energy centers.

The listener's condition prior to hearing the gong, however, can be shaped by the practice of yoga practices specific to the various chakras and the use of mantras, affirmations, and visualizations. In other words, the Gong Yoga teacher can create a fertile ground and set expectations for the listener's experience of the gong as it relates to the chakras that are affected.

For example when playing for the heart chakra, a focus on backbends or devotional chanting might precede the playing of the gong.

The Energy Body and the Breath Cycle

The practice of yoga actually begins with the cycle of breath that repeats over 20,000 times a day. It is breath, or more properly the prana through the breath, that creates movement (asana), energy (pranayama), sound (mantra) and thought (meditation). Working with the basic cycle of inhalation and exhalation while using the gong is the first step to using sound to enhance the energy body (pranamaya kosha) as well as our yoga practice.

The gong may be used to guide and enhance the basic movements of pranayama that make up the breathing cycle of inhalation (**puraka**), exhalation (**rechaka**) and retention or suspension (**kumbhaka**). In the practice of yoga, this full pranayama cycle consists of four phases:

- Puraka (inhalation)
- Abhyantara kumbhaka (retention of breath after the inhale)
- Rechaka (exhalation)
- Bahya kumbhaka (suspension of the breath after the exhale)

A simple way to use the gong in a pranayama practice is to signal each breath phase. At the beginning of the inhale (*puraka*), the gong is gently struck and the inhale continues until the sound disappears. The breath is then retained in (*abhyantara kumbhaka*) for a time equal to the inhale. Then the gong is struck and the exhale begins (*rechaka*) and continues until the sound disappears. The breath is then suspended out (*bahya kumbhaka*) for a time equal to the exhale. The cycle begins again when the gong is struck again.

The gong player must learn to time the strike and moderate its intensity so that the resulting sound lasts for 10 to 15 seconds. Alternatively, the player can muffle or silence the gong after the 10 to 15 second interval.

In addition to serving as a timer, the gong can also be played during one or both of the kumbhaka phases while the breath is held in or held out.

By consciously suspending the breath, the whole system becomes controlled as we stop nervous impulses in different parts of the body and start to harness the brain wave patterns. Since it is the movement of prana (breath) that enables the mind to think, when this movement is suspended, the mind becomes quiet. During deep meditation the breath naturally becomes suspended for a short period of time, and it is in this interval that pranayama truly occurs. As Patanjali, the author of the Yoga Sutras, observed: "Pranayama is the **cessation** of the movement of inhalation and exhalation." (*Yoga Sutras* 2:49).

It is during this period of breath cessation that the gong can be used to re-pattern consciousness and clear *samskaras*, or past life energies. When the breath is suspended out, for example, it is common for deep fears associated with death to come to the surface. The gong can overlay those fears with its own pranic and sonic field and effectively neutralize them when played correctly. When the breath is retained in, the gong can be played to encourage the circulation of prana from the heart outward into the energetic body. This could be done, for example, by playing from the center of the gong outward while the breath is held in, and then released or exhaled with a definite strike.

Ultimately, the gong can be played during pranayama to induce the state of *kevala kumbhaka* (or *stambhavritti pranayama*), in which the breath is simply stopped, without breathing in or breathing out. According to the yogic texts, this state is the highest form of pranayama practice.

"He who is successful in the absolute state of kevala kumbhaka, without breathing in or out, finds nothing in the three worlds beyond his reach." (*Vasishtha Samhita*)

"When the breath can be stopped for three *ghatikas* (75 minutes), the yogi can realize all the attainments he wishes for without doubt." (*Shiva Samhita* 3, 62)

While such a state may seem unreachable to the ordinary practitioner, the sound of the gong can create a transcendent trance-like experience in which the movement of the breath seems to disappear or is paused almost indefinitely. When the gong is played in a repetitive, slow, and even manner for an extended period of time, allowing the hypnotic sound to build softly like a far-reaching wave, the practitioner can sit in meditation and focus on the movement of the breath at the tip of the nose and enter a state approximating non-breathing or kevala kumbhaka.

Pranayama Practices and the Gong

All the formal yoga pranayama practices may be enhanced through the sound of the gong. In effect, the gong multiplies and directs the flow of prana through the energy body when played with the various breathing exercises.

While there are hundreds of pranayama techniques and variations, they can all be categorized as to the effects they create, much like the asanas or physical postures, as either being cooling

(Langhana), warming (Brimhana), or balancing (Samana). Pranayamas can also be categorized as to a secondary effect of being tranquilizing, vitalizing or balancing. Depending upon the combinations of these various qualities for each pranayama, the gong may be played at certain rhythms, volumes and playing areas to enhance the effects of each pranayama.

The following table of the twelve most common pranayama practices in the Hatha and Kundalini traditions indicates the qualities of each one and the gong practices that accompany it.

Pranayama	Quality	Effect	Sound	Rhythm
Sitali or Sitkari	Langhana	Tranquilizing	Soft to Medium	Slow
Chandra Anga	Langhana	Tranquilizing	Soft	Slow
Chandra Bhedana	Langhana	Tranquilizing	Soft	Slow
Bhramari	Langhana	Tranquilizing	Soft	Medium
Kapalabhati	Langhana	Vitalizing	Medium	Fast
Nadi Shodhana	Samana	Balancing	Soft to Medium	Slow
Agni Pran Breath of Fire	Samana	Vitalizing	Medium to Loud	Fast
Viloma	Samana	Varies	Varies	Varies
Ujjayi	Brimhana	Balancing	Soft to Medium	Slow to Medium
Surya Bhedana	Brimhana	Vitalizing	Medium	Medium
Surya Anga	Brimhana	Vitalizing	Medium	Medium
Bhastrika	Brimhana	Vitalizing	Loud	Fast

Sitali or Sitkari Pranayama (Cooling or Hissing Breath)

Sitali pranayama, or the cooling breath, and Sitkari pranayama, or the hissing breath, reduce body heat and soothe the emotions. They are differentiated from most pranayamas in that the inhalation occurs through the mouth. These two breath practices quiet the mind and create muscular relaxation that can help induce sleep. The practices also remove pain in the head and face areas, reduce blood pressure and acidity, and detoxify the liver. In the *Hatha Yoga Pradipika* (2:58), it is said that practicing Sitali pranayama cures an enlarged stomach or spleen, lowers excess fever, counteracts poisons and reduces hunger and thirst. Sitkari pranayama has the added benefit of keeping the teeth and gums healthy.

Breath Technique: Sitali Pranayama is performed by extending the tongue outside the mouth and curling it so it forms a tube (if unable to curl the tongue, focus on the center of the extended tongue) and then drawing the breath in over the tongue. The tongue is then drawn in, the mouth closed, and the exhale is through the nose.

For Sitkari pranayama, the teeth are lightly held together and the lips separate so the breath is drawn through the teeth. The exhale is done through the nose with the mouth closed.

Gong Technique: The gong is played softly at a medium-low volume with a slow rhythm. The intention behind the playing is cooling and calming.

Chandra Anga (Moon Path Breath)

Chandra Anga, more popularly known as the Moon or lunar breath, works primarily with the Ida Nadi to bring about coolness, relaxation and tranquility. The breath works powerfully on the right hemisphere of the brain, and has been useful in accessing mental patterns and unconscious habits. This predominantly activates the parasympathetic nervous system and *manas shakti*, the mental or lunar energy.

Breath Technique: The breath is controlled by inhaling and exhaling through the left nostril while blocking the right nostril. The breath may be continuous. An advanced practice is to retain the breath as long as the inhale and the exhale (1:1:1 ratio). The ratio can slowly be increased with practice to 1:2:2 and eventually 1:4:2.

Gong Technique: The gong is played to activate the Ida Nadi during the pranayama practice by striking the gong at the beginning of each inhale and exhale. When inhaling through the left nostril, the gong is played with an upward strike at percussion point 9. When exhaling through the left nostril, the gong is played with a downward strike at percussion point 9. The rhythm should be slow to allow for a full inhale and exhale and the volume is soft. The intention behind the playing is receptivity and nurturing.

Chandra Bhedana (Moon Piercing Breath)

Chandra Bhedana, more popularly known as the Moon Piercing breath, works with Ida Nadi to bring about relaxation and alertness. The breath works on the right hemisphere of the brain and the parasympathetic nervous system.

Breath Technique: The breath is controlled by inhaling through the left nostril and exhaling through the right nostril, alternately blocking off the nostril not being used. The breath may be continuous for excellent effect. An advanced practice is to retain the breath for as long as the inhale and the exhale (1:1:1 ratio). The ratio can slowly be increased with practice to 1:2:2 and eventually 1:4:2.

Gong Technique: The gong is played to activate the Ida Nadi during the pranayama practice by striking the gong at the beginning of each inhale and exhale. When inhaling through the left nostril, the gong is played with an upward strike at percussion point 9. When exhaling through the right nostril, the gong is played with a downward strike at percussion point 3. The rhythm should be slow to allow for a full inhale and exhale and the volume is soft. The intention behind the playing is relaxation and releasing.

Bhramari (Humming Bee Breath)

Bhramari pranayama, more popularly known as the humming bee breath, produces a soothing effect on the mind and nervous system while also reducing blood pressure and ameliorating throat ailments. It has traditionally been used to deal with anxiety, anger and insomnia, as well as healing body tissues following operations. Significantly in the practice of Gong Yoga, the breath facilitates the awareness of all sound and subtle vibrations and awakens psychic sensitivity. In the *Hatha Yoga Pradipika* (2:68), it is said that by practicing this pranayama one becomes "lord of the yogis and one's mind is absorbed in bliss."

Breath Technique: The breath is done by with the lips gently closed, teeth slightly relaxed and not touching, and the jaw muscle loose. The ears are closed with the index or middle finger pressing the earflaps closed, with the elbows out to the sides and the upper arms parallel to the grounds. Inhale through the nose and with the mouth closed, exhale slowly with a deep steady hum in the head, smooth, even and continuous. The sound is soft and deep, making the front of the head vibrate.

Gong Technique: The gong is played with a medium soft and sweeping swishing sound by lightly and rapidly moving the mallet around the surface. The intention behind the playing is inclusive and encompassing so that the two sounds blend outside and inside.

Kapalabhati (Forehead Shining Breath)

Kapalabhati, also known as the Skull Shining or Forehead Shining Breath, is one of the six basic cleansing practices of yoga (the shatkarmas). The name refers to its invigoration of the entire brain, and particular the frontal lobe (forehead). The breath is cleansing and energizing while simultaneously slowing down the activity of the mind (*vrittis*).

Breath Technique: The breath is distinguished by an active exhale and passive inhale. The inhale occurs naturally after the exhale is forced. The inhale and exhale together take about one second, and are done consecutively for 20 repetitions, or one round. The breath is then inhaled fully and retained comfortably and then exhaled normally. After a few regular breaths, up to 5 to 10 more rounds may be performed. Advanced practices include retaining the breath at the end of a round and applying *mulabandha* (root lock), as well as increasing the number of repetitions in a round and the number of rounds.

Gong Technique: The gong is played in rhythm with the fast breath, almost like a quick tapping on the gong and medium loud in volume, with each strike signaling an exhale. The gong may be played at any percussion point, but typically gets best results when played with upward strikes below percussion point 12. At the end of the round (10-50 repetitions), the gong is struck once loudly to signal the end and the breath is retained comfortably as the sound decays. The intention behind the playing is to create an upward flow of invigorating and clearing energy.

Nadi Shodhana (Alternate Nostril Breath)

Nadi Shodhana, more popularly known as alternate nostril breathing, is one of the most beneficial and basic pranayamas practiced in yoga. The name translates as purification of the energy channels (*nadis*) and prepares the subtle body to handle the increased flow of prana that comes from the practices of yoga. Moving the breath through the left nostril opens the Ida Nadi while right nostril breathing is associated with the Pingala Nadi. When both major nadis are balanced and open, meditation begins and intuition awakens. The practice brings a balance to the sympathetic and parasympathetic nervous systems and balances the emotions. When this pranayama is practiced with the gong, there is an experience of prana moving more directly and openly into the energy channels with the breath.

Breath Technique: The breath is controlled by first inhaling through the left nostril while blocking the right nostril, then exhaling through the right nostril while blocking the left nostril. Then the breath is inhaled through the right nostril, with the left nostril still blocked. Complete the cycle by exhaling through the left nostril with the right nostril blocked. The cycle repeats by inhaling through the left nostril and continuing as desired.

Gong Technique: The gong is played to activate the Ida and Pingala Nadis during the pranayama practice by striking the gong at the beginning of each inhale and exhale. When inhaling through the left nostril, the gong is played with an upward strike at percussion point 9. When exhaling through the right nostril, the gong is played with a downward strike at percussion point 3. When inhaling through the right nostril, the gong is played with an upward strike at percussion point 3. When exhaling through the left nostril, the gong is played with a downward strike at percussion point 9. The rhythm should be slow to allow for a full inhale and exhale and the volume is soft to moderate. At the end of the practice, still or silence the gong, inhale through both nostrils, retain the breath, and then exhale as the gong is struck near the center. The intention behind the playing is balance and purity.

Agni Pran (Breath of Fire)

Agni Pran (fire breath), more popularly known as Breath of Fire, accompanies many Kundalini Yoga exercises and is independently used as a separate pranayama practice. The breath is vitalizing and balancing, encouraging both detoxification and alertness, and focuses the mind while oxygenating the body. The benefits of this breath are numerous and as it activates the energy center at the solar plexus (the third chakra) which is associated with the fire element in yogic physiology. It burns the impurities in the body and purifies the nervous system. The breath is enjoyably energizing.

Breath of Fire helps detoxify the lungs, mucous linings, blood vessels, and other cells. It expands the lung capacity and increases physical endurance. It balances sympathetic and parasympathetic nervous systems and strengthens the nerves. It expands and energizes the body's electromagnetic field. It focuses the mind, elevates the mood, and alleviates depression. It reduces addictive impulses for foods, drugs, and smoking. It boosts the immune system and stimulates glandular secretions. It creates a harmonic resonance among all the body's systems and synchronizes its biorhythms. It purifies and oxygenates the bloodstream within three minutes of practice.

Breath of Fire may be done as a separate practice to energize the physical and energetic bodies.

Breath Technique: The breath is distinguished by a quick and equal active inhale and active exhale through the nose as if lightly panting with the mouth closed. There is an equal intensity and length of the inhale and the exhale, at the rate of 1 to 3 breaths per second. The heart is lifted and the solar plexus lightly dances with the breath, yet the movement is not forceful or contractive. The breath is rhythmical (equal length between inhale and exhale) and quick (1 to 3 breaths per second) so a continuous light panting breath through the nose is accomplished without strain. While breath of fire may consist of 60 to 180 inhalations and exhalations per minute, it is physiologically one continuous breath. The lungs are never completely emptied or filled during the breath. Instead, air is baffled or vibrated in and out of the lungs by the motion of the diaphragm at the navel point.

Gong Technique: The gong is played playing moderately fast and at a medium to loud volume. The rapid rhythm of the breath can be matched with a similar quick playing rhythm on the gong, striking the surface at the rate of 1 to 2 times per second. The strikes are generally made upward near the top of the gong. The intention behind the playing is to energize, balance and uplift.

The following pranayama practice demonstrates the effectiveness of using the gong to amplify the effects of the Breath of Fire.

Agni Gong (Fire Gong) Exercise

Assume a meditative posture and raise the arms over the head and separate the hands (palms facing out) about two feet (30 centimeters) apart. Close the hands into fists with the thumbs outside and pointing at a 45-degree angle upward. Close the eyes and focus at the brow point or third eye (sixth chakra).

1. Begin the breath of fire, lifting the arms up and very slightly back to open the heart. Continue the breath of fire at the same rhythm throughout the exercise.
2. After 30 seconds, begin playing the gong steadily and moderately fast at the top of the gong, about two thirds up from the center and below the rim at a light to moderate volume.
3. After another 30 seconds, increase the rhythm and slowly increase the volume.
4. After another 30 seconds, again increase the rhythm rate and volume.
5. After another 30 seconds, hold the rhythm rate but increase the volume so that the sound of the breath disappears into the sound of the gong.
6. After 30 seconds at the loud volume, make 2 or 3 powerful strikes with a crashing and releasing sound at points of your choosing. Then remove the mallet from the gong and let the sound decline naturally while continuing the Breath of Fire.
7. After 30 seconds as the sound diminishes, inhale very deeply and retain the breath and posture for 15 seconds or until the sound disappears into silence.
8. Exhale. Relax the hands down into a meditative posture. Meditate at the third eye for 60 seconds or more.

Viloma Pranayama (Segmented Breath)

Viloma Pranayama, also known as segmented breath or reverse breath, is distinguished by pausing the breath during inhalation and/or exhalation. The pausing segments the breath and is a reversal of the normal continuous breath flow. The pauses during the breath flow create a finer control of the breathing process and deepens the relationship to the experience of prana. It is an excellent practice to extend breath duration and retention and to expand breath capacity. The pauses may occur in different ratios to create specific benefits for the practitioner. The most commonly practiced Viloma breath ratios and their benefits are summarized in the following table.

Viloma Breath Ratios	Effects
1 Part In : 4 Parts Out	Meditative, balancing, purifying
4 Parts In : 1 Part Out	Energizing, elevating, clearing
4 Parts In : 4 Parts Out	Simulating, strengthening
3 Parts In : 3 Parts Out	Neutralizing, heart opening
4 Parts In : 8 Parts Out	Releasing, eliminating, calming
8 Parts In : 1 Part Out	Energy, stress relieving
8 Parts In : 4 Parts Out	Builds energy and focus
8 Parts In : 8 Parts Out	Creates endurance and stamina
10 Parts In : 10 Parts Out	Balances brain and metabolism
16 Parts In : 16 Parts Out	Complete glandular tune-up

Breath Technique: The breath is a complete inhale and exhale, but paused, or interrupted, by stopping the inhale or exhale for one second. The breath is not sniffed or forcefully pulled in or pushed out. Instead the breath is simply stopped several times, according to the ratio practiced. For example, on a 4:4 ratio, the inhale is paused when the breath is ¼ inhaled, then paused at ½ inhaled, then again ¾ inhaled and finally paused when fully inhaled. The exhale is done by letting ¼ of the breath exhale, then ½ the breath exhaled, then ¾ the breath exhaled, and finally all the breath is exhaled.

Gong Technique: The gong is struck for each part of the inhale and the exhale, approximately every 2-3 seconds, giving time for a one-second pause between each part. At the end of the inhale and the exhale cycle, the sound of the gong fades for 3-5 seconds before the next cycle. On the inhale cycle, the gong is sequentially struck above the center of the gong and graduating to near the top, stepping up the volume almost imperceptibly with each strike. On the exhale cycle, the gong is sequentially struck below the center of the gong and descending to near the bottom, diminishing the volume with each strike. The intention behind the playing is to create a rhythmical and almost hypnotic state by pulsing the gong.

Ujjayi (Psychic Breath)

Ujjayi Pranayama, also known as the psychic breath and translated as the victorious breath, opens the subtle states of the mind and may be practiced in any position (standing, sitting, lying down) and with many techniques (asana, mantra, and meditation). The breath reduces hypertension, mental tension, turns the mind inward and increases psychic sensitivity. In the *Hatha Yoga Pradipika* (2:51-53), it is said that practicing Ujiya pranayama removes phlegm, stimulates digestive fire (*agni*), and removes disorders of the energy channels (*nadis*) and tissues (*dhatu*).

Breath Technique: The breath is controlled by gently contracting the glottis in the back of the throat so that a soft hiss or whisper is created in the throat (audible only to the practitioner). This is best accompanied by a simultaneous light contraction or natural lift in the abdomen with a minimum of effort. Both inhale and exhale are long and deep through both nostrils.

Gong Technique: The gong is played to imitate the hissing sound of the breath by building the sound through small rapid strikes in one area, varying the rhythm from slow to moderate and increasing and decreasing the sound back and forth between soft and medium loudness. The intention behind the playing is watery and soothing.

Surya Anga (Sun Path Breath)

Surya Anga, also known as the Sun or solar breath, works primarily with Pingala Nadi to bring about focus, awareness and energy. The breath works powerfully on the left hemisphere of the brain, and has been useful in expressing mental creativity and connecting with the external world. This predominantly activates the sympathetic nervous system and *prana shakti*, the vital or solar energy. In the *Hatha Yoga Pradipika* (2:63), it is said that "when the body is tired, inhale through the right nostril."

Breath Technique: The breath is controlled by inhaling and exhaling through the right nostril only while blocking the left nostril. The breath may be continuous for excellent effect. An advanced practice is to retain the breath as long as the inhale and the exhale (1:1:1 ratio). The ratio can slowly be increased with practice to 1:2:2 and eventually 1:4:2.

Gong Technique: The gong is played to activate the Pingala Nadi during the pranayama practice by striking the gong at the beginning of each inhale and exhale. When inhaling through the left nostril, the gong is played with an upward strike at percussion point 3. When exhaling through the left nostril, the gong is played with a downward strike at percussion point 3. The rhythm should be slow to medium and allow for a full inhale and exhale and the volume is medium. The intention behind the playing is warming and elevating.

Surya Bhedana (Sun Piercing Breath)

Surya Bhedana, more popularly known as the Sun Piercing breath, works with Pingala Nadi to bring about warmth and projection. The breath works on the left hemisphere of the brain and the sympathetic nervous system. In the *Hatha Yoga Pradipika* (2:50), it is said that practicing this pranayama purifies the brain and destroys the imbalances present in the vata (wind) dosha.

Breath Technique: The breath is controlled by inhaling through the right nostril and exhaling through the left nostril, alternately blocking off the nostril not being used. The breath may be continuous for excellent effect. An advanced practice is to retain the breath for as long as the inhale and the exhale (1:1:1 ratio). The ratio can slowly be increased with practice to 1:2:2 and eventually 1:4:2.

Gong Technique: The gong is played to activate the Pingala Nadi during the pranayama practice by striking the gong at the beginning of each inhale and exhale. When inhaling through the right nostril, the gong is played with an upward strike at percussion point 3. When exhaling through the left nostril, the gong is played with a downward strike at percussion point 9. The rhythm should be slow to medium and allow for a full inhale and exhale and the volume is medium. The intention behind the playing is outgoing and focusing.

Bhastrika (Bellows Breath)

Bhastrika, also known as Bellows Breath because of the forceful pumping, is the most energizing pranayama of yoga. The breath is heating and builds the internal fire of the physical and pranic body. It increases oxygen levels, reduces carbon dioxide, stimulates the metabolic rate, and flushes out wastes and toxins while massaging the organs, particularly the liver, and improves digestion and elimination.. In the *Hatha Yoga Pradipika* (2:66-67), it is said that practicing this pranayama arouses kundalini and breaks open the three psychic pranic knots (*granthis*) so the kundalini may rise.

Breath Technique: The breath is a strong active exhale and inhale with an exaggerated movement of the diaphragm and abdomen. One inhale and exhale cycle takes two seconds for beginners and may be increased to one cycle per second and then two cycles per second. Generally the breath is practiced in rounds of 10 to 30 breaths and from 5 to 10 rounds. Beginners may start by breathing through both nostrils. Eventually the breath is done for one round through the left nostril only, ending with a deep inhalation through the left nostril and retention. Then a round is done for the right nostril only. Finally a round is done with both nostrils. The cycle of left, right, and both nostrils may be repeated from 3 to 10 times. At the end of a round, the inhaled breath may be retained for several seconds and then exhaled suspended out for several seconds. Normal breathing may be practiced between the rounds.

Gong Technique: The gong is played in rhythm with the breath, loudly and quickly, with a strike for each breath cycle (inhale and exhale). The strike rate will be one to four times every two seconds, and should be played louder than the sound of the powerful breath. The gong may be played at any percussion point, but typically gets best results when played with upward strikes above the center of the gong (Up 0 percussion point). If retention of the breath is practiced, at the end of the round the gong is struck loudly one time to signal the end of the round and the breath is inhaled and retained comfortably as the sound decays. The gong is struck again to signal the exhalation. If suspension of the breath follows after exhalation, the gong is struck at the end of the suspension when it is time to inhale again. The intention behind the playing is fiery and forceful.

The Gong Yoga Teacher's Practice: Pranayama

The Gong Yoga teacher creates a relationship with prana, the breath, and the gong by practicing pranayama while playing. Simply stated, the player breathes into the gong and with the gong.

Consciously breathing while playing the gong is a powerful pranayama practice for the player. By connecting the breath to the movement of the mallet and the playing process, the Gong Yoga teacher can direct prana into the sound, as well as cultivate and conserve their own prana. The more prana the player can bring into the playing process through conscious breathing techniques, the more transformational the sound becomes.

The conscious breathing can be long deep breathing or it can be a modified Breath of Fire (or Agni Pran) or continuous Ujiya breath as the gong is played rhythmically. For specific single strikes, a conscious inhale occurs when the mallet is pulled away from the surface and the exhale occurs when the mallet strikes the gong. Breathing the mallet into the gong in this manner creates a pranic charge that is amplified through the sound and reaches the listener.

When the Gong Yoga teacher maintains a conscious awareness of the breath while playing, the level of prana transferred both into the room and from the player is significantly experienced.

Similarly, the students can be instructed to use their breath awareness to bring more prana by consciously directing their breath into different areas of the body as the gong is played. This can be done to create an opening in asana, a release during relaxation, or a focus during meditation that connects sound to breath in a new and powerful way.

I am the taste of the water,

The light of the sun and moon.

I am the sound in the ether,

And the possibility within you.

Bhagavad Gita (7:8)

Mantra and the Gong: Playing for the Emotional Body

Mantra and the sound of the gong affect the manamaya kosha, the layer of existence between the breath body (pranamaya kosha) and the knowledge body (vijnanamaya kosha), thereby creating the bridge from the grosser to the more subtle practices of yoga. When mantra is used or when the gong is played, the manamaya kosha is strengthened and healed, much like asana for the physical body and pranayama for the energy body.

Because it affects the emotional layer, the sound of the gong can bring emotional releases, especially when heard the first several times. Crying or laughing may be common, as well as experiencing transient states of anxiety, fear, love or bliss, as emotional reorganization is brought about by the sound of the gong.

Gradually as the manamaya kosha interacts with this sound, the various emotional states subside and the general feeling is well-being. From this calm and neutral emotional center, it becomes easier to experience the meditative mind contained in the vijnanamaya kosha.

The relationship between the gong, mantra, the emotional body, and the inner sounds of yoga is one of the most profound in the practice of Gong Yoga.

The Gong, Mantras and the Science of Naad

All sound has a common origin with the universal sound current. All music, all spoken words, all mantra possess to some degree a fundamental frequency and a specific sound essence that is known as **Naad**. This sound essence is the vibrational harmony that connects the finite to the infinite. When we hear sounds that are closely aligned with this universal resonance known as the Naad, we tune in to the infinite consciousness that is the source of all sound.

Mantras are especially potent vehicles to carry the Naad and were the first recorded yoga technique, predating the more common practices (at least in the Western world) of asanas and pranayama. As powerful as mantras are for creating a change in consciousness due to their ability to align us with the Naad, it is the Gong that most closely approximates the Naad in its purest state and vibration.

Within the gong are all mantras, all sounds, all words, and all voices, and it is not uncommon for people to seeming hear different musical instruments playing in he sound of the gong. When the gong is used with mantra, we purify and accelerate the effects of the mantra on the manamaya kosha. Using the gong with mantras is one of the most natural expressions of Gong Yoga, and can be achieved in three ways:

- Mantras are played while the gong is played.

- Mantras are chanted while the gong is played.

- Mantras are repeated silently while the gong is played.

Playing Mantras with the Gong

A simple way to experience the power of mantras with the gong is to play recorded mantras and the gong simultaneously. The recorded mantra provides a soundtrack that the gong player can interact with by playing over, under, or along with the recorded sound.

When the gong is played with a recorded mantra, the gong player may interact with the mantra in several ways. One option is to begin playing the mantra before the gong is struck and allow the listener to fully hear the mantra and experience its rhythm and vibration. After awhile, the gong player can begin playing the gong softly in a supporting rhythm or cadence that is consonant with the mantra. At this stage, the sound of the mantra dominates over the sound of the gong that simply serves to accentuate and not obliterate the recorded mantra.

A second option is to start by playing the gong first and then bringing in the sound of the recorded mantra. The gong player plays the gong softly enough so the mantra can be heard, but, unlike the first option, the gong remains the dominant sound and the mantra is experienced almost subliminally.

A third option is to start either with the recorded mantra or the gong, and then alternate the gong playing so that at times the mantra dominates the listener's experience, and at other times the gong is louder than the mantra. Indeed, the gong may eventually completely overwhelm the sound of the mantra until it simply disappears and then magically re-appears as the gong is played softly. The alternating duet between the volume of the gong and the volume of the mantra re-directs the focus of the listener until the two sounds blend into a greater synergistic whole.

When selecting a mantra to play with the gong, consider its rhythm, cadence and strength. A simple mantra is best, as well as a mantra with a strong carrying tone and rhythm that can complement and compete with the powerful sound of the gong.

Chanting Mantras with the Gong

Chanting a mantra as the gong is played increases the prana of the mantra and brings its vibration deeper into the listener's awareness. The active participation between the chanter and the gong player is somewhat akin to the practice of kirtan whereby the voice of the individual is assimilated into the common group sound (supplied by the gong) and produces a sense of sonic communion.

Unlike playing the gong with a recorded mantra, playing the gong with a mantra chanted by one or more individuals requires the gong be played at a consistent volume so the sound of the mantra can be clearly heard. In other words, the gong becomes a partner in the sound current produce by the mantra and neither dominates nor disappears as the mantra is chanted.

Mantras of simple repetitive sounds work best when chanting with the gong, such as bija mantras (seed mantras of one or two syllables) and ashtang mantras (mantras with 8 distinctive sounds).

Amplifying Mantras with the Gong

If the gong is large enough (generally 38 inches or 100 cm), there is the opportunity to chant mantras near the gong when it is not being played and have the sound of the mantra reverberate through the gong and be heard. In this way, the gong serves as a transmitter, amplifier, and transformer of the human voice, translating the spoken mantras into the language of the gong and allowing it to chant with the practitioner.

The ability of the gong to capture any sound in the room and then re-sound it makes it a powerful instrument to have in a yoga class whether it is played or not. Whenever mantras are chanted or music is played in a room with the gong, these sounds are subtly captured and returned by the gong, even when inaudible to the human ear, producing a vibrational complexity that affects the consciousness.

Furthermore, once struck, the vibrations of a gong resonate at the molecular level for *40 years*! For all practical purposes, the gong is always chanting or resonating, regardless if it is being actively played or not.

Silent Mantra with the Gong

Chanting a mantra silently as the gong is played strengthens the subtle body of the practitioner and directs the flow of prana produced by the gong. Similarly to using mantra with asanas and pranayamas, repeating a silent mantra with the gong directs the mind and clears the subconscious.

Mantras consisting of simple repetitive sounds work best when chanting silently with the gong, such as bija mantras (seed mantras of one or two syllables) and ashtang mantras (mantras with 8 distinctive sounds).

The silent use of mantras with the gong works well for people who may have fears or resistance around the sound of the gong, as well as those who may be suffering from traumatic stress or shock. The silent mantra creates a connective link between the listener and the gong that gives a sense of control to the practitioner.

The advantage for the gong player is that silent mantra allows for more freedom in how the gong is played. For the practitioner, silent mantra can create a specialized and deeper internal focus and processing than mantras played or chanted out loud.

Chakra Bija Mantras with the Gong

An effective use of mantras with the gong is to chant the traditional bija (seed) mantra for each chakra while the gong is struck to activate the corresponding chakra. The mantras may be done silently or out loud. The following chart shows the sounds and the corresponding areas of the gong to be struck for the seven chakras.

Chakra	Mantra (silent)	Mantra (out loud)	Gong Area
First Muladhara_	LAM	LANG (lung)	Above bottom rim
Second Svadhishthana	VAM	VANG (vung)	Higher above bottom rim
Third Manipura	RAM	RANG (rung)	Below center
Fourth Anahata	YAM	YANG (yung)	Above center
Fifth Vishuddha	HAM	HANG (hung)	Higher above center
Sixth Ajna	AUM	ONG (ong)	Below top rim
Seventh Sahasrara	Silence	Silence	Silence gong

Pronunciation guidelines for chanting the mantras out loud are as follows:

The bija mantra LANG is pronounced *lung* with the 'L' sound produced by placing the tongue behind the upper teeth. The mantra is made up of two sounds that are almost equal in length, 'LA' and 'NG.'

The duration for the two sounds is the same for all the chakra bija mantras. Notice the common sound 'NG' is created by vibrating the sound inside the cranium. It is said that the 'NG' sound is the *nada bindu*, or the primal cosmic sound that created all sounds in the universe.

The bija mantra VANG is pronounced *vung* with the 'V' sound produced by the lips as though making a 'FF' sound.

The bija mantra RANG is pronounced *rung* with the 'R' sound produced by curling the tip of the tongue to the roof of the mouth.

The bija mantra YANG is pronounced *yung* with the 'Y' sound produced with the tongue pressed against the soft palate at the front of the roof of the mouth.

The bija mantra HANG is pronounced *hung* with the 'H' sound produced at the back of the throat.

The bija mantra ONG is produced from the back of the throat and the front of the open mouth.

Nada Yoga and the Inner Sounds

Nada Yoga divides sound into the inner sounds, discovered by the yogi in meditation, and the outer sounds, such as music and the gong that are conveyed through the sensory organs. Being able to experience the inner sounds is considered to be the highest form of Nada Yoga, and this occurs when the consciousness or prana is centered in the top-center region of the head (anterior fontanelle), or what the yogis call the *Brahmrandhra*, during the advanced stages of mediation and pranayama.

Yet the use of external sounds, such as practiced in Gong Yoga, can also create a focused awareness and a heightened sensitivity to all vibration that can lead the practitioner to an experience that is similar to that produced by hearing the subtle inner sounds.

These inner sounds have been compared in various yogic texts to external sounds created by musical instruments. By replicating these internal sounds through musical instruments and the gong, we can create an experience of Nada Yoga. Here are descriptions from the major works on yoga of the different stages of the inner sounds:

Hatha Yoga Pradipika

In the first stage, the sounds are surging, thundering and jingling like kettle-drums. In the second stage, the sounds are like the conch and bells. In the final stage, the sounds are like the flute and the bee.

Shiva-Samhita

The first sound is the hum of the bee, then a flute, then a harp and gradually the sounds of ringing bells and then a roar like thunder.

Nadabindu Upanishad

At first the sound is like the gentle ocean, then the kettle-drum and waterfall. Later the sound becomes like the tabor or small drum, then a big bell and a military drum. Finally the sound is that of a tinkling bell, the bamboo flute, then the harp and the sound of a humming bee.

Darsana Upanishad

First the sound of a conch blast (sankha-dhvani), then a clap of thunder, and finally the roaring of a mountain stream.

Hamsa Upanishad

The sounds begin as a whisper, then the sound of a bell. Next are the conch, the lute, and the cymbal. Then come the flute, the drum, the double drum, and finally the roaring thunder.

Although these descriptions differ, the general experience is one of a lesser to a greater sound. The gong can approximate most of these sounds when skillfully played (note especially the "clap of thunder"). Here is a suggested soundscape, from five different yogic texts, to externally re-create the inner sounds heard by the yogi in meditation by using musical instruments, including the gong. Each instrument may be played by moving from the top to the bottom.

Hatha Yoga Pradipika	Siva Samhita	Nada Bindu Upanishad	Darsana Upanishad	Hamsa Upanishad
Gong	Humming	Gong	Conch	Humming
Drums	Flute	Small Drum	Drums	Bell
Conch	Harp	Big Bell	Gong	Conch
Bells	Bells	Big Drum		Lute
Flute	Gong	Small Bell		Cymbal
Humming		Flute		Flute
		Harp		Drums
		Humming		Gong

The gong can also be played by itself for 2 to 3 minutes through each of the six successive stages, from the subtle to the most profound, moving from top to bottom, as follows:

Stages of Sound	Gong Playing Technique
First	Slow single centering strikes, medium soft
Second	Light sparkling strikes around the top rim
Third	Medium diagonal strikes (percussion points 2 > 8, 10 > 4)
Fourth	Strong center strikes (percussion points Up 0, Down 0)
Fifth	Crashing strikes upper half of gong
Sixth	Light whispering strikes above bottom rim

Shanmukhi (Yoni) Mudra and the Inner Sounds

Shanmukhi mudra may be used to create a state of sensory withdrawal, or pratyahara, to go inward and listen to the inner sounds. The Sanskrit word *shan* means six and *mukhi* means face or gate. Shanmikhi mudra involves using the fingers to close the six gates of perception or openings in the face – the two eyes, two ears, and two nostrils – to limit sensory input. The mudra is also called Yoni mudra as the word *yoni* also means a cave or the womb where sensory impressions are decreased.

How to Do it: Bring the palms in front of the face with the elbows. Close the ears with the thumbs. Close the eyes with the index and middle fingers by gently pressing the eyelids. Inhale deeply and close the nostrils with the ring fingers. Retain the breath as long as comfortable while closing the ears, eyes and nostrils with the fingers. After some time, release the pressure of the middle fingers and slowly breathe out. You can also keep the fingers on the nostrils without closing them to perform this without breath retention. Listen to the silence or inner sounds. Practice 3 to 11 minutes or as long as comfortable, then remove the fingers and lower the arms.

Shanmukhi (Yoni) Mudra and Hearing the Gong

Shanmukhi mudra may also be used to listen to the gong and constitutes a form of gong yoga meditation. The teacher begins playing the gong as students connect to the breath. After a few moments, the students perform Shanmikhi mudra, using the option to not block the nostrils and instead breathing normally. By sealing off the ears and eyes, a new experience of the sound of the gong is created that is deeply internalized in the listener.

Using Other Sounds with the Gong

For the yogi, the gong is not simply a musical instrument to be played or orchestrated with other instruments. Yet its powerful sound can be used with other musical sounds to re-create the the inner sounds of Nada Yoga.

The most obvious examples of gongs as part of a greater sound experience are the traditional gamelan orchestras of Indonesia in which there may be flutes, metal bowls, thick metal bars and other percussion instruments. In keeping with this classical approach, suitable instruments to be used with the gong are other metal percussion instruments, woodwinds, and drums.

In particular, metal bowls and chimes seamlessly complement the gong soundscape, while native flutes and the conch work well during periods of silence. The *sitar* (or harp) and *vina* (zither) are also old friends with the gong. The Australian didgeridoo, while not used in the original yoga practices, creates a contrast of earthly sonorous sounds with the ethereal sound of the gong. In many cases, these instruments are used during interim periods when the gong is silent.

The Gong Yoga Teacher's Practice: Mantra

Chanting mantras silently and out loud while *playing the gong* can be profound and transformational for both the player and the listener. Just as practicing pranayama without mantra is not pranayama, playing a gong without mantra is simply – well, only playing the gong!

Chanting mantras while playing the gong connects the prana and consciousness of the gong player to the gong and powerfully directs the prana into the sound of the gong and the consciousness of the listeners. In some ways, this is one of the greatest and most powerful secrets of teaching gong yoga.

While chanting mantras out loud may not always be possible or even advisable in some teaching situations and environments, the teacher can always chant a mantra silently as the gong is played. Play in the rhythm and cadence of your silently chanted mantra, and let mantra inform and guide your playing. In this manner, the gong will magnify the effects of the mantra many times over.

Meditation and the Gong: Playing for the Knowledge Body

One of the most effective uses of the gong in the practice of yoga is its ability to naturally induce a state of spontaneous meditation, regardless of the background or experience of the practitioner. Indeed, people who have never had a formal practice or experience of meditation are able to enter into a physiological and psychological state of meditation through the sound of the gong.

Part of its ability to create a state conducive to meditation is that the sound of the gong has an affinity for activating the crown chakra that connects the listener to a consciousness that exists beyond time and space. One of the gong's earliest uses was to be played at the time of death to allow the subtle body to leave the physical body through the crown chakra, as postulated in some yoga teachings.

Throughout its history the gong has also been played to create a heightened state of psychic sensibility. It was played to awaken intuition so that prophets and mystics could more easily foretell the future. The gong was considered to be a portal to God because its playing increased a profound state of intensified sensory perception through sound that allowed the listener to experience the self in a new way.

To understand how the gong can be played for meditation in a yoga practice, we first need to distinguish what yoga practices facilitate the meditative state to occur.

Yoga Techniques and Meditation

The popular Western practices of yoga are drawn from the Hatha and Kundalini traditions, and meditation will be discussed in this context, as opposed to the practices of Raja Yoga as described in the Yoga Sutras.

Essentially in these traditions, meditation occurs as a result of employing the yogic techniques of asana, pranayama, mudra and mantra or sound in a synergistic manner to prepare the physical, energy, and emotional bodies to experience the knowledge body (vijnanamaya kosha). Lets look at these four foundational techniques in the practice of Gong Yoga meditation.

Asana and Gong Meditation

The experience of the gong as played for relaxation is profoundly different then when played for meditation. This difference primarily occurs due to the asana requirement in yoga that meditation can only occur when the body is in an upright-seated posture and not when in a relaxed supine state. In yoga, meditation is the process by which the movement of energy through the spine and chakras opens the higher centers of consciousness. This movement only effectively occurs when the spine of the practitioner is in a perpendicular relationship to the earth's magnetic field so that energy can move upward.

While the gong may be enjoyed in a transformational way when relaxing on the back, the experience is not properly called meditation unless a seated posture is used (including siting in a chair, as long as the spine is in perpendicular alignment). Another consideration is how posture affects our orientation in time. Supine postures, as occur in sleep or deep relaxation, create an orientation to the past, such as in the dream state. Standing positions, such as occur when walking or moving through space, create an orientation toward the future as we move forward. Seated postures, such as occur during reflection and self-absorption, create an orientation to the stillness of the present, which is another characteristic of meditation.

Pranayama and Gong Meditation

Conscious awareness of the breath is a requirement in the practice of Gong Yoga meditation. All meditation begins with a conscious connection to the breath, as the movement of prana is intimately associated with the movement of the mind. Without some sort of breath awareness, at least initially, the state of meditation is difficult to create and maintain.

When the gong is played, one of its major effects is to create a movement of prana through the body. This rhythmical and resonating movement of prana through the sound of the gong deeply affects the nature of the mind and the arising of thoughts. Often the mind seems to stand still or is suspended by the sound of the gong. This occurs because the movement of prana begins to move in accordance with the sound of the gong and not in its usual erratic or vacillating nature. A new pranic pattern is imprinted when the gong is played, and this can be greatly enhanced through a conscious connection with the breath.

If students are challenged by the gong as it begins its energetic re-programming of the body, mind and emotions, it is helpful to remind them to simply create an aware connection to the breath. This breath awareness allows the prana that is moved by the gong to more easily be integrated into the emerging new pattern of energy. When this is accomplished, the meditative mind naturally occurs. In this respect, breath awareness, or a modified form of breath control or pranayama, aids in creating the experience of meditation when listening to the gong. Without the breath awareness, there may be a resistant to the movement of prana that the gong produces and an inability to enter fully into meditation.

Mantra (Sound) and Gong Meditation

Obviously the yogic technique of using sound (or mantra) is paramount in practicing Gong Yoga meditation. The common error in playing the gong for meditation is to assume that one only needs to experience the sound, much like hearing music, to create the desired effect. There is a fundamental difference, however, between hearing and listening, and this difference is vital in the practice of Gong Yoga meditation.

Hearing is a passive process, and sometimes unconscious, whereas listening is active and completely conscious. Listening to the gong is what allows its sound to produce a state of meditation and for the listener to completely merge with the outer and inner sound that is the goal of using mantra and sound in yoga.

Guru Nanak expressed the virtue of listening over 500 years ago when he recited the following in a heightened state of mystical revelation: "Listening, the technology of yoga, and the secrets of the body are revealed. …Listening, and intuitively grasping the essence of Meditation."

Actively listening to the sound of the gong during meditation can be accomplished in several ways. One effective method, which can also be done when practicing mantra, is to internalize the outer sound into the body or mind. One way to do this is to feel or localize the sound of the gong into the spine, feeling the sound move through the body and vibrating along the central channel or Sushumna. Another way to is actively listen to the sound as it enters both ears, distinguishing the subtle difference in sound between right and left. Allowing the sound to vibrate inside the head or various other areas of the body also can create a deeper identification with the sound of the gong. Sensing the tactile sensation that sound can create on the surface of the skin, inside the ears, or even the eyelids creates a deeper identification with the sound. Sometimes even sensing the sound moving along the floor and entering the base of the spine can be a profound experience.

If you are visually oriented, the sound can be given colors or allowed to create images at the brow point or third eye. You can also see the sound as it moves around the room and through the body. By exploring other forms of synesthesia, such as tasting or even smelling the various sounds the gong creates, different cognitive pathways open that allow us to deeply listen to the gong in a meditative manner. Primarily, listening to the gong during meditation is a willful and active engagement of the senses to first identify the sound as coming from the outside but ultimately existing inside the listener.

In reality, the sound of the gong only exists in the mind of the listener due to its unique combination of acoustic undertones that is created in playing, and so no two people hear the gong in the same manner. This entirely personal perception of the gong's sound is due to its undertones. These undertones, which are produced when loud tones are sounded together, are known as combination tones. Acousticians consider combination tones to be a physiological phenomenon, rather than an acoustical one, because the tones are actually synthesized within the inner ear of each listener by the vibration of the cochlea, or extremely delicate hairs. The gong thus produces an inner sound as well as an outer sound. It is this dual sound that takes each listener deeper into their own experience of being so that the sound of the gong becomes individually unique to each person and leads them into the inner realm of deep meditation.

Mudras and Gong Meditation

The last technique of Gong Yoga meditation, the performance of mudras, is likely the most important to create the state of meditation. A mudra is commonly thought of as a hand position or gesture in which the fingers touch each other in order to seal and direct the flow of prana. More generally, mudras may also involve muscular locks (*bandhas*), eye positions or gazes (*drishtis*), and certain body positions (*asanas*).

When various mudras are used in a yoga practice along with the sound of the gong, the movement of prana in the energy body can be optimally directed to produce a state of a spontaneous state of meditation. Indeed, all gong meditation is primarily mudra-based and, as mentioned, may involve the fingers, eyes, muscular locks, and body positions to integrate the sound of the gong more deeply into the practice. Mudras work primarily to attune and balance the energies of the first three koshas, physical, energetic and mental, so that the knowledge body, the fourth kosha is strengthened.

While mudras are a necessary component of all yogic meditation practices, they play an even more critical role in Gong Yoga Meditation. Without mudras, there can be no experience of meditation using the sound of the gong because the mudras are essential to direct the prana created by the sound to the different areas of the physical and subtle body that support meditation.

There are over 3500 known mudras in the practice of yoga and all of them can be used with the sound of the gong. The gong supports all mudras, and any mudra can more effectively channel the energy of the gong for healing, pranayama, and meditation. Here are a few hand (*hast*) mudras that are known to specifically facilitate meditation with the gong.

Pran Bandha Mudra

A simple and effective hand mudra to use for Gong Yoga mediation is Pran Bandha, which collects, binds and commands the life force (*pran*) that is produced and directed by the sound of the gong. The mudra is performed by holding the two small fingers of each hand down with the thumb and extending the two large fingers up, side by side. The hands are held at shoulder level, palms facing forward. The hands are pulled slightly back so a pressure is created between the shoulder blades and the spine is tightened and lengthened. There is a sense of opening the central channel of the body, or Sushumna, so that energy can rise through the body. The eyes are closed and fixed toward the tip of the nose. Be aware of the tips of the two extended fingers as you listen to the sound of the gong.

Sahasrara Bandha Mudra

There are many variations of Sahasrara mudra in which the hands are interlocked or clasped over the crown of the head. Sahasrara refers to the crown chakra, or the seventh energy center, which exists about four inches about the top of the head. A basic version is to interlace the fingers and bring the hands 4-6 inches (10-15 centimeters) over the top of head. The arms are pulled slightly back so that the hands are over the center of the skull. There is a constant

Pran Bandha Mudra

Sahasrara Bandha Mudra

Humkara Mudra

Gyan Bandha

light pull on the hands as if they could be pulled apart. The eyes roll up to the top of the head as if to look up into the hands. This mudra greatly facilitates the natural opening of the crown chakra that the sound of the gong produces.

Humkara Mudra

This Tibetan Buddhist mudra that crosses the hands over the heart has many different expressions, depending upon how the hands and fingers are held. The mudra brings equanimity, neutrality and balance to the heart and mind. The simplest version has the left hand crossing over the center of the chest and the right hand crosses over the left hand, locking energy at the heart chakra. Another variation is to cross the wrists, not touching, with the thumb tip touching the index finger tip of both hands. Many mudras can be adapted to this practice by performing the same mudra with each hand and then crossing the two hands with the right in front over the left over the heart center.

Gyan Bandha Mudra

This mudra uses the classic Gyan mudra (sometimes called Chin or Jnana mudra) that touches the thumb tips to the index finger tips of both hands. In Gyan Bandha mudra, the two individual circles formed by Gyan mudra are interlocked with each other by joining them together like a chain link in front of the heart. The interlocked circles do not touch each other but float in space. The eyes are one-tenth open and look down toward the interlocked chain. This mudra has the ability to completely still the mind and lock the thoughts and is especially useful when playing the gong in a rhythmical and hypnotic manner.

Mehtab Benton

Mudras for the Chakras

As the gong can be played to activate and access the seven major chakras and different gongs may also be used to work on specific chakras, specific mudras may be held for each of the chakras. You can refer to the section on chakras for how to play the gong for each chakra mudra.

There are many different mudras for the chakras. The following ones are some of the simplest to perform.

First Chakra (Muladhara Mudra)

Technique: Touch the tip of each index finger touch to the tip of each thumb. Extend the other fingers out, touching the sides together. Rest the hands palms down toward the earth. Perform *mulabandha,* or the root lock, by slightly contracting the anal sphincter, sex organs and navel point.

Second Chakra (Swadhisthana Mudra)

Technique: Open the hands, palms up. Hold the right hand below the navel point and above the lap with the palm turned up. Rest the back of the left hand in the right palm. Connect the two thumbs tips together. (Men should reverse the hand position).

Third Chakra (Manipura Mudra)

Technique: Bring the hands together in front of the navel point with the four fingers joined together, tips touching, Pull the hands slightly apart, keeping the fingertips touching. Cross the left thumb over the right thumb. (Men should cross the right thumb over the left thumb.)

Fourth Chakra (Anahata or Lotus Mudra)

Technique: Bring the hands in front of the heart center and join the heels of the palms together. Pull all the fingers back away from each other and then join the sides of the little fingers and thumbs together, making a shape like an open lotus or flower.

Fifth Chakra (Vishuddha Mudra)

Technique: Interlace the fingers with the palms facing up and relaxed in a comfortable position. Connect the thumb tips together and pull them upward to make a circle between the palms and the thumbs.

Sixth Chakra (Ajna Mudra)

Technique: Bring the hands together and join the four fingers by pressing the second knuckle of each finger together. Turn the palms down and pull the thumbs down and touch the thumb tips together. Now extend the middle fingers up straight from the other fingers and touch their two tips together, pointing upward.

Seventh Chakra (Sahasrara Mudra)

Technique: With palms facing down, interlace the fingers and cross the thumbs, left thumb over right thumb. (Men reverse the position.) Extend the little fingers up and touch the tips together.

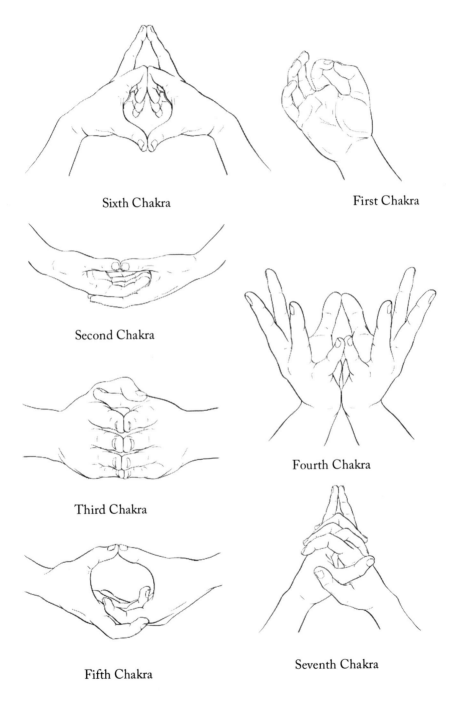

Sixth Chakra

First Chakra

Second Chakra

Fourth Chakra

Third Chakra

Fifth Chakra

Seventh Chakra

Mudras for the Planets

Given that there are gongs tuned to the various planetary energies, there are also traditional mudras from Vedic or Indian astrology that may be used when specific planetary gongs are played in order to enhance the unique energy of each one.

In addition, any gong can be played in a manner that is consonant with the primary quality associated with that planet according to Vedic (Indian) Astrology in order to activate or balance the energy associated with that planet. The primary playing style for each planet is also specified.

Notice that there are no traditional yogic mudras for the outer planets (Uranus, Neptune, and Pluto) so only the seven visible planets are represented by the following mudras. Each mudra is named after the Sanskrit name of the planet associated with the finger, or area of hand, as follows:

Sun (Surya Mudra)

Technique: Touch the thumb tip to the ring finger tip.

Gong Playing: Steady, strong and bright. Also playing the Sun Planetary Gong.

Named after the Sun (Surya), this mudra is also called Ravi Mudra (another name for the Sun) and, like the Sun, gives revitalizing strength, excellent health, immunity, nerve strength, stability and outwardly directed energy. It is also used to strengthen potency and efficacy.

Moon (Chandra Mudra)

Technique: Join the outside of the hands together below the little finger to the base of the palms.

Gong Playing: Nurturing, variable and feminine. Also playing the Sidereal Moon or the Synodic Moon Planetary Gong.

Named after the Moon (Chandra), this mudra enhances our receptivity and intuition and brings a balance to our emotions and our thoughts as well as to our fantasies and our plans.

Mars (Mangala Mudra)

Technique: Make a fist of the hand with the thumb extended or curled inside.

Gong Playing: Aggressive, fierce and fiery. Also playing the Mars Planetary Gong.

Named after Mars (Mangala), this mudra is formed by curling the fingers into the palm and bringing the thumb outside the fist or extended up. Bringing the thumb to the base of the ring finger and making a fist around the thumb can also form it. This mudra increases courage, vitality, strength, assertion, and ability to overcome obstacles.

Mercury (Buddhi Mudra)

Technique: Touch the thumb tip to the little finger.

Gong Playing: Playful, clever and quickly. Also playing the Mercury Planetary Gong.

Named after Mercury (Buddhi) the messenger of the gods, this mudra enhances all areas of communication. It gives quickness to the mental processes, increases analytical ability, and develops intuition and psychic faculties. It is also beneficial for commerce and prosperity.

Jupiter (Gyan Mudra)

Technique: Touch the thumb tip to the index finger.

Gong Playing: Expansive, benign, and thoughtful. Also playing the Jupiter Planetary Gong.

Named for the wisdom (*gyan*) of Jupiter, this mudra is also called Chin Mudra or Jnana Mudra and is the most practiced of the planetary mudras. This mudra receives and integrates knowledge and brings calmness, expansion, and understanding. Since the dispelling of ignorance (*avidya*) is the first step toward enlightenment, this mudra is often used in meditation and pranayama practices. It is also associated with opportunity and good fortune.

Venus (Shukra Mudra)

Technique: Interlace the hands with thumbs resting side by side and not crossing. Fingers are interlaced so men press the right thumb on the mound and left little finger is on bottom. Women press the left thumb on the mound with right little finger on the bottom.

Gong Playing: Easy, sensual and spontaneous. Also playing the Venus Planetary Gong.

Named after Venus (Shukra), this mudra channels sexual energy into love and compassion and balances our sensuality.

Saturn (Shani Mudra)

Technique: Touch the thumb tip to the middle finger.

Gong Playing: Very slow, metered and methodical. Also playing the Saturn Planetary Gong.

Named after Saturn (Shani), the lord of Karma, which represents discipline, hard work, duty, responsibility, and selfless service, this mudra is used to give patience and perseverance so we can understand the lessons of time. It produces calmness, purity and humility.

BASIC PLANETARY MUDRAS

Surya
Mudra
(Sun)

Chandra
Mudra (Moon)

Mangala
Mudra
(Mars)

Budha
Mudra
(Mercury)

Gyan
Mudra
(Jupiter)

Shukra
Mudra
(Venus)

Shani
Mudra
(Saturn)

Playing the Gong for Meditation

Playing the gong for meditation is significantly different than playing the gong as an accompaniment for asanas, pranayama or relaxation. To support the state of meditation, the gong should be played to create a sound that locks and engages the mind instead of impressing or entertaining it. In other words, the cleverness or personal expression of the gong player should be subordinated to creating a neutral state of mind in the meditator.

Ideally when the gong is played for meditation, it creates a deep absorption, a vanishing of separation in the mind of the listener until there is a sense of merger between the sound of the gong and the meditative mind.

This state of absorption in sound until all else dissolves save the bliss of experience is known as Laya Yoga. As the listener becomes absorbed by the external sound of the gong, the distinction between the listener and the sound dissolves into oneness. The ability of the gong to create a sound unique to each listener so that the mind becomes entranced and stilled makes it a powerful instrument for inducing a meditative state.

With the surrender of the lower mind to the sound of the gong, the listener enters into the transcendental state of *shuniya* or a zero point of complete stillness, where inner truth can be accessed and visions spontaneously arise. In this respect, the gong is the yogi's instrument for creating a spontaneous meditative state that only requires the listener to let go and let gong.

The guidelines for playing the gong for mediation are:

- Maintain a consistency in rhythm and volume so as to not distract the listener.

- Create predictable and returning patterns in the playing, usually in the mid-area of the gong to bring balance and neutrality.

- Alternate between playing near the center of the gong and around the rim of the gong to re-direct the mind inward.

Binaural Beats and Gong Meditation

The gong is very adept at producing what are termed binaural beats, or binaural tones, by simultaneously creating one sound of two different frequencies that are heard by the listener as one tone. When this occurs, brainwave frequencies begin to align with the tones to create a state of brainwave entrainment that leads to deep meditation.

To practice creating binaural beats with the gongs, two mallets of different sizes are struck slightly out of sync in a repeated pattern to create a pulsing sound. Ideally there is only a small offset in the frequencies of the two tones created by the two mallets. This beat can also be approximated with only one mallet, by quickly striking two areas slightly off-center so that two tones blend into one sound.

An advanced practice is to meditate between two gongs. The two gongs are played in the offsetting manner as previously described for one gong so that the sound from one enters the left ear and the sound from the other enters the right ear. The gongs are played in such a close rhythm and offset that the listener distinguishes the two sounds as only one. This replicates the effect of binaural sound that is often created through the wearing of headphones.

The Gong Yoga Teacher's Practice: Meditation

When teaching Gong Yoga, the gong player should prepare by practicing meditation to awaken intuition and create a neutral space free of the ego's agenda. Ideally the meditation is done within one hour before playing the gong.

The meditation can consist of simple pranayamas, recitation of mantras, or performing asanas. Yoga sets (kriyas) and meditations that work on the fifth and sixth chakras are particularly effective in preparing the teacher to play the gong. Here are examples of simple and short meditations that activate the flow of prana through the higher chakras (4, 5, 6, and 7) before playing the gong:

Meditation to Open the Heart and Play with Compassion

Sit in a comfortable meditative posture. Block the right nostril with the thumb or finger of the right hand. Inhale smoothly and fully through the left nostril only. Exhale for an equal length of tie through the pursed lips. The left hand can rest on the center of the chest or heart chakra. After 5 minutes, relax the hands and breath. Meditate for 2 more minutes on the natural flow of the breath

Meditation to Activate the Throat Chakra

Sit in a comfortable meditative posture. Interlace the fingers so that the palms face down and held slight out from the heart. The thumbs relax open and point back to the body.

Inhale and move the interlaced hands quickly up to the brow point or third eye. Exhale and move them quickly down to the heart again, passing back and forth over the throat chakra. Make the movement rapid, almost once per second, so the breath becomes almost like the Breath of Fire (Agni Pran).

After 3 minutes, inhale to the level of the third eye, retain the breath for 20 seconds and pull the hands. Exhale and relax.

Meditation to Awaken Intuition and Third Eye

Sit in a comfortable meditative posture. Focus at the two nostrils and the third eye (brow point). Imagine inhaling only through the left nostril and up to the brow point. Then imagine exhaling only through the right nostril. Now inhale through the right nostril to the brown point and exhale back down through the left nostril. Switch sides and continue back and forth, breathing through alternate nostrils without using the fingers, for 3 to 7 minutes or longer.

Meditation to Open the Crown Chakra

Sit in a meditative posture. Interlace the hands and press them on top of the head. Press the tongue against the roof of the mouth. Roll the eyes up as if to look through the top of the head. Begin Breath of Fire and continue for 5 minutes. Inhale, hold, press the hands down and the tongue up. Exhale and release the hands and tongue.

Ritual and the Gong: Playing for the Bliss Body

In using the kosha model in the practice of Gong Yoga, the bliss body or the anandamaya kosha, is accessed through the technique of ritual. Along with mantras, the practice of ritual is one of the oldest practices of yoga as described in the Rg Veda, and even today in India and beyond, it is the fire rituals and the pujas (ceremonies) that still play an important part in the spiritual evolution of the yogi and yogini. Indeed, the common feature among every spiritual tradition and yoga practice is the performance of ritual, and the practice of Gong Yoga lends itself easily to using this technique to experience the final and fifth layer of existence, the anandamaya kosha.

The word ritual comes from the Latin *ritus* that means to fit together. In the practice of yoga, the ritual is what fits or connects together the finite with infinite, the form with the formless, and the transient with the eternal. Ritual is a gesture or action performed in the material world of the five elements that connects us to the transcendent plane of spirit. Ritual is the relationship we create between the Individual Self with the Universal Self, and the gong is uniquely suited to performing this connection.

The Gong and Its Role in Rituals

The primary function of the gong across all cultures was to mark and create a ritual. The gong has been involved in every kind of human activity, from the earthly to the ethereal. In Buddhist monasteries, gongs call the attention of the gods. In ancient Greece, they opened the realm of the dead. In Borneo, they are beaten to frighten away storms. In Ceram, gongs are given as wedding gifts. In Assam, they are used as funeral pyres. During war, gongs intimidate enemies and gather troops. In peace, they celebrate festivals and accompany dances. Even the ritual of coming to a formal meal was announced by the dinner gong in the early twentieth century.

The gong has played an important role in ceremonies, rituals, and inner journeys among all the world's peoples. Deaths, births, marriages, and initiations were all accompanied by the sounding of the gong. For thousands of years, across all civilizations, all who hear it instinctively recognize the power of the gong to announce or mark a time of transition, of new beginnings or final endings. When the gong is played, the body, mind and spirit change through this timeless ritual and ethereal sound.

The gong may be used alone to create the experience of ritual and access the anandamaya kosha in a yoga class. The opening of the class with one or more strikes of the gong, or the closing of the class by simply sounding the gong, can signify the ritual transition betwwen profane and sacred space. When the gong is played consistently this way to begin and/or to end a Gong Yoga practice, it signals to the practitioner that a ritual is occurring that is beyond ordinary consciousness.

In addition to these simple opening and closing rituals,, the gong player may create their own ways to connect their energy to the energy of the gong and the higher self. Simply bowing the head, touching the heart, or giving a silent blessing can be enough to change from the mundane to the sacred work of playing the gong.

The Five Elements and Performance of Rituals

Rituals are constructed from elemental materials, or the *mahabhuta tattvas* of earth, water, fire, air and ether. By working with these material elements, we can construct rituals that take us beyond our earthly sensibilities. These physical elements of ritual comprise the most ancient language that speaks to everyone and may be represented in several ways.

Element (Tattva)	Represented By:
Earth (Prithvi)	Sacred stones, flowers, statues, precious metals, incense
Water (Jala)	Blessed water, blood, wine, reproductive fluids, elixirs
Fire (Agni)	Bonfires, candles, open flames, lights, sun, illumined objects
Air (Vayu)	Singing, prayer, mantra, feathers, the breath, wind instruments
Ether (Akash)	Gongs, bells, drums, chimes, stringed instruments

An elaborate gong ritual can be constructed by using some or all five of these fundamental elements. For example, a Gong Yoga session may be introduced by the lighting of incense (*prithvi*), the sprinkling of purified water (*jala*), the lighting of a candle (*agni*), the repetition of a mantra (*vayu*), and the strike of the gong (*akash*). When the gong is used in a ritual with other elements, it should always be the initiating and/or terminating element as all things come from ether (*akash*) and return to ether.

The Gong Yoga Teacher's Practice: Ritual

The Gong Yoga teacher may incorporate ritual into the class in several ways. A simple ritual is to cover the gong at the end of a playing session (and consequently uncovering it at the beginning). The covering is a sign of respect for the hidden mysteries of the gong, acknowledging its ability to reveal what is hidden from us when it is unhidden by the player. Practically, the covering of the gong also prevents the electrostatic attraction of dust and particulates that can affect the sound of the gong and eventually harm its surface.

Another pragmatic ritual is the periodic cleaning of the gong with a soft cloth and vinegar and water, or an appropriate cleaning solution. Cleansing practices of all types, from bathing to fasting, figure prominently in many rituals and spiritual practices, and the cleaning of the gong reminds us of the purity we are to bring to our playing. Again in a practical manner, cleaning the gong surface preserves the purity and crispness of the sound when it is played.

A more esoteric clearing of the gong can be done through the ritual application of an essential oil, preferably sandalwood or essence of amber. Care must be taken that the oil is very, very lightly applied or rubbed onto a cloth and then on to the surface of the gong; otherwise, the surface will become oily and hold onto dust and eventually affect the mallet as well. The idea is to subtly bring the clarifying fragrance into the aura of the gong and not massage the oil into it. Sandalwood has been used for centuries to open the higher chakras and cleanse the aura.

Some players have a ritual of asking the gong to guide them through their playing and teaching, or simply making an offering of their playing to a higher entity. Other players may wear certain clothing, sacred malas or jewelry, or carry sacred objects on their person when playing the gong.

The purpose of all these rituals is simply to connect the gong player to a higher guidance that exists beyond the teacher's ego and human agenda.

Opening Mantra as Ritual

One of the most significant and powerful rituals is to use an opening or centering mantra before the gong is played in order to attune the player to the power of the sound of the gong. This linkage between the player and the gong creates the intuitive relationship that allows the gong to play the player as well as the player to play the gong.

In Kundalini Yoga, the specific linkage between the gong player and the gong is made through a series of three mantras. Each of the following mantras is repeated silently or chanted before the gong is played.

AD GUREY NAMEH
JUGAD GUREY NAMEH
SAT GURU NAMEH
SIRI GURU DEV A NAMEH

ONG NAMO GURU DEV NAMO

AD SUCH JUGAD SUCH HAIBHEE SUCH
NANAK HOSEE BHEE SUCH

The first mantra brings you before the timeless teacher, to lay aside your ego, and to allow the wisdom through all the ages to guide you, and is translated as follows:

AD GUREY NAMEH
(I call upon the teacher who exists at the Beginning)
JUGAD GUREY NAMEH
(I call upon the teacher who teaches through all times)
SAT GUREY NAMEH
(I call upon the teacher who teaches from the Truth)
SIRI GURU DEV A NAMEH
(I call upon the unseen subtle teacher of all)

The second mantra links to the creative energy of the universe, the feminine creative power that rules music and all forms of expression, the sound of ONG, of creation itself:

ONG NAMO
(I call upon the Infinite Creative Energy)
GURU DEV NAMO
(I call upon the divine transcendent teacher)

The third mantra takes the mind to the point where sound exists in the eternal moment of truth, beyond polarities and indistinguishable from the sound and the producer of the sound.

AD SUCH
(The truth before all beginnings)
JUGAD SUCH
(The truth through all ages)
HAIBHEE SUCH
(The truth at this moment)
NANAK HOSEE BHEE SUCH
(The truth that is ever true)

Once these mantras are used with the proper intention, the gong player plays what is needed at the present moment and not from the ego of a performer. The karma of the playing becomes dharma and elevates both the player and the listener.

Mantras from other spiritual and yogic traditions may also be used as part of the ritual opening. For example, an offering and mantra may be given to Saraswati, the Vedic goddess of music, arts and knowledge. Honey is the traditional ingredient offered to this goddess of music on the altar. This frequently used mantra may also be used to invoke the energy of Sarawsati before playing the gong:

OM AING SARASWATYE NAMAH OM

The seed or bija mantra **AING** can also be repeated by itself to invoke the energy of the goddess of music, knowledge, sound and arts.

Another useful energy to invoke is that of Ganesha, the deity that removes all blocks and brings us knowledge of the divine. Two simple and powerful Ganesha mantras are:

OM GAM GANAPATAYE NAMAH

OM SHRI GANESHAYA NAMAH

Finally, simply invoking the name of your teacher or that feeling which represents the divine to you is a most effective ritual to open the channel from the player to the infinite.

Relaxation and the Gong: Playing for Integration

As we complete the journey through the five koshas using the techniques of asana, pranayama, mantra, meditation and ritual with the gong, we finish the integration of these energy bodies into wholeness through the experience of relaxation.

Experiencing the gong during relaxation at the end of a yoga class is perhaps one of the most common ways people encounter the healing and transformational sound of the gong. Yet without adequate preparation and awareness on the part of the student, as well as intentionality and understanding by the teacher, the gong relaxation can become a low energy or *tamasic* experience, much like a nap or a warm bath.

While listening to the gong while napping or resting in a semi-conscious state (gong bath), is enjoyable, the opportunity that a well-done relaxation to the gong can provide is missed. There are preparations and practices, as well as playing techniques by the teacher, to create the experience of a profound gong relaxation.

The basic guidelines for Gong Yoga relaxation are: 1) Yoga practices are done prior to relaxation; 2) Preparation for the relaxation is conducted by the teacher; 3) The gong is consciously played by the teacher to induce and maximize the experience of relaxation; 4) The relaxation is done in a state of awareness with a pure and light (*sattvic*) quality.

Yoga Practices for Relaxation

Most uncomfortable experiences that people may have with the gong usually occur because the gong is not played in a yogic environment and participants are not ready to receive the sound.

For the most part, almost any yoga class with an appropriate balance of postures and breath work will create a receptive state for gong relaxation. It is not necessary that the class itself be a Gong Yoga class. It is only required that the practices in the yoga class be authentic or follow a specific style or recognized lineage.

If other techniques and practices are borrowed from non-yogic traditions or created by the teacher, the results may be unpredictable. Remember that you are creating Gong Yoga relaxation, and while a relaxation that occurs after a mix of various physical, mental or emotional practices can be healing and beneficial, it also poses uncertain outcomes. You certainly can use other modalities with the gong as therapy, **if you are a skilled practitioner in that modality.** The gong is a powerful instrument for transformation so staying within the yoga tradition provides you, as a yoga teacher, a tested method in which to work.

Preparation for Relaxation

The preparation for gong relaxation follows a sequence of yoga practices that address the physical, energetic and emotional bodies by using the techniques of asana, pranayama, and visualization.

The Physical Environment

The place for the gong relaxation should reduce sensory stimulation as much as possible. Dimmed lights or covering the eyes is important as sight increases the response of the sympathetic nervous system that takes us into action. The body may be covered lightly to reduce unwanted tactile stimulation, such as air circulation, and to increase the body temperature that precedes a relaxed state. Smell is a potent and sometimes overlooked stimulator and distractor; especially food odors and scents that can arouse distracting memories and emotions.

While the sound of the gong can mask outside sounds, reducing ambient noise is important and it may be helpful to lightly cover the ears or top of the head, or turn the sound of the heating or air conditioning systems off. The gong will still be effective even if the ears are lightly covered and the covered filtered sound can reduce anxiety that some people may have regarding the powerful sound of the gong. Even with the ears covered, the gong will be able to accomplish its work.

Be aware that all hearing aid devices must be turned off before the gong is played. As much as possible, the physical environment should facilitate sensory withdrawal, or *pratyahara*, in order to maximize the effect of the sound of the gong.

Preparing the Physical Body

Ideally asanas or *kriyas* (sequences of exercise with yoga techniques) are done to release tension and prepare the body for relaxation. The asanas immediately preceding relaxation should be slow and cooling (*langhana*). The asanas do not have to be elaborate or lengthy; simple head turns or neck rolls, flexing the ankles or turning the hands, drawing the knees into the chest while on the back, all enhance the ability of the body to relax.

Relaxation is optimally done in a supine position, using variations of *savasana*, or corpse pose. In environments where lying down is not an option, relaxation can be done seated in a chair or on the floor, provided the hips are slightly elevated.

While the classic corpse pose is done on the back with the hands and arms slightly apart, and palms turned upward, the palms can be turned down to accommodate the shoulders and the knees can be bent or supported under the knees to aid the lower back. The pose can also be done lying on one side (preferably the left side) with the knees pulled up and the head supported on the arm or thin cushion.

If the primary purpose of the gong playing is to create deep physical relaxation, then the feet should be pointed toward the gong in order to ground the body. If the intention is to dissociate the ethereal or astral body from the physical body during relaxation to create a sense of lightness or release, then the head may be pointed toward the gong. For those who are easily spaced out, or susceptible to vata derangement, then the top of the head can be covered or wrapped with a blanket. A light cushion or eye pillow over the eyes and forehead can be beneficial for inducing relaxation.

Preparing the Energy Body

Working with the breath through breathing practices is the most effective way to prepare the energetic or subtle body for gong relaxation. The breathing practices may be done before or during the relaxation. Breathing practices immediately before relaxation should be cooling (*langhana*) or balancing (*samana*) in effect.

Some ideal pranayamas to induce relaxation are:

- Breathing through the left nostril only
- Inhaling left, exhaling right
- Alternate nostril breathing
- Sitali (tongue extended) breathing
- Humming Bee breath

When entering relaxation on the back, attention can be directed to an easy diaphragmatic breath, focusing on the rise and fall of the stomach or diaphragm, or upon a full body breath, inhaling from the feet to the crown of the head and exhaling from crown to feet. A simple way to create relaxation is to gently extend the length of the exhalation so it becomes twice as long as the inhalation.

A more passive relaxation breath is to begin relaxing on the right side of the body for 3-5 minutes and that will gently shift the dominant breathing pattern to the left nostril and activate the parasympathetic nervous system. After a few minutes roll onto the back or remain on the right side if more comfortable.

Preparing the Emotional Body

The emotional body can be prepared for gong relaxation through visualizations, affirmations, and silent mantra.

The teacher may repeat one or more of the following affirmations out loud, one to three times, and then have the student repeat the affirmation silently. Depending upon the energetic or emotional state of the practitioner, or the intention for the relaxation, affirmations may be selected according to which chakra or major emotional issue is being addressed as the following table illustrates.

CHAKRA	AFFIRMATIONS
FIRST Muladhara	I am safe. I am secure. I am grounded. I am prosperous. I am here.
SECOND Svadhisthana	I am connected. I am spontaneous. I am worthy. I am creative. I am deserving.
THIRD Manipura	I am able. I am strong. I am willful. I am self-sufficient. I am determined.
FOURTH Anahata	I am compassionate. I am neutral. I am willing. I am balanced. I am accepting.
FIFTH Vishuddha	I am truthful. I am clear. I am effective. I am receptive. I am expressive.
SIXTH Ajna	I am perceptive. I am intuitive. I am focused. I am guided. I am ready.
SEVENTH Sahasrara	I am aware. I am trusting. I am divine. I am aligned. I am One.

Playing the Gong for Relaxation

Balancing the sympathetic and parasympathetic nervous systems through sound sequences that alternatively create contraction and expansion, tension and extension, and finally pressure and release is an effective way to play the gong for relaxation.

Unlike playing the gong for meditation and pranayama in which consistent patterns are followed to induce concentration and focus, playing the gong for relaxation requires the player to engage the listener in a guiding and sometimes challenging manner in order to create a release of tension and removal of blocks that inhibit relaxation.

A classic relaxation technique in therapy and yoga is progressive muscle relaxation, or PMR, in which areas of the body are first contracted and then relaxed in order to create an awareness of the residual tension and stress that may be inherent (and hidden) in the body of the practitioner. In other words, pressure is consciously applied and the consciously released, giving the practitioner control over the physically stressed areas in the body.

While effective for many people, PMR with contraction can cause some people to feel more tension and become more stressed. Fortunately, the gong can be played in such a way that pressure can be applied through sound and then released through sound rather than the physical contraction that can create discomfort. More importantly, the gong goes beyond dealing with the simple muscular tension, which is symptomatic and not causative of stress, and addresses the root cause of stress by rebalancing the nervous system.

Stress and the inability to relax is fundamentally experienced as a result of the sympathetic nervous system (the fight or flight response) being overactive and the parasympathetic nervous system (which supports relaxation) being unable to turn back on.

The gong works through the sympathetic and parasympathetic nervous systems to create deep relaxation through playing sequences that are termed build and release cycles.

Build and Release Cycles for Gong Relaxation

Simply put, a build and release cycle occurs when the gong is played in a repetitive pattern, often with an increase in rhythm, volume, or both, in order to create an expectancy or inner tension in the mind of the listener that continues to build and build until a release from the tension is delivered through a culmination or completion of the building pattern.

An apt comparison is the sexual tension that builds to a heightened intensity and then climatically releases through orgasm, resulting in relaxation and a sense of completion.

For example, a simple build and release cycle is to repeatedly strike one point on the gong, gradually building its rhythm or volume to a point of intensity, and then breaking the playing pattern with a single (or multiple) strike that releases the mind and nervous system of the listener.

The building of the sound through repeated patterns over time builds an expectancy and even desire in the listener for the pattern to be released. This has the same effect of the sympathetic nervous system (the desire to break away from the pattern) that muscular contraction has on the physical body.

When the release strike breaks the pattern, the sympathetic nervous system can shut down and the parasympathetic nervous system of relaxation can now assert itself. To effectively retrain the listener to shut off the sympathetic nervous system and turn on the parasympathetic response often requires three build and release cycles be done over the 7 to 15 minutes of a gong relaxation.

While the loud volume or fast rhythm of the gong during these building cycles may seem counterintuitive to inducing deep relaxation, they serve the same function as applying stressors (such as muscle contraction) in a conscious manner in order to create deep release when the stressors are removed.

The Gong and Yoga Nidra

One of the most profound ways to create relaxation with the gong is through a guided process known as Yoga Nidra, or yogic sleep. Yoga Nidra induces deep relaxation, heightens awareness, enables self-diagnosis, integrates changes, and accelerates healing. It is a powerful tool for therapeutic change that is accomplished over an extended (30 to 60 minute) relaxation period.

The practice of Yoga Nidra purifies the deep impressions of the individual's *samskaras*, the driving and often hidden karmic forces behind many of our actions and conditions. Essentially, the state of Yoga Nidra gives access to the mind that is underneath our normal processing, fantasizing and imagining consciousness. It is an excellent tool for attenuating and eliminating habit patterns that are the root causes of physical and psychological problems that manifest in long-term stress and an inability to relax.

While Yoga Nidra can be practiced in many ways, there is a standard sequence for a Gong Yoga Nidra relaxation session. Notice how this sequence follows the kosha model to create a journey of holistic healing through all five layers of existence.

Opening the Space – At the beginning of a Yoga Nidra practice, the participants relax on the back. Blankets or yoga props may be used to keep the body comfortably still. Give a reminder to remain awake and aware in order to receive the full benefits of the practice, and to simply follow the teacher's voice and listen to the sound of the gong.

The teacher opens the space by gently striking the gong three times. In the ensuing silence, the teacher asks the participants to select a precise, clear and positive intention or resolve for the session. This positive resolve is known as a *sankalpa*. The Sanskrit word means a resolution or determination, and is a basic tool in initiating a yogic healing process to awaken innate healing energies. A typical sankalpa might be, "I experience radiant health," or "I am free of all pain." The sankalpa should be in the present tense as if it has already occurred. Ask them to silently repeat it to themselves, and then strike the gong once and announce, *"The practice of Yoga Nidra has begun."*

Body Awareness - While in a state of relaxation after setting the intention, the teacher directs the participant's awareness to the different areas of the body. By rotating the participant's awareness through all areas of the body in an automatic and spontaneous fashion, a body-mind state is created that begins the process of integration. Generally, a specific sequence is used to direct body awareness, beginning with the right hand, the right side, moving to the left side, to the back of the body, to the front of the body, the head, face, and back down to the legs. The example given later in the sample script may be followed. During this segment, the gong is not played. This practice awakens the anamaya kosha.

Breath Awareness – After the rotation of consciousness, an awareness of the breath is established, either through counting or breathing into different areas or points on the body. This awakens the flow of prana and energy to every cell in the body. The example given later in the sample script may be followed. The gong may be optionally played during this segment to direct the inhale and exhale or retention or suspension of the breath. This practice awakens the pranamaya kosha.

Sensation Awareness – Now feelings and emotions are awakened, experienced, and removed through a directed focusing on pairs of opposites, such as hot and cold, joy and sadness, love and fear, light and dark. This contrasting of opposites through words or imagery allows for emotional balancing and relaxation and integration of the brain hemispheres. The example given later in the sample script may be followed. During this segment, the gong is not played. This practice awakens the manamaya kosha.

Guided Meditation - This stage of Yoga Nidra uses visualizations by the participant based upon suggestions from the instructor. The guided visualization awakens the third eye of the participant and begins the inner journey into the subconscious. This process develops concentration and dissolves the distinctions between the conscious and unconscious mind, allowing it to completely relax. The teacher can create or use a guided visualization of their own or may use the example script given later. During this segment, the gong may be played to underscore or emphasize a particular visual image as long as it does not overwhelm the participant's ability to follow the teacher's visualizations. This practice awakens the vijnanamaya kosha.

Relaxation and Integrations - The stage of Yoga Nidra allows the participant to experience the bliss body or anandamaya kosha through the extended playing of the gong. In this stage, the gong is played intuitively for 7 to 31 minutes. More than one gong or gong player may participate. Three or more build and release cycles may be included in the session, as well as periods of near silence. At the end of this segment, there should be several distinctive gong strikes to signal the ending, and then allow for one minute of total silence.

Closing the Space - The participants are brought back into the body by directing the breath consciously in and out several times. The gong is no longer played. Before they move their body, the teacher reminds the participants of their original intention, or sankalpa, from the beginning of the session. They are asked to mentally repeat their intention three times. The session ends with the participants gently moving and stretching. Have them slowly come up to a seated posture. Close the session with a gong strike, a chanted mantra, a prayer or a blessing. If they are with others, have them turn to someone and discuss their experience. If they are alone, make yourself available as a sounding board for their experience. Do not judge or direct the conversation. Simply affirm what you are hearing.

Within these guidelines, there is much flexibility in constructing a Gong Yoga Nidra session, and ideas can be garnered from various books and examples of Yoga Nidra practices. You can also write your own scripts and experiment with different images and guided visualizations. Two example scripts follow.

Gong Yoga Nidra: Integration through Sound

This Gong Yoga Nidra script incorporates the sound of the gong as an integral part of the narrative visualization. As you read the script, please modify it for your speaking and teaching style.

It is not uncommon for some people to fall asleep during the practice. To encourage them to stay awake and be present to receive the full benefits of the practice, keep the voice strong and directed. You may find it easier to be seated as you read the script and use a floor stand for the gong so it can be easily played without getting up and down.

A Yoga Nidra session often takes a little longer than you might expect as you do not wish to rush the experience and you will need to provide pauses for integration.

(1) Opening the Space

Relax comfortably on your back. Feel and connect to the easy flow of your breath. (Silent pause)

(The gong is struck 3 times softly.)

Allow a conscious intention to arise in your mind for this session of Yoga Nidra. It should be a short, positive affirmation in the present moment, such as "I am healed in every cell of my body" or "I am relaxed with each breath I take." Allow the intention to enter your consciousness and then silently repeat it three times to yourself. (Silent pause)

(The gong is struck one time.)

The practice of Yoga Nidra now begins. Relax deeply but remain awake and aware. Completely relax and follow the sound of my voice. Repeat to yourself, "I will remain awake. I will remain aware. I will fully experience this moment."

(Silent pause. The gong is struck one time.)

(2) Body Awareness

Now let you awareness quickly move to each area of the body that I name. Simply take your awareness there and then move immediately to the next area. (Silent pause. Then speak slowly.)

Right hand ... right palm ... right wrist ... lower right arm ... elbow ... upper arm ... right shoulder ... right armpit ... right side of body ... right waist ... right hip ... right thigh ... kneecap ... calf muscle ... right ankle ... right heel ... top of right foot ... bottom of foot.

Left hand ... left palm ... left wrist ... lower left arm ... elbow ... upper arm ... left shoulder ... left armpit ... left side of body ... left waist ... left hip ... left thigh ... kneecap ... calf muscle ... left ankle ... left heel ... top of left foot ... bottom of foot.

Top of head ... forehead ... right eyebrow ... left eyebrow ... right eyelid ... left eyelid ... right eye ... left eye ... right nostril ... left nostril ... right cheek ... left cheek ... upper lip ... lower lip ... chin ... jaw... throat ... right chest ... left chest ... navel ... upper abdomen ... lower abdomen ... right thigh ... left thigh ... right knee ... left knee ... right calf muscle ... left calf muscle ... right ankle ... left ankle ... right foot ... left foot.

While right leg ... whole left leg ... both legs together ... whole right arm ... whole left arm ... both arms together ... whole of the head together ... whole of the back together ... whole of the front together ... the whole body together ... the whole body together ... the whole body together.

(Silent pause. The gong is struck one time.)

(3) Breath Awareness

Now bring your awareness to your breath. Become aware of the movement of the breath. Feel the breath as it enters the nostrils. Feel the breath as it leaves the nostrils. Feel the movement of the breath throughout the body. Feel the rise and fall of the diaphragm with each inhale and each exhale. (Silent pause)

Now focus on the breath entering and leaving at the tip of the nose. Feel the breath entering and leaving the nostrils. Sense the movement of the breath moving from the tip of the nose to the third eye point above the eyebrows. Allow the breath to move back and forth between the tip of the nose and the third eye. Inhale up to the third eye. Exhale down to the tip. Feel the breath travel from the nose to the brow point and from the brow point to the nose. (Silent pause)

Now begin to count the breaths as you inhale from the tip of the nose to the third eye and exhale down from the third eye to the tip of the nose. Count backwards silently from thirty, as follows: Inhaling Thirty, Exhaling Thirty. Inhaling Twenty-nine, Exhaling Twenty-nine. Inhaling Twenty-eight, Exhaling Twenty-eight. Keep counting backwards. If you lose count, start over again at Thirty and count each breath as it moves in and out. Breathe consciously and slowly. Feel the breath moving in and out with each count.

(Silent pause for 2-3 minutes. The gong is struck one time.)

(4) Sensation Awareness

Now let your breath and counting relax. Continue to let your awareness rest on the easy flow of your breath. Remain awake and aware. Remain awake and aware, as I name objects and you should try to visualize them on the levels of feeling, awareness, emotion and imagination as best you can.

(Silent Pause)

You should jump your mind from image to image, not concentrating on any one image, but keep moving and allow all sensations and feelings to quickly arise and disappear.

(Silent pause. The gong is struck one time. Then the following images are spoken.)

Cold winter day... Cold winter day

Leafless tree in the sun ... Leafless tree in the sun

Frightened dog barking ... Frightened dog barking

Black stones in a clear stream... Black stones in a clear stream

Old woman crying ... Old woman crying

Knife in an empty glass ... Knife in an empty glass

Apple pie baking ... Apple pie baking

Child in an empty room... Child in an empty room

Ashes on a wooden floor ... Ashes on a wooden floor

Wind banging door... Wind banging door

Smiling Buddha ... Smiling Buddha

Broken window in the rain... Broken window in the rain

Kittens nursing with claws... Kittens nursing with claws

White roses blooming ... White roses blooming

Tombstone covered in blood... Tombstone covered in blood

Restless tiger in a cage... Restless tiger in a cage

Snowflakes falling on fire... Snowflakes falling on fire

Yogi in a cave ... Yogi in a cave

Bells ringing on a rope... Bells ringing on a rope

Mother holding sleeping child ... Mother holding sleeping child

Lying in a warm bath ...Lying in a warm bath

A torn and patched coat ... A torn and patched coat

Incense burning on an altar... Incense burning on an altar

Field of sunflowers ... Field of sunflowers

Full moon rising ... Full moon rising

(Silent pause. The gong is struck one time.)

(5) Guided Meditation

Let your eyes relax and turn upward. Let your eyes relax upward. Let your awareness take you on an inner journey. Go deeper and deeper inside. Become a witness of yourself. Become a watcher of the story that unfolds within you. Become the observer beyond time and space. (Silent pause)

See yourself standing on the beach of an infinite ocean, calm and quiet, as the gentle waves roll up to your feet. Feel the wet sand beneath you and the warmth of the sun upon you. Smell the salt in the wind and see the birds flying over the water. Feel the cooling wind on your skin. Listen to the sound of the waves, and hear the birds calling. Listen and hear. Listen and hear. And from the distance, hear the sound of a gong from far away.

(The gong is struck softly and allowed to fade completely away.)

As you turn from the ocean toward the sound of the gong, you see a cool green jungle. From the palm tress, a path leads from the beach and disappears into the jungle. From deep within the jungle, you hear the gong again, like a softly beating heart.

(The gong is played with a heart beat rhythm and fades away.)

You take the path into the jungle and walk toward the sound of the distant gong. With each step, the sound of the gong grows and calls you to come closer.

(The gong is played slightly louder and fades away.)

You come to a clearing in the jungle and before you is a magnificent gong hanging between two trees. There is no one around, and as you walk toward the gong the sound grows and swells and surrounds you.

(The gong is played with a strong rhythm and then with a single strong strike, it fades completely away.)

Standing in front of the gong, you close your eyes in gratitude. As you open your eyes, you see your reflection on the shinning surface of the gong, like a mirror, looking back at you.

The reflection in the gong is the image of the person you are becoming. It is your most divine self, your most radiant being, your most loving nature, that looks back at you, holding you in infinite compassion and acceptance. See the reflection, smiling at you, accepting you and reminding you that the person that is looking and the person that is reflected are both the same, forever one, forever eternal, and completely perfect in this moment.

(Silent pause.)

(6) Relaxation and Integration

The gong is played for 7 to 15 minutes and then lasting silence.

(7) Closing the Space

Inhale gently and fully. Exhale. Let your breath return to your conscious control. Inhaling and exhaling. (Pause) Now remember your intention and affirmation you made at the beginning of relaxation. Repeat the affirmation silently three times. Let it be so. Now deepen the breath and begin to move the fingers and toes. Circle the hands around the wrists and the feet around the ankles. Reverse the circles. Please inhale the arms over the head and stretch in both directions. Bring the hands together over the heart and rub the palms together and rub the feet together. Bring your knees into you chest and rock side to side and then roll over to one side. Slowly bring yourself up to sitting. (A mantra can be chanted to close the session or simply hold in silence.) *The practice of Yoga Nidra has now ended.* (Single gong strike.)

Participants should talk and share their experiences to process and integrate the profound changes of this practice and take their time to re-enter the world from this sacred space.

Gong Yoga Nidra to Balance the Chakras

This Gong Yoga Nidra script uses simple supported asanas that may be done on the back during the guided meditation. While most Yoga Nidra sessions do not use movement, in this case the postures create a deeper opening into the journey through the chakras. Please modify for your speaking and teaching style.

(1) **Opening the Space** – Same as previous session.

(2) **Body Awareness** – Same as previous session.

(3) **Breath Awareness** – Same as previous session, or use the Point-to-Point breathing exercise or other breathing exercises that may be done on the back.

(4) **Sensation Awareness** – Same as previous session or create your own imagery and symbols to access the unconscious mind.

(5) **Guided Meditation**

Let your awareness move to the base of your spine. Breathe into that space and feel the sensations around the base of the spine. Let the breath amplify all sensations and feelings around the base of the spine. Is there a sense of contraction or expansion ... Lightness or heaviness ... a color or an image? Let the breath move to that area of your body. Now draw the knees into the chest with the hands and hold the knees down. Focus and breathe into the base of the spine.

(The gong is played for the first chakra, near the bottom of the gong while the posture is held for 1 to 2 minutes. Then silence.)

Now release the posture and relax into the breath. Breathe into the hips and pelvic area. Let the breath amplify all sensations and feelings around the pelvic area. Is there a sense of contraction or expansion ... Lightness or heaviness ... a color or an image? Let the breath move freely. Now bring the soles of the feet together and pull the heels up so that the knees fall open to the sides, like an open butterfly. Focus and breathe into pelvic area.

(The gong is played for the second chakra, above the bottom of the gong, for 1 to 2 minutes. Then the gong is silenced.)

Now release the posture and relax into the breath. Begin to breathe into the area around the navel point and solar plexus. Let the breath amplify all sensations and feelings around the abdomen area. Connect to the rise and fall of the diaphragm. Is there a sense of contraction or expansion ... Lightness or heaviness ... a color or an image? Let the breath move to that area of your body. Now slide the hands under the hips palms down and pull the knees into the chest. Gradually extend your legs out between 6 inches (15 centimeters) and three feet (one meter) above the ground. Bend the knees if you need to protect you back, but keep the feet off the floor. Focus and breathe into navel point area. Keep the abdominal muscles engaged.

(The gong is played for the third chakra, right below the center of the gong, for 1 to 2 minutes while the posture is held. Then the gong is silenced.)

Now lower the legs and relax into the breath. Begin to breathe into the area around the heart. Breathe into the heart and breathe out from the heart. Let the breath open the heart area. Let the breath amplify all sensations and feelings around the heart area. Connect to the breath moving in and out of the heart. Is there a sense of contraction or expansion ... Lightness or heaviness ... a color or an image? Let the breath move to that area of your body. Now begin to press the heart upward through the ribcage. Keep the back on the floor but maintain a constant upward pressure on the heart as if you could push it up, as if a string was lifting the chest and heart upward. Keep the upward pressure and breathe; breathe into the heart.

(The gong is played for the fourth chakra, right above the center of the gong, for 1 to 2 minutes. Then the gong is silenced.)

Now relax the chest, relax the heart, and release all the pressure around the heart center. Breathe and relax. Begin to breathe into the area around the throat. Breathe into the throat and hear the sound of the breath in the throat. Breathe in and out from the throat and let the breath open the throat area. Let the breath amplify all sensations and feelings around the throat. Connect to the breath moving in and out of the heart. Is there a sense of contraction or expansion ... Lightness or heaviness ... a color or an image? Let the breath move to that area of your body. Now slide the hands under the hips again, palms down, and gently lift the head and bring the top or the back of the head on the floor so the neck is comfortably arched and the throat is opened. If the neck is uncomfortable, release the head onto the floor and continue hearing the sound of the breath in the throat

(The gong is played for the fifth chakra, between the center of the gong and the rim, for 1 to 2 minutes. Then it is silenced.)

Now relax the head and neck and gently rock the head side to side along the floor. Swallow and release any tension Relax the neck, and release all the pressure around the throat center. Breathe and relax. Begin to breathe into the area above and between the eyebrows. Draw the breath into the brow point, as if the breath can enter and leave through the third eye. Imagine the brow point as the lens of a camera opening to receive the breath into the body, and breathe in and out through the third eye. Imagine the breath as a shaft of light that enters the body as you inhale and then projects from the third eye you exhale. Let the breath amplify all sensations and feelings around the third eye. Connect to the breath moving in and out of the brow point. Is there a sense of contraction or expansion ... Lightness or heaviness ... a color or an image? Let the breath move to that area of your body. See any images, any colors, or any symbols that might appear on the screen of your third eye. Now roll the eyes strongly up to the third eye point and hold the inner gaze steadily with focus and intention. Keep the eyes locked upward and inward, behind the root of the nose and back into the brain.

(The gong is played for the sixth chakra, below the top rim for 1 to 2 minutes. Then the gong is silenced.)

Now relax the gaze and the eyes. Let the eyes completely relax. Breathe and relax. Begin to breathe into the area at the top of the head. Take the breath all the way up to the crown of the head. Feel the breath entering the top of the head as you inhale and feel the breath leaving through the top of the head as you exhale. Breateh in and out from the top of the head, gradually extending the breath above the head, a few inches, a few inches more, and finally as far as the mind can project, drawing the breath in from infinity and out from infinity. Sense the vastness beyond the physical body, feel the expansion of self above time and space. Now press the tongue against the roof of the mouth and roll the eyes upward as if you could look through the top of the head.

(The gong is played for the seventh chakra, at the edge of rim near the top of the gong with light upward expansive strikes. Finally the gong is played all along the rim, starting from the top and sweeping around to the bottom and back to the top is several circles of increasing rhythm the top rim for 1 to 2 minutes while the posture is held. Then the gong is silenced.)

Now relax the eyes, relax the tongue, relax the breath, and relax the whole body. Breathe and relax. Feel the wholeness of the body. Feel the whole body together. Breathe through the whole body, from the soles of the feet to the crown of the head. Let the breath move through all the chakras, along the spine, along the whole body. And relax... relax... relax.

(6) Relaxation and Integration

The gong is played along the axis of the chakras, from bottom to top and top to bottom, for 7 minutes and then fades to a lasting silence.

(7) Closing the Space – Same as previous session.

The Gong and Styles of Yoga

The gong can be easily integrated into all the Western styles of yoga, which tend mostly to be variations on the Hatha and Kundalini Yoga traditions.

Outside of Hatha and Kundalini traditions, which are further described in this chapter, the gong can be prominently used in the practices of Laya Yoga, Mantra Yoga, Raja Yoga, and Nada Yoga. Given the right circumstances, the gong can be an instrument for even practicing Bhakti and Karma Yoga.

Kundalini Yoga and the Gong

The most popular style of yoga associated with the gong is Kundalini Yoga as taught by Yogi Bhajan. In fact, without Yogi Bhajan and Kundalini Yoga, it is unlikely that the development of Gong Yoga would have occurred.

The gong was integrated into Kundalini Yoga classes by the early 1970s, primarily as a way to rebuild the nervous systems of the drug culture hippies recently turned yoga students. Yogi Bhajan often played the gong during meditations at the end of class and also taught several yoga sets in which the gong was played during the exercises and relaxation. His instruction to the dozens of Kundalini ashrams that emerged worldwide in the 1970s and 1980s was to have an ashram gong that could be played to heal all who came to the classes.

Although there are a limited number of Kundalini kriyas (yoga sets) that explicitly specify playing the gong, the gong can be used in a Kundalini class in much the same way that Kundalini music is played during the class, as a way to focus the mind, raise the vibrations and connect the students to the Naad, or universal sound current.

Mehtab Benton

In many ways, Kundalini Yoga is the most welcoming style of yoga in which to play the gong as classes tend to be done in a meditative sequence with the eyes often closed, using floor postures instead of standing postures. In addition, the teacher does not leave the front of the classroom to make adjustments or give extensive physical demonstrations, but holds the space through verbal instructions and so remains within easy access to the gong.

Sound is used extensively in Kundalini classes, through mantras, songs, and live music, so students are comfortable integrating the gong into their yoga practice. Beginning and intermediate students often comment that practicing breath of fire, the signature pranayama of Kundalini Yoga, is much easier when the gong is played as it helps maintain a steady rhythm of the inhale and exhale.

Other classical Kundalini Yoga practices, such as Sat Kriya, Kirtan Kriya (Sa Ta Na Ma), and Morning Call (Ek Ong Kar mantra), lend themselves well to practice with the gong.

Sat Kriya

How to Do It: Sitting on the heels, raise the arms above the head and interlace the fingers and cross the thumbs. Extend both index fingers together in the air above the crown of the head. Breathe as needed to chant the mantra SAT NAM (in this case, the sound *sat* rhymes with "but" and *nam* rhymes with "mom"). On the sound SAT, contract the navel point and project the sound. On the sound NAM, relax the contraction and let the sound escape from the third eye, connecting the third chakra to the sixth chakra. Chant at the rate of 8 times per ten seconds. After 3 minutes, inhale and apply the root lock, mulabandha, and then relax with the exhale.

Playing the Gong: The gong is struck below the center area on SAT firmly and with a lighter strike below the top rim on NAM, playing the gong in the areas of the third and sixth chakra. At the end on the inhale, let the sound of the gong naturally decay as the energy is pulled up with the root lock.

Sat Kriya

Kirtan Kriya (Sa Ta Na Ma Meditation)

How to Do It: Sitting in a meditative pose, chant the four sounds of SA TA NA MA out loud as the thumb is touched successively to the index finger (SA), middle finger (TA), ring finger (NA), and little finger (MA). Each repetition takes about 5 seconds. After 2 minutes chanting out loud, continue with a whispered sound for 2 more minutes. Then repeat the mantra silently for 4 minutes as you continue to touch the thumb to the four fingers with the silent sounds. Return to a whispered chant for 2 more minutes, and then finally chant out loud for the last 2 minutes. At the end, inhale and stretch the arms over the head, twist to the left, twist to the right, and then exhale to the center. Inhale again with arms still over the head and shake the arms and hands. Exhale and keep shaking. Inhale and keep shaking and then exhale the arms and hands down.

Playing the Gong: The gong is struck for each sound made, either out loud, whispered or silent. The gong is first struck upward at percussion point 6, then upward at percussion point 9, again upward at percussion point 12, and downward at percussion point 3. Repeat the 6-9-12-3 playing sequence throughout the meditation, at medium volume when chanting out loud, medium to soft volume when whispered, and then softly when chanted silently.

Long Ek Ong Kar Sat Nam Siri Wahe Guru Meditation

How to Do It: Sit in a meditative posture with the thumb touching the index finger tips in gyan mudra and close the eyes. Inhale and chant the sound EK from the base of the spine (root chakra) in a short projective burst, using about 10% of the breath. On the same breath, vibrate the sound ONG at the pelvic area (second chakra) for half of the remaining of the breath, then finish the remaining breath by chanting the sound KAR at the navel point (third chakra). Inhale a deep second breath and chant the sound SAT at the heart (fourth chakra) for almost half the breath. Then chant the sound NAM at the throat (fifth chakra) for almost the rest of the breath, saving a small mount of breath for the sound SIRI chanted at the brow point (sixth chakra). Take a half breath inhale and chant the sound WAHE at the top of the head (seventh chakra) and let the final sound GURU be released into the aura around the body (eighth chakra). The full chant takes approximately 40 to 45 seconds. Repeat the full chant for 7 minutes or more as desired. Then inhale and apply the root lock, mulabandha, pull the energy up through the chakras and then relax with the exhale.

Playing the Gong: The gong is struck at each of the seven chakra points along the vertical axis of the gong, beginning above the bottom rim with the sound EK and working up to below the top rim with sound WAHE. With the sound GURU, the gong can be played around the rim or simply allowed to decay after the seventh strike. It may be necessary to muffle or still the gong after the first breath is exhausted (after KAR is chanted), again after the second breath (after SIRI is chanted), and finally at the end (after GURU is chanted) to create a pause the next repetition of the chant.

Hatha Yoga and the Gong

The most popular style of yoga in the Western world is Hatha Yoga, a system associated almost exclusively with the practice of asanas or postures. Because of the need to demonstrate and occasionally assist with the postures, it is often necessary to have a gong player as a dedicated accompanist so the teacher can be free to direct the performance of the asanas.

Ideally the gong player is also a Hatha teacher or an experienced practitioner so they can anticipate the energetic effects of the various postures as well as the sequencing needs of the teacher.

The gong can be very effective in a Hatha class when postures are held for several breaths, freeing the teacher to play the gong and use the sound to focus the student's attention.

The other consideration in using the gong in a Hatha class is to strike the right balance between giving enough space for the teacher to instruct and guide and using the gong effectively. It may be necessary to muffle or silence the gong more often when using it in a Hatha class.

Vinyasa Flow Yoga and the Gong

Playing the gong with the Vinyasa Flow styles of yoga, which consist of repeated movements and asana sequences connected with the breath, bring both opportunities and challenges in the teaching of Gong Yoga.

The challenge of playing the gong in the Vinyasa Flow environment is to match the rhythm of the gong with the flow of the practice. The gong must seem to ride on the breath of the practitioners, neither hurrying nor delaying the flow of the postures that arise from an inherent rhythm that is guided by the teacher's instructions and the collective movement of the students. Without this subtle attunement of the playing rhythm of the gong to the flow of the practice, the sound becomes intrusive and frustrating. To be able to play the gong effectively for this style of yoga, one must be an accomplished practitioner as well.

The opportunity of using the gong is Vinyasa Flow yoga classes is the ability to create a flowing rhythm that is maintained by the gong, thus freeing both student and the teacher from directing and attempting to create the group conscious and movement that makes up a flow practice.

The gong can be used to signal a vinyasa or transition from one posture to the next with a strike. Also, the gong can be used as the timer for holding one posture and from moving into the next asana.

Ashtanga Yoga and the Gong

The Ashtanga style of yoga popularized by Pattabhi Jois presents special opportunities for the Gong Yoga teacher with its consistent regimen of postures that are repeated over six series.

Because each Ashtanga class follows a format of invariable sequences, students learn the series of postures over time and can become independent of following the teacher's directions. There is less need for the teacher to talk students through the postures and that frees space for both the teachers and the students to go deeper into the sound of the gong when it is played in class. On the other hand, the Ashtanga teacher spends much time with the demonstration of postures and making adjustments. Because of the student-intensive nature of the practice, Ashtanga teachers can benefit greatly by having a separate gong player for the class.

Another use for the gong in Ashtanga Yoga is to use it as a counter for the five breaths that most postures require. A consideration, however, is that many times the group breathing of the class, in which the breath is heard, serves as personal soundtrack for the movement that might be diluted by the sound of the gong.

One contraindication for the Ashtanga practice while using the gong is that in general the gong should not be played while the student (or the teacher!) is in headstand, a posture that is often held for 25 breaths in the Ashtanga finishing sequence. The effect of the gong on the crown chakra is profound and its sound can be overly activating and disturbing for an extended headstand practice.

On the other hand, the last posture of the Ashtanga finishing series, Tolasana (or Utpluthi), in which the body is lifted off the ground and supported on the arms and hands while in Lotus pose, is one of the best asanas in the series to play the gong, usually in a fast and moderately loud volume to create a climatic upward surge of energy at the end of the class and before relaxation.

Restorative Yoga and the Gong

Restorative Yoga uses blankets, blocks, bolsters and other props to provide support to hold passive postures for an extended length of time. This static and relaxing approach to yoga is a natural application for the gong.

When postures can be held for three minutes or more, the sound of the gong can deepen the experience and create great release. When feasible, holding a single restorative posture for eleven minutes while the gong is played can give optimum benefits as the glandular system is completely rebalanced.

Perhaps the three best restorative poses for a gong relaxation are Supported Child Pose, Supported Hip Openers, and Supported Heart Opener. These poses work on different chakras and organs and can also be done at the end of any regular yoga class as well as being part of a Restorative Yoga class.

Supported Child Pose (Salamba Balasana)

How to Do It: Sitting on the heels, fold forward over a stack of folded blankets or a bolster so the head and chest are supported off the floor. Turn the head so the neck is comfortable. Relax for 3 to 5 minutes in this position, and allow the breath to move deeply into the body.

Playing the Gong: Like many restorative poses, the gong is played softly and slowly, with downward strokes on the bottom half of the gong. Let the gong match or guide the breath to 4 to 8 strikes or

breaths per minute, allowing the sound to be regular and monotonic. After 3 minutes, let the gong become softer and softer for the last 1-2 minutes of the posture.

Supported Heart Opener (Supta Anahata Chakra)

How to Do It: Lying on the floor, place folded blankets or a bolster under the knees to support the hips. Place a rolled blanket below the shoulders so the heart s lifted and another rolled blanket under the neck to support the head. Let the arms fall open above your shoulders, elbows comfortable bent. Relax for 3 to 5 minutes in this position, and allow the breath to move through the heart.

Playing the Gong: The gong is played with a heartbeat rhythm around the center. The rhythm remains steady, with a single beat followed by a quick double-beat to approximate the heart sound. After 3 minutes of medium soft playing, the volume and strikes can increase for one minute and then soften for the final minute.

Supported Hip Openers (Supta Baddha Konasana)

How to Do It: Sitting on the floor, bring the soles of the feet together and le the knees fall open to the sides. Place folded blankets or blocks under the knees to support the hips. Place a bolster under the back if you desire and slowly lower the back to the floor. Let the arms fall open to the sides. Relax for 3 to 5 minutes in this position, and allow the breath to move across the hips and pelvic area.

Playing the Gong: The gong is played in a soft and watery manner in the lower third of the gong between the center and the rim. This playing area affects the second chakra. After 3 minutes of medium soft playing, the volume and strikes can increase for one minute and then soften for the final minute.

Prenatal Yoga and the Gong

Playing the gong in prenatal yoga classes can be relaxing for mothers-to-be and enjoyable for the babies. Many mothers feel positive movement of their babies in response to a gong well-played.

While the commonly expressed concern for using the gong in a prenatal yoga class is to avoid playing it so that it disturbs the baby, in reality the rule is to not play the gong loudly or aggressively in such a manner that creates anxiety or fear in the mother. For the most part, the baby in the amniotic fluid of the mother experiences the sound of the gong in a softly filtered way, like hearing the gong played under water, and responds positively. However, the baby is sensitive to the emotional state and reactions of the mother and will not enjoy the gong if the mother is experiencing anxiety around it.

The mother's sensitivity to the gong increases in the last trimester, and it can bring up fears if played loudly or aggressively. In such cases, the gong should be played in a soft and soothing manner. One specialized use of the gong during the last trimester is to bring the baby into a better birthing position. Some midwives have even used the gong to turn or spin a baby who is breeched.

This can be done by playing the gong in a manner that brings deep relaxation while holding one or more of these yoga asanas described here.

Uttana Shishosana (Extended Puppy Pose)

Also known in Yin Yoga as Anahatasana (Heart-melting Pose)

This yoga posture appears to be a cross between Child's Pose (Balasana) and Downward Dog (Adho Mukha Svanasana) and has many health benefits, including helping with flexibility of the spine and relieving the symptoms of chronic stress and insomnia. It is also an excellent position to create the proper alignment of the baby before delivery, or to turn or spin the baby.

How To Do It: Come onto the hands and knees, shoulders over wrists and hips over knees with the arms should width apart. Extend the arms out on the floor, reaching away from you, palms down, as you bring your forehead to the floor. The hips stay up in the air, above the knees, with the thighs approximately perpendicular to the floor. If there is tightness, you can place a bolster or cushion under the forehead and bring the arms closer back to the body. Hold the posture for up to one minute, or up to three minutes if comfortable.

Playing the Gong: The gong is played on the bottom half with soft downward strokes at a slow and regular pace.

Bitilasana (Cow Pose)

This yoga posture is often paired with the Cat Pose (Marjariasana) to perform Cat-Cow movement. Cow has several health benefits, including releasing tension in the low back and regulating the thyroid gland. It is also an excellent position to create the proper tilt of the hips before delivery, or to turn or spin the baby.

How To Do It: Come onto the hands and knees, shoulders over wrists and hips over knees with the arms should width apart. Allow the belly to sink toward the floor and lift you head to look straight ahead. Close your eyes. Hold the posture with easy long breathing for up to one minute, or up to three minutes if comfortable.

Playing the Gong: The gong is played on the bottom half with firm downward strokes at a regular pace.

Vasti Udayana (Pelvic Lift)

This yoga posture is used therapeutically to strengthen the back and is an excellent hip and pelvis opener that provides the benefits of a backbend. This can be a strenuous prenatal pose and should not be held for long periods of time. It is an excellent strengthener to prepare for delivery and is another position to create the proper tilt of the hips before delivery, or to turn or spin the baby.

How To Do It: Come onto the back and bend the knees so the feet are flat in the floor in front of the hips. Place the arm palms down beside the body. As you inhale, press the hips off the floor, using the

Mehtab Benton

feet, legs, hands and arms. As you exhale, slowly lower the hips back to the floor. Repeat several times as comfortable.

Playing the Gong: The gong is played on the top half with a short upward strike when inhaling and on the bottom half with a short downward strike when exhaling. After the hips relax down, the gong is played softly for a minute.

Children's Yoga and the Gong

Playing the gong for a children's yoga class has special requirements depending upon the age group. For children over the age of 12, the gong can generally be played as for adult yoga students. The gong does affect the glandular system so after children enter puberty, the gong can be a welcome balancing influence on the pituitary and pineal glands. Children of this age can enjoy a gong relaxation for up to 10 minutes with good benefit. Extended gong playing may produce anxiety in some children and can be too challenging for their nervous systems.

For younger children, the gong should be introduced as a musical instrument by demonstrating how the various sounds are produced, and even inviting them to gently strike the gong to create a relationship with it. They may wish to sit with their eyes open as the gong is played instead of closing the eyes or lying down. In some cases, they can hold a simple yoga pose while the gong is played almost like a soundtrack.

Excellent results have been obtained with special needs children by using the gong in yoga classes. Autistic children are especially attracted to the gong when they are allowed to play it, although care must be taken to not play the gong overly loud for them.

Children with attention deficient disorders can learn to focus better when the gong is played in postures or short meditations. While it is no surprise that the gong has been successfully used in yoga classes for blind children, deaf children are also fascinated by the gong and benefit from the vibration that is transmitted through the floor and around the room.

Yoga for Seniors and the Gong

Playing the gong for seniors and populations who may be chair-bound has special rewards. The special consideration for a Gong Yoga class for seniors is to make sure that the students do not have their hearing aids on when the gong is played. Have them turn the hearing aid completely off or remove it before the gong is played. Amplification of the gong through hearing aids can create pain and possible injury.

The gong should be played slowly and softly for people over the age of 75. The idea is to soothe and not challenge the listener or to create anxiety with overly loud sounds.

An easy and enjoyable yoga exercise using the gong for seniors is to have them imagine the sound like the waves of the ocean and to allow their breath to move up and down with the sound. If movement is desired, the students can move their hands and arms slowly up and down in rhythm with the gong while sitting in a chair.

Guidelines for Teaching Gong Yoga

Depending upon the class structure and the playing skill of the teacher, the teacher can both instruct the class as well as play the gong. This works well with relaxation and meditation when the students need little guidance from the teacher.

On the other hand, if the teacher needs to actively guide the students through an asana practice or otherwise be fully engaged in instruction, then a second person may be needed to play the gong. Such an arrangement requires a good rapport between the teacher and gong player so as to strike an appropriate balance between spoken instruction and the playing of the gong. The gong should be played at a very low level, if at all, if the teacher needs to speak or interact with the students. At the same time, the teacher needs to be sensitive when it is better to remain silent and let the gong do its work.

The gong player should always be in a subservient role to the teacher, neither speaking nor instructing the students, once the class has begun. In addition the gong player needs to be tuned in to the changing needs of the class as it unfolds and be ready to quickly support the teacher. Each yoga class develops a rhythm of its own according to the students and energy in the room, and the gong player must be open to change and accommodation.

Regardless if the teacher plays the gong or is assisted by a gong player, the class needs to be orchestrated to maximize the impact of the sound of the gong. There should be sufficient listening space as the gong is interweaved into the class experience. Realize that the gong is never simply background music. It creates a dominant undertone and audible presence that moves and changes energy from moment to moment, breath to breath.

Mehtab Benton

Teaching and Playing the Gong

Here are some helpful guidelines when teaching Gong Yoga:

- Do not give complicated verbal instructions to the students while the gong is played. While it is better to not speak at all while the gong is playing, realize you will have to project loudly if you must say something vital.

- Do not over orchestrate the class with multiple gong sessions. Playing the gong a few times will often be sufficient.

- Let students know when you are about to play the gong if they do not already expect it.

- If some students in class have never heard the gong before, prepare them for the experience with instructions to relax into the sound and use the breath to allow the experience to be received. Perhaps even have them watch you strike the gong the first time so they can see the sound being made.

- Be cognizant that some people may react negatively to the sound of the gong the first time they hear it, particularly if they have issues around trust, letting go, tightly held boundaries, or a history of unpleasant associations with loud or unusual sounds. On the other hand, these same people can develop a healthy and appreciative relationship with the gong once it begins to clear out feelings of anxiety and old traumas.

- Be aware that whenever the gong is played, it will open and change energy. People may process emotional clearing from the gong as they continue through the rest of the class and this may color the experience of the remainder of the class.

- Bring people out of the gong space gently, with the soothing sound of your voice or a period of silence. Do not rush the transition from listening to the gong to actively doing a yoga posture as there can be a disassociation from the physical body when listening to the gong.

Gong Maps and Playing Techniques

These gong maps can help refine your playing techniques and are based upon the premise that different playing areas of the gong produce different effects in the listener. These effects can be implemented in all the methods of yoga: asanas, pranayama, meditation and relaxation.

The Top and Bottom Areas of the Gong

Imagine a horizontal line across the face of the gong connecting percussion point 9 to percussion point 3 that divides the gong into an upper horizontal half and a bottom horizontal half. Each of these areas can be played to create different effects as shown in the map.

The Side Areas of the Gong

Imagine a vertical line down the center of the gong connecting percussion point 12 to percussion point 6 that divides the gong into an right vertical half and a left vertical half. Notice that while the top and bottom areas are the same for all players, the side nearest the player (inside) is the right vertical area of the gong if the player is right-handed and the left side of the gong if the player is left handed. Each area can be played to create the effects as shown in the map.

The Four Energy Areas

Finally, the gong can be divided by a horizontal axis that bisects the center of the gong and a vertical axis from top to bottom.

The resulting quadrants the two intersecting axis produce create four energy areas that can be played to achieve certain effects in a yoga practice, such as either to energize or to relax, or to elevate or to ground. Intuitively, the upper half of the gong elevates, the bottom half grounds, the far side of the gong projects and the inner side of the gong receives. The map of the four energy areas is for the right-handed player and is mirrored for left handed players.

Playing the Top Area of the Gong

Creates Elevating Energy
Affects the Upper Body
Stimulates Prana Vayu
Increases Brimhana
Supports Upward Moving Postures
Affects Chakras 5, 6, 7

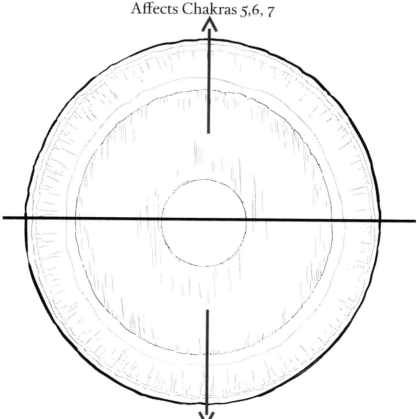

Playing the Bottom Area of the Gong

Creates Grounding Energy
Affects the Lower Body
Stimulates Apana Vayu
Increases Langhana
Supports Downward Moving Postures
Affects Chakras 1, 2, 3

Playing the Far Area of the Gong
(the area away from player)
Creates Projective Energy
Affects the Analytical Body
Stimulates Pingala Nadi
Increases Brimhana
Supports Outward Moving Postures
Affects Sympathetic Nervous System

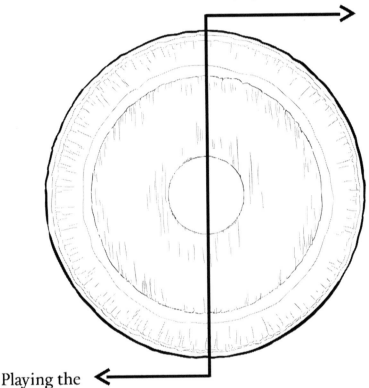

Playing the
Inner Area of the Gong
(the area next to player)
Creates Receptive Energy
Affects the Intuitive Body
Stimulates Ida Nadi
Increases Langhana
Supports Inward Moving Postures
Affects Parasympathetic System

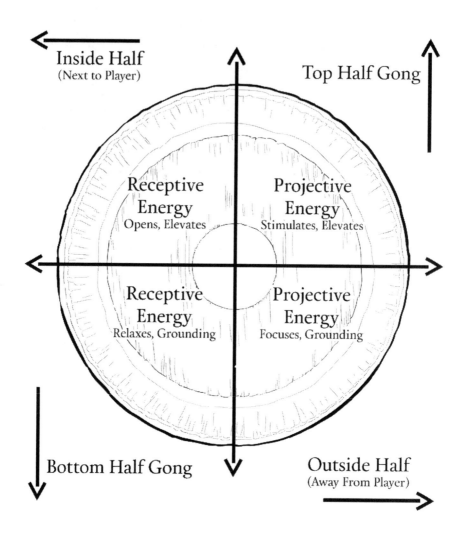

Inside Half
(Next to Player)

Top Half Gong

Receptive
Energy
Opens, Elevates

Projective
Energy
Stimulates, Elevates

Receptive
Energy
Relaxes, Grounding

Projective
Energy
Focuses, Grounding

Bottom Half Gong

Outside Half
(Away From Player)

Mehtab Benton

The Structure of a Gong Yoga Class

There is a difference between playing the gong in your yoga class and teaching a Gong Yoga class, and there is a structure that distinguishes the practice, as follows:

- Gong Opening
- Gong Pranayama
- Gong Kriya
- Gong Meditation
- Gong Relaxation
- Gong Closing

There are many variations within this structure that can be adapted to all styles of yoga.

Gong Opening: Beginning a Gong Yoga Class

Begin the class with a centering mantra. This should be done silently for yourself as the player.

Remain in silence as you strike the gong slowly three times near the center of the gong. Allow the sound to decay between the strikes and fill the room with its sound. After the third strike, remain in silence for as long as the previous strikes took. These three strikes, and the resulting silence, introduce the sound of the gong and correspond to the trinity field concept of consciousness in the practice of yoga.

The first strike represents the waking state of mental consciousness and the gross form of the universe that is contained in the anamaya kosha and the Physical Body (*Sthula Sharira*).

The second strike represents the dreaming state of the active unconscious processing level of the mind and the subtle realm of the universe that is contained in the pranamaya kosha, manamaya kosha, vijnanamaya kosha and the Subtle Body (*Sukshma Sharira*).

The third strike represents the deep sleep state of the mind and its subconscious aspects where the *samskaras*, or impetus for karma arises and the causal realm of the universe that is contained in the anandamaya kosha and the Causal Body (*Karana Sharira*).

The silence that follows the three strikes represents the state known as *Turiya*, or infinite consciousness where the three levels of mind and being are transcended.

After the silence, you can now introduce the class, or you can chant a mantra with the class according to your yoga tradition. For example, a Kundalini Yoga teacher would chant *Ong Namo Guru Dev Namo* three times while an Ashtanga teacher would use the invocation beginning with *Vande Gurunam Charanaravinde*.

After the group chanting ends, the gong can be struck a single time to mark the beginning of formal instruction, or a simply conscious inhale and exhale may be done.

Gong Pranayama: Connecting Sound to Energy

Since the gong works powerfully with moving prana through the body, it is helpful to begin the class with a gong pranayama practice to initiate the flow of breath. This could be a Breath of Fire practice with the gong if you are a Kundalini Yoga teacher, alternate nostril breathing if you are a Hatha teacher, Ujiya breath if you are an Ashtanga teacher, or simple long deep breathing, using the gong to regulate the inhale and exhale.

Gong Kriya: Using Sound With Movement

A kriya is a sequence of asanas, pranayamas, mudras, bandhas, and mantra that create a state of meditation. Some traditions, such as Kundalini and Ashtanga Yoga, have formalized kriyas that are strictly followed by the teachers. While some Hatha styles in the Western world have specific sequences or kriyas they follow in accordance with their tradition, there is often the possibility to create one's own sequence. Regardless of the yoga style or tradition, the kriya in a Gong Yoga class has a specific purpose (such as working on a chakra, an organ, or psychological state) in addition to preparing the practitioner for meditation.

Within this kriya, the teacher can take the opportunity to play the gong with one or more asanas or exercises. A reasonable rule is to play the gong one to three times during the class. For some kriyas, and if appropriate for the specific exercises and class flow, the gong can be played more, following the guidelines already given.

Gong Meditation: Taking the Sound Within

Following the kriya, the Gong Yoga class can lead directly into a gong relaxation and the meditation may be omitted. If a formal meditation is desired, then it may be done before the relaxation.

A meditation should last for a minimum of 3 minutes, although a 7-minute threshold is usually required for the sound of the gong to deeply affect the nervous system and mind. An 11-minute meditation is ideal for experienced students. For advanced practices and workshops, the meditation can be extended to 31-minutes.

Gong Relaxation: Integration and Clearing

If a gong meditation was used, then the relaxation afterwards can be done in silence, at least for a few minutes. Otherwise, the gong may be played as part of the relaxation for a minimum of 7 minutes to fully activate the parasympathetic nervous system. Be aware that a gong relaxation longer than 15 minutes at the end of the class may overwhelm the effects of the kriya and meditation, or change the sattvic state of relaxation into a tamasic nap. At the end of the gong relaxation, there should be a minute of silence before speaking and bringing the students out of relaxation.

Gong Closing: Ending a Gong Yoga Class

The Gong Yoga class may be closed with a mantra, a song, or a blessing. Depending upon the tradition and the energy of the class, the gong can also be struck to signal the closing of the sacred space.

Sat Nam

About Bookshelf Press

Bookshelf Press is a print and electronic publisher of books on yoga, health, Eastern astrology, and literary works of high imagination.

Bookshelf Press retains all subsidiary rights for its books. Rights are available through the publisher for foreign editions and other media adaptations.

Wholesale and retail orders are available directly from the publisher.

www.bookshelfpress.com

Mehtab Benton

Gong Yoga

Healing and Enlightenment Through Sound

Mehtab Benton

Gong Yoga is the first comprehensive book on practicing and teaching yoga with the sound of the gong. You will learn about the origin, history and use of the gong for yoga and meditation as well as its current therapeutic applications for healing and transformation.

The book contains a step-by-step training guide to teach you how to play the gong through a series of practice sessions. You will learn the basic techniques to play the gong as well as advanced techniques to create your own gong playing sessions. You will learn how to structure gong yoga classes and gong yoga therapy sessions for your students and clients.

A comprehensive chapter on Yoga and the Gong describes the chakras, the major energy channels of the body (the nadis), and the five sheaths of existence (the koshas), that are key to understanding how the gong integrates with the practice of yoga. Special sections explain the use of Kundalini Yoga mantras for playing the gong, how to select and care for your gong and additional resources to develop your skills.

Written by a long-time yoga teacher and international trainer of students and therapists in the art of playing the gong for meditation and healing.

*"Information on how to play the gong and the spiritual aspects of the sound of the gong are difficult to find. **GONG YOGA** is a wonderful introduction to all aspects of the gong and the yoga that is associated with it. The interesting history of the gong, its uses in Western and Eastern music, how to play it and the gong's effects on the body's energetic system are all discussed. FIVE STARS!"*

Available from Bookshelf Press and all major booksellers.
www.bookshelfpress.com

CPSIA information can be obtained at www.ICGtesting.com
Printed in the USA
LVOW07s0235140614

389999LV00001B/17/P

Communication in
Palliative Nursing

Communication in
Palliative Nursing

Elaine Wittenberg-Lyles

Joy Goldsmith

Betty Ferrell

Sandra L. Ragan

OXFORD
UNIVERSITY PRESS

OXFORD
UNIVERSITY PRESS

Oxford University Press is a department of the University of
Oxford. It furthers the University's objective of excellence
in research, scholarship, and education by publishing worldwide.

Oxford   New York
Auckland   Cape Town   Dar es Salaam   Hong Kong   Karach
Kuala Lumpur   Madrid   Melbourne   Mexico City   Nairobi
New Delhi   Shanghai   Taipei   Toronto

With offices in
Argentina   Austria   Brazil   Chile   Czech Republic   France   Greece
Guatemala   Hungary   Italy   Japan   Poland   Portugal   Singapore
South Korea   Switzerland   Thailand   Turkey   Ukraine   Vietnam

Oxford is a registered trademark of Oxford University Press in the UK
and certain other countries.

Published in the United States of America by
Oxford University Press
198 Madison Avenue, New York, NY 10016

© Oxford University Press 2013

Library of Congress Cataloging-in-Publication Data
Communication in palliative nursing / Elaine Wittenberg-Lyles ... [et al.].
p. ; cm.
Includes bibliographical references and index.
ISBN: 978-0-19-979682-3
I. Wittenberg-Lyles, Elaine.
[DNLM: 1. Nursing Care—methods.   2. Palliative Care—methods.
3. Communication. WY 152.3]
LC Classification not assigned
616.02'9—dc23
2012021001

9 8 7 6
Printed in the United States of America on acid-free paper

CONTENTS

FOREWORD

Nessa Coyle

Communication is a powerful therapeutic tool. When used well communication can empower patients and families with a sense of control; it can reduce uncertainty and provide a basis for action. Effective communication creates an environment of safety, trust, and hope in times of crisis and threat. The practice of thoughtful clinical communication has the power to strengthen the patient/nurse relationship. In contrast, inattentive communication may deprive the patient of hope, create loss of control, and silence the patient's voice. If the patient and family story is never elicited, queried, or engaged, the quality of care delivered can be diminished and the cost for the institution, exponential. This is especially salient during end-of-life care when nurses face decisions that become memoralized by the patient and family.

Communication is a continuous process of making meaning, occurring consciously and unconsciously, verbally and nonverbally—think of the power of communication as its own clinical practice. Communication is central to nursing care, especially in the setting of progressive disease that will end in the patient's death. All interactions between the patient and health care team are mediated through communication. A function of clinical communication is to reduce uncertainty and to provide a basis for action. Ineffective communication can increase anxiety, impede action, extinguish hope, and lead to a diminished sense of personal dignity as well as feelings of abandonment. Unproductive communication can cause more distress and suffering for patients and their families than anything other than unrelieved physical pain. Because the nurse is at the hub of an interdisciplinary palliative care or hospice team—the channel through which the expertise of various team members is often brought to the bedside—the ability to communicate skillfully with the team is also essential.

How do we communicate—how much does it matter—how can we do better? Elaine Wittenberg-Lyles, Joy Goldsmith, Betty Ferrell, and Sandra Ragan recognize that nothing deserves higher priority than effective palliative care communication and have taken up the challenge. They begin by exploring a number of myths about what constitutes effective communication and the definition of communication itself, preferring to define communication as "the mutual creation of meaning by both communicators." The authors of this volume acknowledge that communication that enables transitions in care and at the end-of-life is difficult but can be taught. They outline a holistic communication model—COMFORT—an acronym for seven principles designed to be taught and implemented in palliative care communication and end-of-life communication. Case examples are liberally used to illustrate each component of the model and to guide the nurse through the process. This is a necessary book and has been long in coming.

PREFACE

The field of palliative care espouses the importance of interdisciplinary care, and this book is a product of the blending of disciplines. It began in 2010 when two scholars with doctoral degrees in communication (Elaine Wittenberg-Lyles and Joy Goldsmith) approached a palliative care nurse researcher and educator (Betty Ferrell) to suggest that perhaps a different paradigm should be applied from their field of communication to understand and advance the concept of communication in palliative nursing. Through their innovative and provocative research in areas such as communication in hospice settings and interdisciplinary team meetings, Wittenberg-Lyles, Goldsmith, and their mentor, a senior scholar in health communication, Sandra Ragan, began to question existing thought and literature related to communication in palliative nursing. Thus began the collaboration that led to this book and a new way of approaching the essential concept of communication in palliative nursing.

The chapters of this book are organized according to the elements of the communication model, COMFORT, developed by these communication scholars (Ragan, Wittenberg-Lyles, Goldsmith, & Sanchez-Reilly, 2008; Wittenberg-Lyles, Gee, Parker Oliver, & Demiris, 2009; Wittenberg-Lyles, Goldsmith, Demiris, Parker Oliver, & Stone, 2012; Wittenberg-Lyles, Goldsmith, & Ragan, 2010; Wittenberg-Lyles, Goldsmith, Ragan, & Sanchez-Reilly, 2010; Wittenberg-Lyles, Goldsmith, Sanchez-Reilly, & Ragan, 2008). Each element is described in detail with supporting communication theory, empirical support, clinical evidence, and case examples. Collectively these elements challenge the notion that communication is simply sending and receiving information or that communication in palliative care is limited to breaking bad news. The intent of this book is to present the COMFORT model as a more honest representation of communication in palliative nursing. Through application of the model, our hope is to improve the care of patients and families while advancing our professional practice. In much the same ways that we move from novice to expert palliative care nurses by refining our skills in symptom assessment, care of the physical body, pain management practice, or grief interventions, we also become expert practitioners through developing proficiency in communication (Dahlin, 2010).

A critical reality, reinforced in this volume, is that no aspect of expert palliative nursing practice can be realized without proficiency in communication. Pain management requires skillful communication to assess the patient's pain, identify and overcome fears of addiction, and provide information about optimal use of analgesics and management of side effects. Similarly, compassionate, skillful listening to the family caregiver's grief, hearing the depth of his or her emotion, and responding verbally and nonverbally with communication that validates the loss and the suffering of the loss are key to quality palliative nursing care. For every aspect of palliative nursing care, communication is not only key, but it is also the foundational substance upon which other critical nursing practices depend.

CLINICAL PRACTICE GUIDELINES FOR QUALITY PALLIATIVE CARE

In 2006, a consortium of the leading palliative care organizations in the United States developed clinical practice guidelines in order to establish quality standards for the practice of palliative care (National Consensus Project for Quality Palliative Care, 2009). This National Consensus Project (NCP) effort was intended to provide shared definitions of the domains of palliative care and to challenge organizations to "reach" to a higher level to promote increased quality in this developing field. The NCP guidelines define each domain but ultimately create the whole concept of quality palliative care.

The NCP guidelines are expressly intended as an interdisciplinary document, representative of the inherent interdisciplinary nature of palliative care, which has been a fundamental characteristic of our field since the origins of hospice as conceived by our founders including Dame Cicely Saunders, Balfour Mount, Florence Wald, and others who challenged the ways that care was provided to the dying (Coyle, 2010). The NCP guidelines direct the interdisciplinary team but also hold special significance to nurses as the providers most often at the bedside of patients and families across all settings of care from diagnosis to death. The NCP domains are listed in Table 1. Following is a review of these quality domains in order to illustrate how essential communication is to every aspect of quality palliative care.

DOMAIN 1: STRUCTURE AND PROCESSES OF CARE

The NCP guidelines begin with this domain as an intentional message of the importance of creating structures that will support each of the domains and collectively promote palliative care. Yet palliative care clinicians in most every setting can easily identify daily operations that obstruct rather than promote effective communication.

Table 1 Domains of Quality Palliative Care

Domain 1: Structure and processes of care
Domain 2: Physical aspects of care
Domain 3: Psychological and psychiatric aspects of care
Domain 4: Social aspects of care
Domain 5: Spiritual, religious, and existential aspects of care
Domain 6: Cultural aspects of care
Domain 7: Care of the imminently dying patient
Domain 8: Ethical and legal aspects of care

The field of palliative care is by its very nature fraught with factors that challenge the goal of supportive structures and processes. Palliative care is complex, multidimensional, and is concerned with care in the most intimate and intense weeks of life. Palliative care requires multiple disciplines, settings, transitions, and enormous cultural variation. Quite often, the well-intended professionals working in this field may believe that effective communication will just happen because, after all, we are compassionate and dedicated clinicians. But the reality is that effective communication will not happen unless the structures and processes of care within an organization support communication.

Technological advances such as electronic medical records, cell phones, e-mail, Skype, and a host of other electronic means can greatly facilitate communication or conversely create significant barriers to communication. The challenge is for administrators and managers in palliative care settings to seriously consider the ways in which policies and procedures can best support effective communication.

Ellington and colleagues (Ellington et al., 2008; Ellington, Reblin, Clayton, Berry, & Mooney, 2012) have recently studied the interactions and communication between hospice nurses, patients, and families through audio recordings of these visits. Their initial findings have described how nurses devote the majority of their communication to topics of physical care. The recordings revealed many encouraging findings such as the tendency for nurses to devote substantial time to building partnerships with family caregivers and patients. Nurses also were flexible and adaptive, altering their communication to the changing circumstances of patients and families as the disease progressed. Ellington and colleagues are continuing their research in nursing communication, which will identify areas needed for more effective communication. Their research and others will help identify structures and processes of care that best support nurses in effective communication.

DOMAIN 2: PHYSICAL ASPECTS OF CARE

The great complexity of communication regarding physical aspects of care prominently involves the experience of symptoms. Communication skills are essential in order to elicit patient pain levels, but there must also be attention to the mitigating factors that influence patient pain tolerance, administration of pain medication, and decision making about treatment options. Varying responses to the question *"How would you rate your pain, on a scale of 0 to 10?"* can be the result of how the question was asked, who was in the room, or the patient's prior life experiences and choices. Communication about physical care involves learning to recognize the mediating effects of stoicism and its impact on pain management administration, recognizing what triggers patient complaints and when patients minimize symptoms, and understanding the inherent connection between physical pain and existential suffering. The dynamics between patients, providers, and family caregivers as well as the relationships between physical problems and other domains such as psychological or spiritual care are prominent when working to provide physical care.

DOMAIN 3: PSYCHOLOGICAL AND PSYCHIATRIC ASPECTS OF CARE

Psychological responses to illness are ever present in palliative care, and attention to these needs is integral to quality care. In this domain, the essential communication skill of listening is paramount. Palliative care nurses listen intently and through careful assessment identify the need for consultation by other professionals. The assessment of anxiety, depression, and other psychiatric responses is critical as is attention to responses to facing the end of life. Attentive communication gives voice to fears, uncertainty, anger, and sadness and also provides opportunity for life review. Nurses hold a special place in these last days and weeks of life as confidantes and as central support to recognize expected psychological responses to life-threatening disease as well as the urgent psychiatric symptoms that can greatly improve quality of life at end of life.

DOMAIN 4: SOCIAL ASPECTS OF CARE

The social domain of quality palliative care includes aspects of the patient's life in relationship with others. Social aspects include issues such as financial impact of illness, family dynamics, and sexuality as well as the very critical aspect of culture. Relational issues are central to the COMFORT model, which guides the remaining chapters of this text. Treatment decisions and the entire family experience of illness are greatly influenced by culture, family communication patterns, other family death experiences as well as a host of other factors. Nurses need to communicate with respect for the family system, honoring the dignity of the patient, and to facilitate bereavement support for loved ones. Effective communication means more than finding "the right words" as it also involves deep and attentive listening, strategic communication with other health care professionals, and a deliberate plan for the communication with the patient and family (Steinhauser, K. E. et. al, 2000).

DOMAIN 5: SPIRITUAL, RELIGIOUS, AND EXISTENTIAL ASPECTS OF CARE

Spiritual care is also an essential element of palliative care, encompassing a broad range of issues both religious and secular in nature. Patients and families face aspects of care such as hopefulness, life meaning and purpose, faith, forgiveness, abandonment from God, relationships with a higher being, and the profound connection to others and the universe.

Communication about spiritual issues is a challenge for most professionals and an area where nurses may feel ill prepared. We call on our spiritual care experts, chaplain, or other spiritual leaders for guidance and support of patients. Yet these issues are also often a topic of the routine encounters between nurses and patients. As a nurse conducts an initial assessment, these concerns may be voiced, and as disease progresses and death nears, it is often a nurse who hears the patient suffering and spiritual distress. In this domain as with the others, skillful communication is a part of nursing assessment and intervention.

DOMAIN 6: CULTURAL ASPECTS OF CARE

The overwhelming influence of culture in palliative care reveals the intertwining forces of cultural beliefs, religion, relationships, family history, and the fragility of family reconciliation. These factors are well described in the literature as influences on patient care (Clayton, Butow, Arnold, & Tattersall, 2005; Kruijver, Kerkstra, Bensing, & van de Wiel, 2000; O'Baugh, Wilkes, Sneesby, & George, 2009). The consequences of decisions and ensuing actions by the patient, family, and health care team are monumental.

DOMAIN 7: CARE OF THE IMMINENTLY DYING PATIENT

Professionals working with the imminently dying across settings know that the final hours are the ultimate test of our ability to provide compassionate care. Regardless of the diagnosis, length of time of the illness, or the highly varied family circumstances, care in the last days and hours is paramount (*Berry & Griffie, 2010*). This is also a challenging time for communication when family caregivers are physically and emotionally exhausted, grief is intense, and when the health care providers also confront the emotional burden of witnessing death and feeling responsible for this intensive care at life's end. The nurse's response and support of family will undoubtedly involve important information about signs and symptoms of approaching death and the dying process but will also respond to the emotions and grief.

Quality-of-Life Model Applied to Cancer Survivors

FIGURE 1 **Quality-of-Life Model**
Ferrell, B & Grant, M. City of Hope Medical Center, last retrieved on August 23, 2012, from http://prc.coh.org

DOMAIN 8: ETHICAL AND LEGAL ASPECTS OF CARE

When prognosis is poor and clear advance care planning is absent, it is not uncommon for intense ethical and legal concerns to become a focal point of care. Issues of proxy decision makers, advance directives, family conflict regarding goals of care, and challenges with communication amid acute illness in intensive care are common (Cherlin et al., 2005; Royak-Schaler et al., 2006). Skillful communication by all involved is essential to avoid disastrous care and potentially contribute to quality care for the patient and family.

Ultimately, communication is the cornerstone of quality of life and quality patient care. Figure 1 illustrates the quality-of-life (QOL) model developed at the City of Hope Medical Center by Ferrell and Grant (Ferrell, 1996, 2008; Ferrell & Grant, 2003), which has been used by many scholars, students, and nurses over the past 20 years. This depiction of QOL includes four key domains of physical, psychological, social, and spiritual well-being. Meeting the needs of patients in each of the areas requires effective communication so that patient needs can be identified, the patient can be heard, and a plan of care can be developed that addresses these needs.

A review of the National Consensus Project domains of quality care illustrates that the need for effective and compassionate communication in palliative care is unquestionable (NCP, 2009). Communication is the essence of our practice. It is the foundation of all that we embrace as palliative care nurses. Communication is in some ways the inherent art of our practice. It is also the skill that we seek to acquire having entered our practice with little preparation for the effective communication that is required hourly in our work as nurses caring for the seriously ill and dying. The chapters that follow provide a new approach for nurses and all professionals to guide this communication.

REFERENCES

Berry, P., & Griffie, J. (2010). Planning for the actual death. In B. Ferrell & N. Coyle (Eds.), *Oxford Textbook of Palliative Nursing* (3rd ed., pp. 629–646). New York: Oxford University Press.

Cherlin, E., Fried, T., Prigerson, H. G., Schulman-Green, D., Johnson-Hurzeler, R., & Bradley, E. H. (2005). Communication between physicians and family caregivers about care at the end of life: When do discussions occur and what is said? *Journal of Palliative Medicine, 8*(6), 1176–1185.

Clayton, J. M., Butow, P. N., Arnold, R. M., & Tattersall, M. H. (2005). Discussing end-of-life issues with terminally ill cancer patients and their carers: A qualitative study. *Support Care and Cancer, 13*(8), 589–599.

Coyle, N. (2010). Introduction to palliative nursing. In B. Ferrell & N. Coyle (Eds.), *Oxford Textbook of Palliative Nursing* (3rd ed., pp. 3–12). New York: Oxford University Press.

Dahlin, C. (2010). Communication in palliative care: An essential competency for nurses. In B. Ferrell & N. Coyle (Eds.), *Oxford Textbook of Palliative Nursing* (3rd ed., pp. 107–136). New York: Oxford University Press.

Ellington, L., Matwin, S., Uchino, B. N., Jasti, S., Dudley, W. N., & Roter, D. (2008). The body's response to health care provider communication: The impact of dominant versus facilitative styles. *Journal of Applied Biobehavioral Research, 13*(2), 67–85.

Ellington, L., Reblin, M., Clayton, M. F., Berry, P., & Mooney, K. (2012). Hospice nurse communication with cancer patients and their family caregivers. *Journal of Palliative Medicine, 15*, 262–268.

Ferrell, B. R. (1996). The quality of lives: 1,525 voices of cancer. *Oncology Nursing Forum, 23*(6), 907–916.

Ferrell, B. (2008). From research to practice: Quality of life assessment in medical oncology. *The Journal of Supportive Oncology, 6*(5), 230–231.

Ferrell B., & Grant, M. (2003). Chapter 9. Quality of life and symptoms. In C. King and P. Hinds (Eds.), *Quality of Life from Nursing and Patient Perspectives* (2nd ed., 199–217). Sudbury, MA: Jones and Bartlett.

Kruijver, I., Kerkstra, A., Bensing, J. M., & van de Wiel, H. (2000). Nurse-patient communication in cancer care: A review of the literature. *Cancer Nursing, 23*, 20–31.

National Consensus Project for Quality Palliative Care (NCP). (2009). *Clinical Practice Guidelines for Quality Palliative Care* (2nd ed.). Retrieved on November 11, 2010 from http://www.nationalconsensusproject.org/guideline.pdf

O'Baugh, J., Wilkes, L. M., Sneesby, K., & George, A. (2009). Investigation into the communication that takes place between nurses and patients during chemotherapy. *Journal of Psychosocial Oncology, 27*(4), 396–414. doi: 915716917 [pii]10.1080/07347330903182291

Ragan, S., Wittenberg-Lyles, E., Goldsmith, J., & Sanchez-Reilly, S. (2008). *Communication as Comfort: Multiple Voices in Palliative Care.* New York: Routledge/Taylor & Francis.

Royak-Schaler, R., Gadalla, S. M., Lemkau, J. P., Ross, D. D., Alexander, C., & Scott, D. (2006). Family perspectives on communication with healthcare providers during end-of-life cancer care. *Oncology Nursing Forum, 33*(4), 753–760.

Steinhauser, K. E., Christakis, N. A., Clipp, E. C., McNeilly, M., McIntyre, L., & Tulsky, J. A. (2000). Factors considered important at the end of life by patients, family, physicians, and other care providers. JAMA: *Journal of the American Medical Association, 284*(19), 2476.

Wittenberg-Lyles, E., Gee, G. C., Parker Oliver, D., & Demiris, G. (2009). What patients and families don't hear: Backstage communication in hospice interdisciplinary team meetings. *Journal of Housing for Elderly, 23*, 92–105.

Wittenberg-Lyles, E., Goldsmith, J., Demiris, G., Parker Oliver, D., & Stone, J. (2012). The impact of family communication patterns on hospice family caregivers: A new typology. *Journal of Hospice and Palliative Nursing, 14*, 25–33.

Wittenberg-Lyles, E., Goldsmith, J., & Ragan, S.L. (2010). The COMFORT initiative: Palliative nursing and the centrality of communication. *Journal of Hospice & Palliative Nursing, 12*(5), 282–294.

Wittenberg-Lyles, E., Goldsmith, J., Ragan, S. L., Sanchez-Reilly, S. (2010). *Dying With Comfort: Family Illness Narratives and Early Palliative Care.* Cresskill, NJ: Hampton Press.

Wittenberg-Lyles, E., Goldsmith, J., Sanchez-Reilly, S., & Ragan S. (2008). Communicating a terminal prognosis in a palliative care setting: Deficiencies in current communication training protocols. *Social Science & Medicine, 66*, 2356–2365.

ACKNOWLEDGMENTS

Though the sparkle of an idea for this collaboration emerged in a hotel room in Lexington, KY, it was the gracefully, generously, and deliciously appointed Italian meal in the home of Michael A. Mollica that brought us together. The authors are also deeply thankful to our editorial assistant, Andrea Garcia, who worked with us throughout every step of this manuscript. Her expert eyes and attention to detail were the secret ingredient to success.

Communication in Palliative Nursing

1

DEFINING AND UNDERSTANDING
COMMUNICATION

I am already a good communicator—what can you teach me? One of the problems communication experts encounter in attempting to teach effective communication is this: everyone already knows what good communication is, and many people believe that communication skills are innate, much like the hardwired ability we are born with that enables us to acquire and to understand language. Yet communication researchers have unearthed a number of myths that are popularly held about what constitutes good communication, even about the definition of "communication" itself. For example, a commonly accepted definition of effective communication is the transmission of information—what is in the speaker's head gets somehow magically transported to the listener's head so that both agree about the content of the message.

What we suggest in this chapter and throughout this text is that communication is, instead, the mutual creation of meaning by both communicators.

This revised definition has rich implications for all of us but particularly for palliative care nurses as they communicate with a host of audiences: physicians, patients, family members, interdisciplinary palliative care team members, and fellow nurses. Seeing the act of communicating as mutually creating meaning rather than transmitting information implies that the traditional roles of speaker and listener (also termed *sender* and *receiver*) do not really make sense. Both communicators are speaking and listening, sending and receiving, in any communication event. Further, both communicators are mutually and reciprocally influencing what the other party will say next or how he or she will react nonverbally. Let's look at an example of how mutual influence works when a nurse asks her dying patient about how the family is dealing with her impending death:

RN: How is your family doing with all of this?
PT: None of them are talking to me.
RN: They might be afraid—you might need to bring it up.
PT: Yes they are.
    (long pause)
RN: You might need to bring it up.
PT: I have a niece and nephew. I haven't seen them in 2 years, and they live right here in town. They said they were coming yesterday, and they didn't. But maybe I was sleeping. I feel like they are using it as an excuse, but I don't

care. They have an excuse now. I was not the most popular person in my family. I'm the oldest, and I've always had to do the most, and sometimes it put me in an unpopular position. I was the tattle-tale. Mommy and Daddy expected me to report everything. (Wittenberg-Lyles, Goldsmith, Ragan, & Sanchez-Reilly, 2010, pp. 69–70.)

In the example above, both nurse and patient affect the other's communication behavior. This may appear a simple notion, yet it has profound implications: how we communicate (what we say verbally and nonverbally) significantly influences communication effectiveness. Analyzing the conversational exemplar above reveals how the nurse's responsiveness to her patient's communication results in repetition of her advice ("you might need to bring it up"). This is offered after the patient's truncated admission that her family *is* afraid and then a lengthy pause: taking into account the verbal utterance of the patient and the long pause, the nurse repeats her advice. The patient's next utterance is an elaborated response to the nurse's original question about how her family is doing. The patient has modified her original response, perhaps because the nurse's repeated advice has freed her to disclose fully her family situation. The nurse now has a deeper understanding of this patient's limited social support as well as how she sees herself in relation to her family. Knowing this may prompt the RN to consult the social worker on the palliative care team.

This mutual influence model of communication (rather than the traditional sender-receiver model) means that both parties are simultaneously and reciprocally designing (encoding), delivering (both verbally and nonverbally), and interpreting (decoding) messages: both are creating the meaning of each other's messages. It also means that both speaking and listening are critical communication skills—for nurse and patient alike.

Epstein and Street (2007) note in their book on communication skills for patient-centered cancer care that clinicians and patients constantly influence each other's communication in ways that facilitate more effective patient care. For example, a patient can use such active communication strategies as asking questions, interrupting, and expressing concerns in an attempt to elicit more interest and more inquiry from the clinician. Concomitantly, if a patient appears passive, clinicians can use facilitative behaviors (e.g., asking for the patient's opinion and concerns, offering encouragement) that might elicit more patient involvement. This is because the clinician's communication "both legitimizes and specifically asks for the patient's views" (p. 6).

Note how this mutual influence might function in a palliative care context:

NURSE: How are you feeling today?
    (lengthy pause before patient responds)
PATIENT: Same as yesterday.
NURSE: When we talked yesterday, you mentioned some pain in your upper abdomen. You said it was a "6"—has it gotten better?
PATIENT: A little.
NURSE: What number would you give it today? I'd really like to know whether you think the new medication is working better. We want you to be as pain free as possible.

PATIENT: Yeah, well I'd say it's about a "4" this morning, so I guess that means that the new meds are working some.

NURSE: Going from "6" to "4" is in the right direction, and I'm glad your pain is less severe, but I think a "4" is still too high. I'd like for us to get your pain down to a "3" or lower. We will work to get the dosage exactly right for you so that your pain will not be more than a "3."

PATIENT: I'm still worried that I won't get enough pain medicine to control my pain.

NURSE: I'll increase your pain meds today to make sure that you're receiving enough medication to keep your pain at a level of "3" or less. That is our number one priority in caring for you: to make you as comfortable as we know how to do.

In the above example, the patient first appears passive, giving only minimal responses to the nurse's questions about her pain level. When the nurse tells the patient that she wants to know the number of the patient's pain level in order to gauge whether the new meds are working so that her pain can be better controlled, the patient gives a more elaborated response. After the nurse's next empathic response and her assurance that they're working to deliver the right dosage, the patient apparently feels trusting enough to disclose that she's still worried about not receiving enough pain meds to control her pain. Can you imagine how this conversation might have played out had the nurse not asked more questions of the patient or had she not expressed empathy for the patient's situation? Worse yet, what would have been the possible consequence of the nurse's replying to the patient's telling her that the pain was "a little better" today: "Oh, okay, well that's good to hear"? It's probable that this remark would have ended the conversation abruptly, that the patient would not have felt any empathy from the nurse, and that the patient's fears about not receiving enough pain meds would have gone undisclosed.

Of course, the verbal messages in this dialogue between patient and nurse are made more complex by both communicators' nonverbal messages—messages that are constantly and often unwittingly being conveyed along with their words. The next section of this chapter will discuss the preeminence of nonverbal communication as it affects the patient care (or task) and the communication climate (or relationship) between nurse and patient.

COMMUNICATION AXIOMS

Two central laws or axioms of communication (Watzlawick, Beavin, & Jackson, 1967) recognize the critical importance of nonverbal communication in every communication context, personal or professional:

(1) **One cannot not communicate.** While this verity may appear simplistic, it reminds us that it is impossible *not* to be sending messages when we are interacting with another. All of our words, gestures, facial expressions, gaze, touch, and tone of voice communicate loudly. Even our silence is profoundly communicative. The person we are talking to will attribute meaning to silences,

pauses, hesitations, and other nonverbal communication. For example, in the dialogue above, the long pause between the nurse's question ("How are you feeling today?") and the patient's response ("Same as yesterday") might indicate several things to the nurse: she might interpret the pause to mean that the patient really doesn't believe that the nurse is interested in how she's feeling, or that the patient wishes to deliberate about her answer before responding, or that the patient is feeling too bad to want to answer the question at all, among other possible meanings. Whatever the meaning, it is vital to remember that both communicators will try to make sense of the other's verbal and nonverbal (e.g., silence) messages. This leads us to the second law.

(2) **Every message has two levels of meaning: the content level and the relationship level**. In professional contexts, we often speak of these as the *task* and *relationship* levels since message content generally concerns the "tasks" of communication—for example, instructing, diagnosing, encouraging, supporting, and so on. "Relationship" refers both to how communicators interpret the content message and also to how they see the relationship between them: for example, if the nurse in our conversation above asks the patient, "How are you feeling today?," the content is obviously an inquiry designed to get information about the patient's status. But the relationship level of meaning is determined by how these words are spoken: if the nurse is glancing at the patient's chart while she asks the question, if she doesn't make eye contact with the patient, if she is standing at the door rather than at the patient's bedside, the patient likely will interpret the question as phatic (or as a rote greeting rather than a genuine inquiry) and will see the nurse—and their relationship—as distant, perhaps cold and unfeeling.

While the content level of a message is conveyed by the words themselves, the relational level generally is manifested by nonverbal communication. We are often unaware of the nonverbal messages we are communicating—we don't hear our tone of voice or see our facial expressions or appreciate what touch, distance, and timing might be communicating to the other. Yet our nonverbal messages are powerful in communicating meaning and relationship; according to an eminent psychologist, Mehrabian (1981), nonverbals communicate three dimensions of relationship-level meaning: power or influence, affection or liking, and responsiveness or attentiveness or inattentiveness to others.

Not only does nonverbal communication help communicators interpret their messages and assign relationship cues; it is also preeminent because most of the meaning of a message (some researchers says as much as 80%) is communicated through nonverbal means, not through words. This may be because we believe that nonverbal communication is more credible than verbal communication and that nonverbal communication is not under our conscious control as much as verbal communication and is thus more believable. We also know that when verbal and nonverbal messages contradict each other (or are incongruent), we are much more likely to believe what the nonverbal messages are telling us. For example, in the above conversation, the nurse's verbal communication ("How are you feeling today?") appears to exhibit her genuine concern for the patient and her need for this information in order to facilitate the patient's care. But if she asks this question as she reads the patient's chart, failing to make any eye contact, the patient is likely to believe that the nurse is uncaring. That is, the patient attributes meaning to the interaction by believing that the inattentive nonverbal messages are more telling than what the nurse says. For this reason, it is imperative that we bring our nonverbal communication into conscious awareness and that we attempt to make what we say and how we say it match.

NONVERBAL CODES

Nonverbal communication has been defined as all those behaviors other than words themselves that form a socially shared coding system (Burgoon, 1994). That nonverbal communication is "socially shared" assumes that people recognize (decode) the meaning of nonverbal behaviors within their social/cultural settings, though it does not imply that nonverbal communication is necessarily universal in its meaning. We all have heard jokes about how leaders of state traveling abroad unwittingly have used a nonverbal sign (such as making a "V" with the index and third fingers) to signify "victory," only to learn that this sign communicated an obscene expression in the culture in which they found themselves. Yet it is also true that some nonverbal behaviors *are* understood cross-culturally—for example, smiling generally means the same thing across cultures (Afifi, 2007).

To complicate the nonverbal picture further, communication researchers divide nonverbal communication into seven different codes or forms (Afifi, 2007). All seven of these codes can be sending messages simultaneously, or only one or more codes can be utilized. The seven codes—kinesics, haptics, proxemics, physical appearance, vocalics, chronemics, and artifacts—are described in the next section.

Kinesics involves every form of movement of the body, including gestures, eye contact, and body position. Kinesics is particularly important in health care contexts as affect (or emotional) displays—body movements that express emotion without the use of touch or verbal accompaniment. Many kinesic gestures are understood across cultures; for example, sadness is expressed by constricting the eyes and forehead region, flattening the cheeks, and showing a slight downward curve of the mouth.

Nonverbal immediacy, which is a cluster of nonverbal behaviors that communicate how much one is involved in the interaction, is a concept that has been shown to be effective in many professional contexts. It involves several kinesic channels (eye contact; body orientation—toward or away from the other; body lean—forward or backward; and head nods) as well as behaviors from other nonverbal codes: interpersonal distance (proxemics) and touch (haptics). Immediacy is a critical concept in health care interactions as it demonstrates how physically and emotionally accessible the health caregiver is to the patient—changes in the level of immediacy will dramatically affect interaction outcomes. For example, if the nurse in the previous interaction is reading the patient's chart while she inquires about how the patient is feeling, this will show nonimmediacy, or lack of involvement to the patient and may elicit a delayed or minimal response. On the other hand, if the nurse asks the same question and accompanies it with eye contact, a forward body lean, and a touch of the patient's hand, the patient might respond more completely, interpreting the nonverbal communication as indication that the nurse is fully involved in the interaction. Nonverbal immediacy is an excellent example of the concept of mutual influence in communication. It will be further detailed later in this chapter when the COMFORT model is introduced and also will be discussed at length in Chapter 2.

While not as elaborated as kinesics, the other six nonverbal codes include:

Haptics—the use of touch, which in professional contexts can be task related but can also convey relational messages of warmth and caring. This is, of course, a critical component of palliative care.

Proxemics—the way we use space and distance. As nurses, it is generally acceptable to invade a patient's "personal bubble of space" whereas this might be considered offensive and inappropriate in other contexts. However, personal space remains an important element to be assessed by nurses and respected.

Physical appearance—includes body type and clothing, both of which influence perception. A nurse's unprofessional appearance communicates an important image to patients. Nurses similarly develop perceptions about patients based on their physical appearance—this may be the first "red flag" to nurses signaling potential depression or other psychosocial needs.

Vocalics—include all aspects of the voice—volume, pitch, accent, rate of speech, pauses, tone, and so on. The way we use our voices communicates loudly on a relational level. Communication accommodation theory suggests that we moderate our speech and vocalics to either be similar to (to converge with) or be different from (to diverge from) the person to whom we're talking. That is why MDs and nurses who use medical jargon—or who talk to patients in a condescending tone of voice—are perceived as distancing themselves from their patients. And, of course, patients perceive this distancing as relationship distancing, believing that the caregiver is not emotionally accessible to them.

Chronemics—the use of and perception of time. If nurses devote only minimal time to talk with a patient, if they only take the time for administering medications and procedures rather than stopping to hear patients' concerns and fears, they are likely perceived as uncaring. The gift of time is vital not only to our close interpersonal relationships but also to our patients and to other health caregivers. While time is very limited in most clinical settings, even a few minutes devoted to active listening and presence can make an enormous impact.

Artifacts—the presence of physical and environmental objects. Nurses are often physically separated from their patients by objects in the patient's room: bedrails, bedside tables, medical equipment, and the like. Such barriers can reduce emotional connection or relationships unless the nurse intentionally employs those nonverbal behaviors that promote immediacy: for example, touch, pleasant tone of voice, and sustained eye contact while seeking to eliminate artifacts when possible. A nurse sitting for a short time at the bedside versus standing at a distance and separated by bedrails can greatly impact communication.

If we look again at the dialogue on pages 3–4 and insert appropriate nonverbal communication (in brackets) to complement the words used by the nurse, we see dramatic changes in the effectiveness of the nurse's questions and responses:

NURSE: How are you feeling today? [walking to patient's bed as she asks this question and pulling up a chair at patient's bedside]
(lengthy pause before patient responds)

PATIENT: Same as yesterday.

NURSE: When we talked yesterday, you mentioned some pain in your upper abdomen. You said it was a "6"—has it gotten better? [asked in a caring tone of voice]

PATIENT: A little.

NURSE: What number would you give it today? I'd really like to know whether you think the new medication is working better. We want you to be as pain free as possible. [lightly touching patient's hand]

PATIENT: Yeah, well I'd say it's about a "4" this morning, so I guess that means that the new meds are working some.

NURSE: Going from "6" to "4" is in the right direction, and I'm glad your pain is less severe, but I think a "4" is still too high. I'd like for us to get your pain down to a "3" or lower. We'll monitor your pain very closely and will work to get the dosage exactly right for you so that your pain will not be more than a "3." [said with sustained eye contact and with an encouraging tone of voice]

PATIENT: I'm still worried that I won't get enough pain medicine to control my pain.

NURSE: Can we talk a little more about why you are worried? [With this probing question, conversation can ensue that attempts to discover the source of the patient's fears about inadequate pain control. Throughout the conversation, the nurse will sustain eye contact, speak in a gentle, reassuring tone, and lightly touch the patient if this seems appropriate.]
I'll increase your pain meds today to make sure that you're receiving enough medication to keep your pain at a level of "3" or less. That is our number one priority in caring for you: to make you as comfortable as we know how to do.

Equally important in the interaction is the nurse's attentiveness to the patient's nonverbal responses. We've already mentioned that a perceptive nurse will note the lengthy pause that occurs after she asks how the patient is feeling today. If the patient's eventual response ("same as yesterday") is said in a wooden tone of voice and/or if the patient mutters this without establishing eye contact, this should alert the nurse that she must continue to probe gently in order to communicate to the patient that she really cares. Later in the dialogue when the patient discloses that she's worried about not getting enough pain medication, the nurse should also be responsive to accompanying nonverbals (e.g., frowning and other facial expressions) that further communicate the patient's fear and concern.

In sum, the nurse should be as attuned to and responsive to a patient's nonverbal communication as she is to a patient's words. If the nonverbal communication belies the words (for example, in our dialogue above, if the patient answers—"Oh, I'm feeling on top of the world" with a sneer and a sarcastic tone of voice in response to the nurse's query), then the nurse likely will believe the nonverbal message. She might then smile and question again, "Okay, how are you *really* feeling?" It is essential that nurses be aware of the message that their own nonverbal communication carries as well as those messages conveyed by the patient's nonverbals. Since such messages are frequently "under the radar," nurses must train themselves to be particularly sensitive to this aspect of communication.

Of course, the skill of close listening is paramount in detecting the nuances of both verbal and nonverbal communication. Likewise, the use of silence can be an important communication strategy: recall that the axiom "one cannot not communicate" (p. 6) means that pauses and lengthier silences in conversation will still have communicative import. In addition, nurses can use silence as a means of probing further into a patient's feelings and concerns. Both listening and silence will be discussed in more detail in Chapter 4, "Mindful Presence."

TASK AND RELATIONSHIP AND THE FIVE ROLES OF NURSING

We have mentioned that the content of a message can also be considered the *task* of the interaction, particularly in professional contexts, and that the other dimension of meaning in the message, *relationship*, refers to how the interactants perceive the relationship between them. Specific aspects of *task* and *relationship* pertinent to palliative care will be discussed more thoroughly in Chapter 2; this next section deals with how the five nursing roles (Pavlish & Ceronsky, 2009) also demonstrate the task and relationship goals of communication.

Pavlish and Ceronsky (2009) explored oncology nurses' perspectives of palliative care through narrative analysis of participants' descriptions of life experiences. Findings from the nurses' focus group interactions revealed five primary nursing roles: teaching, caring, coordinating, advocating, and mobilizing. Seven professional attributes occurred in all five of these roles: clinical expertise, honesty, family orientation, perceptive attentiveness, presence, collaboration, and deliberateness. Note that each of the five primary nursing roles involves communication in which both task and relationship are conveyed:

> **Teaching**—A sample quotation illustrating this role was: "You help them figure out what they're going to do about comfort, pain control, spirituality and help them maximize their days" (2009, p. 406). *Task* is communicated in that nurses are preparing patients and their families to make informed decisions, including those regarding symptom management. *Relationship* is interpreted by patients and families as they receive nonverbal cues from the nurse's tone of voice, her use of touch, and eye contact.

Caring—A sample quotation illustrating this role was: "I talk about the hard stuff with them. Sometimes I put an arm around them and say, 'I am so sorry for what you have to go through. What can I do to help you?'" (2009, p. 406). *Task* and *relationship* are communicated simultaneously in the act of caring. Note that the "hard stuff" gets talked out (task) while the nurse uses touch (an arm around the patient) to communicate her emotional accessibility and concern (relationship).

Coordinating—A sample quotation illustrating this role was: "We have to be diplomatic and work with the whole team, I mean everyone from environmental services to chaplains to pharmacy, everyone. It's a big difference when we're all working together" (2009, p. 406). Again, in performing the role of coordinating, nurses must attend both to *task*—that is, getting everyone to work together—and *relationship*—communicating diplomatically and carefully with each team member as well as with the patient and his/her family.

Advocating—A sample quotation illustrating this role was: "So we have to advocate for patients and bring up these [needs] to doctors" (2009, p. 406). Advocacy is obviously the primary *task* of communication in this role, yet, because of the sensitivity of talking to patients, their families, and medical staff about patients' and families' quality-of-life (QOL) issues, nonverbal communication that signifies *relationship* must also be chosen with care and appropriateness.

Mobilizing—A sample quotation illustrating this role was: "We assess them and try to bring help into [the care situation] as much as we can" (2009, p. 406). Responding to patients' and families' changing needs requires *task* communication that is "attentive, assertive, and resourceful" (p. 406). Yet mobilizing also relies on nonverbal communication that is congruent with these messages and that exhibits a caring *relationship*.

It is of further interest to note that four of the seven professional attributes of palliative care nurses that are exhibited in all of these five nursing roles (Pavlish & Ceronsky, 2009)—honesty, family orientation, perceptive attentiveness, and presence—inherently emphasize the preeminence of relationship as these attributes are manifested. In discussing the attribute of *honesty*, research participants talked about the importance of remaining in a caring relationship, even when the patient is in denial, and accepting patients "where they are with the disease" (p. 407). They stressed the importance of being honest in end-of-life situations without taking all hope away: for example, "You have to be truthful without knocking the pins out from underneath them" (p. 407). Likewise with *family orientation*, nurses attended to relationship goals, including teaching families how to relate to a dying loved one, assisting families to accept a patient's preferences for end-of-life treatment, and helping them prepare for the grieving process. Perhaps *perceptive attentiveness* is the attribute in which relationship is manifested most by palliative care nurses: responding to a patient's unspoken needs requires finely tuned nonverbal sensitivity. Nurses in the study commented on "recognizing the need in someone's eyes" and "feeling the need in the room" (p. 407). This attentiveness is especially valuable in sensing a patient's psychological needs; as one nurse expressed, "Physical needs might not change often, but emotional needs change all the time" (p. 408).

The attribute of *presence* is, of course, all about relationship: described as "calmness or peacefulness" and "spiritual and existential connection" (2009, p. 407), presence is that quality that makes patients and their families feel that their nurses are there for them. "Listening carefully," "speaking last," and "making people feel cared about" were all listed as examples of presence (p. 408). One nurse saw presence as caring as she stated: "Palliative always comes with care behind it, which means we're able to take the care path rather than focusing just on all the nursing tasks that have to get done" (p. 408). Surely this nurse understands the nexus of task and relationship.

The task and relationship dimensions of the five roles of palliative care nursing and the corresponding seven professional attributes that nurses exhibit in these roles are further supported by Epstein and Street (2007), who discuss six functions of patient–clinician communication in their book on patient-centered communication in cancer care. These six functions include:

- Fostering healing relationships
- Exchanging information
- Responding to emotions
- Managing uncertainty
- Making decisions
- Enabling patient self-management

As do the nurses' roles and attributes, each of these functions involves both task and relationship goals and, concomitantly, task and relationship communication in order to achieve these goals. Epstein and Street (2007, p. 4) further provide examples of patient-centered clinician communication:

NONVERBAL BEHAVIORS

- Maintaining eye contact
- Forward lean to indicate attentiveness
- Nodding to indicate understanding
- Absence of distracting movements (e.g., fidgeting)

VERBAL BEHAVIORS

- Avoiding interruptions
- Establishing purpose of the visit
- Encouraging patient participation
- Soliciting the patient's beliefs, values, and preferences
- Eliciting and validating the patient's emotions
- Asking about family and social context
- Providing sufficient information
- Providing clear, jargon-free explanations
- Checking for patient understanding

- Offering reassurance
- Offering encouragement and support

There is remarkable similarity between these listings and the five roles and seven professional attributes of palliative care nurses outlined by Pavlish and Ceronsky (2009). All of these authors describe ideal patient–clinician communication, particularly when that patient is suffering from cancer or another life-threatening illness: it is communication characterized by an alignment of verbal and nonverbal messages that are directed to treating both the patient's physiological and psychological concerns, not to merely treating the patient as his/her disease.

INTRODUCING THE COMFORT MODEL

We know that palliative care nurses must face many communication challenges as they deal with patients and families confronting end of life, and yet there are few guidelines currently for teaching nurses end-of-life communication skills. The ELNEC Project (End-of-Life Nursing Education Consortium Training Manual, 2010) curriculum and other palliative nursing educational programs have applied a physician-derived model for delivering bad news, SPIKES (setting, perception, invitation, knowledge, empathy, and strategy/summary) (Baile et al., 2000; Buckman, 2005). A number of deficiencies exist in this model and other physician-based communication training protocols—including (1) the approach to communication as sender-receiver rather than as mutual influence and hence the communication priority on dispensing information, (2) the emphasis on the dyad of physician–patient rather than the multiparty inclusion of family and other health care providers, and (3) the failure to address the ongoing concerns of patients and families after a patient has received bad medical news. These deficiencies as a whole necessitate the need for a new model of palliative care communication, one that embraces the nurse's various roles and professional attributes (Pavlish & Ceronsky, 2009) and one that is built around patient-centered communication.

Based on their empirical research on medical communication training in palliative care, family communication at end of life, and conversations among hospice and palliative care staff, patients, and families (Ragan & Goldsmith, 2008; Ragan, Wittenberg, & Hall, 2003; Ragan, Wittenberg-Lyles, Goldsmith, & Sanchez-Reilly, 2008; Wittenberg-Lyles, Greene, & Sanchez-Reilly, 2007; Wittenberg-Lyles & Thompson, 2006) as well as several years of participation in a medical school elective on geriatric and palliative care, in a palliative care facility, and in a number of hospices (Goldsmith, Wittenberg-Lyles, Rodriguez, & Sanchez-Reilly, 2010; Ragan, Wittenberg-Lyles, Goldsmith, & Sanchez-Reilly, 2008; Sanchez-Reilly, Wittenberg-Lyles, & Villagran, 2007; Villagran, Goldsmith, Wittenberg-Lyles, & Baldwin, 2010), communication scholars (and editors of this textbook) Wittenberg-Lyles, Goldsmith, and Ragan developed a set of themes critical to palliative care. They then organized these themes into a communication curriculum, COMFORT, an acronym for seven principles designed to be taught and implemented in early palliative care communication and breaking ongoing bad news in life-limiting illness contexts.

These principles find their theoretical roots in patient-centered care and also in the narrative medicine movement (Charon, 2004). Narrative medicine, which subscribes to our communication model of mutual influence and coconstructed conversational outcomes, privileges and values the stories of both patients and clinicians. It is intrinsic to the practice of palliative care in that the founder of the modern hospice movement, Dame Cicely Saunders, listened to and collected the stories of illness and suffering of more than a thousand of her dying patients. Through these stories, she developed a more expansive understanding of pain so that she came to see pain as not merely physical but also psychological, spiritual, and existential (Saunders, 1967). Because palliative care nurses must address all these aspects of pain in their patients, and because listening to patients' and family members' stories is fundamental to clinical practice, we believe that a narrative approach to palliative nursing is a pivotal place of convergence between clinical and communication studies (Wittenberg-Lyles, Goldsmith, & Ragan, 2010).

The COMFORT model (Table 1.1) is thus offered to assist nurses in their practice of narrative nursing and patient-centered communication in end-of-life care. The following section will briefly describe the seven principles of COMFORT—communicate,

Table 1.1 The COMFORT Model

The COMFORT Model	Communication Skills to Develop
C—Communicate	• Learning to bear witness
	• Using person-centered messages
	• Recognizing communication expectations
O—Orientation and opportunity	• Gauging health literacy levels
	• Acknowledging vulnerability
	• Understanding cultural humility
	• Formulating a pathway of care
M—Mindful presence	• Practicing empathy
	• Engaging in active listening
	• Demonstrating cultural humility
	• Employing nonverbal communication
F—Family	• Viewing the family as an open or closed system
	• Recognizing predictable family communication patterns
	• Responding to the varying needs of family caregivers
O—Openings	• Identifying pivotal events of change in patient/family care
	• Communicating despite tension
	• Practicing complementary disclosure
R—Relating	• Embracing the multiple goals of a patient/family
	• Accepting inherent conflicts in goals
	• Using communication with patient/family to practice care
T—Team	• Contributing to interdisciplinary collaboration
	• Distinguishing successful collaboration from group cohesion

orientation and opportunity, mindful presence, family, openings, relating, and team—which also organize the remaining chapters of this book and are discussed in detail in Chapters 2–8. We emphasize that these seven themes or principles are not a linear guide or algorithm as most of the physician-based communication protocols are; rather, they are principles that should be used concurrently and reflectively as palliative care nurses care for patients/families with life-limiting illness (Wittenberg-Lyles, Goldsmith, & Ragan, 2010).

Communicate

A detailed discussion of this principle is found in Chapter 2. *Communication* describes behaviors that constitute a narrative nursing approach, namely, the use of verbal clarity and nonverbal immediacy (sustained eye contact, forward lean, nodding to indicate understanding, avoidance of fidgeting). Both of these behaviors exemplify a patient-centered approach to care: using language that is clear, unambiguous, and understandable not only communicates more accurately but also communicates more compassionately; likewise, using congruent nonverbals that signify physical and emotional accessibility (i.e., nonverbal immediacy) conveys empathy, support, and understanding to patients.

Practice Example

A nurse must explain to a patient and his family the typical side effects of a round of chemotherapy that the patient will soon undergo.

Communication Behaviors

The nurse first tries to elicit the patient's understanding of and concerns about his chemotherapy (narrative nursing approach). She uses language that is free of medical jargon and that is direct and unequivocal (verbal clarity) while maintaining sustained eye contact with the patient, leaning toward him, and nodding after he has spoken (nonverbal immediacy). As a result, the *task* of the encounter (giving information) is achieved with *relationship* warmth and caring. The patient and his family perceive that the nurse is concerned with his overall quality of life, not just with the physical effects of the chemotherapy.

Orientation and Opportunity

A detailed discussion of this principle is found in Chapter 3. *Orientation and opportunity* occur when the nurse communicates the entire story of the patient's prognosis and options for care so that understanding occurs (i.e, *orientation*) and then helps educate the patient and her family about all options for treatment and care (i.e., *opportunity*). Nurses must practice this principle with the full awareness that patients' limited health literacy skills may hamper their ability to make optimal health care decisions; thus, nurses must serve to support and nurture health literacy. A patient's vulnerability due to her incomplete understanding of her disease and its projected course, available treatment options, and involvement in research protocols needs to be acknowledged and addressed so that the patient can receive optimal care—as well as care that is self-selected. Helping patients and their families articulate and prioritize health care goals and then helping them implement such goals with a pathway of care are paramount.

Practice Example

A very elderly (and thus marginalized) patient must make a decision to have heart surgery that carries significant risks. The palliative care nurses assess her health literacy as extremely limited and yet must explore the surgical option with her and help her find an optimal pathway of care.

Communication Behaviors

Using the same verbal and nonverbal behaviors as described above (under "*Communicate*"), the nurse must first be completely aware of the patient's vulnerable status and then must attempt to educate the patient about the risks that surgery would entail. With the patient's and family members' assistance, the patient's goals of care must then be determined, and the full range of options—curative and palliative—must be explored. The primary *task* of this encounter (helping to educate the patient and establish a pathway of care) is thus achieved with empathy for the patient's limited health literacy and the use of verbal clarity and nonverbal immediacy to establish rapport and support (*relationship*).

Mindful Presence

A detailed discussion of this principle is found in Chapter 4. *Mindful presence* involves those psychological attributes of staying in the moment, refusing to prejudge patients, families, and ensuing interactions, and adapting to rapid changes in these interactions. Staying in the moment entails a reduction of self-talk and predetermined scripts; the nurse is willing to operate without a script as she recognizes the complexity of the end-of-life situation and the need for adaptation and spontaneity. As Wittenberg-Lyles, Goldsmith, and Ragan (2010) describe it, "characteristics of mindful self-monitoring include an ability to describe your inner experience, adopting more than one perspective, openness to possibilities, curiosity, and attentiveness" (p. 287).

Practice Example

A palliative care nurse is making a routine visit to an elderly female patient who resides in a group home. He is aware that the patient is dying of heart disease, but recalling that she appeared content and physically stable when he saw her last week, he anticipates a routine, quick visit. When he arrives, he finds the patient sitting alone in a dark room, appearing withdrawn, and ignoring the nurse's presence. The patient responds with only minimal utterances to the nurse's questions, yet she does not report any pain.

Communication Behaviors

Since mindful presence is as much a psychological attribute as a communication behavior, this nurse must adopt a mindset that permits him to quickly adapt to the situation: it is not as he expected. While it might be tempting to judge his patient as depressed given her behavior (after all, she is in a comfortable family setting and is not experiencing physical pain), mindfulness entails a complete lack of judgment and a willingness to adapt to the patient's interaction needs. In this case, narrative nursing comes to the forefront, for the nurse must try to elicit the patient's story: what are the causes of her sadness? What has changed since his visit with her last week? In the course of their interaction when the patient complains that she feels imprisoned in the group home and at age 92 knows she's capable of driving although that privilege has been denied her, the nurse needs to hear her out without prejudgment or a scripted admonishment or solution. While he may not succeed in changing her feelings or materially improving her quality of life (*task*), he can at least exhibit caring, empathic, verbal and nonverbal communication, which assures her of a supportive *relationship*. And because he is willing to take the time to hear her story, he might enable his patient to be open to possibilities for improved quality of life that she has overlooked.

Family

A detailed discussion of this principle is found in Chapter 5. *Family* acknowledges that both patient *and* family members form the unit of care in palliative care interactions. The principle of *family* also means that nurses recognize the complexity of multiparty communication in this context in that both the patient's needs and family members' needs must be considered. Further, family is seen as a conduit to the patient: it carries primary responsibility for the implementation of patient care and as such is viewed as a partner in the caretaking process. Honoring family members in this way also entails encouraging their voices and their stories in family meetings that help to establish and to clarify the patient's goals of care.

Practice Example

The palliative care team meets with four family members of their comatose dying grandmother, who does not have an advance directive. The goal of the meeting is to try to determine what their grandmother's wishes would be regarding aggressive treatment at end of life, and DNR (do-not-resuscitate) orders.

Communication Behaviors

The communication *task*, in this case, is daunting: the palliative care nurse, along with other team members, must help the family arrive at consensus about their grandmother's end-of-life care. In doing so, they must mindfully listen to each family member's perspective and story; they then need to facilitate problem solving and conflict resolution if family members are divided about the course of care. Even if the discussion gets heated, nurses must exhibit supportive, empathic, verbal and nonverbal communication in order to assure family members that their opinions are valued and that they are considered a vital component of the unit of care (*relationship*).

Openings

A detailed discussion of this principle is found in Chapter 6. *Openings* are those critical opportunities in patient care in which nurses' skilled and strategic communication can create the possibility for positive change. Such opportunities frequently occur around painful transitions in patient care (e.g., initial diagnosis, decisions about treatment options, disease recurrence). Through their roles as mediator, coach, and advocate with patients and their families, nurses can help reframe these moments of tension so that they become opportunities for resilience and coping.

Practice Example

Mr. Jones was a 68-year-old man with a 40-year history of chronic illnesses including diabetes, obesity, hypertension, and COPD (chronic obstructive pulmonary disease). Over the past year, he has also developed renal failure. Mr. Jones, his family, and his primary care physician have discussed his declining health status, recent new diagnosis of heart failure, and the resulting decline in his QOL and function. Over the weekend, he informed his family that he is "done" and wants to discontinue his renal dialysis, recognizing that this decision will lead to his death. His wife and daughter are appropriately sad but support and understand his decision. His brother, age 60 and also diagnosed with renal disease and heart failure, has strongly opposed his decision and insisted they all come in to the renal clinic today so that the staff can "straighten this out." He is very hostile toward Mrs. Jones and is emotionally distressed yet strongly advocating for his brother's care.

Communication Behaviors

This case example illustrates tremendous opportunity for nursing. The nurse in the renal clinic can apply the principle of *opening*, using this change in the patient status and goals of care to facilitate family communication. Careful assessment, listening to each family member's perspectives, and being present to the tension will be essential to facilitating the next phase of care.

Relating

A detailed discussion of this principle is found in Chapter 7. *Relating* means that nurses are willing to meet patients and their families where they are in their acceptance and understanding of their disease and its course. This principle thus may entail a repetition of prognosis and treatment options to patients/families regardless of how many times they have heard the bad medical news. As a patient's/family's awareness level deepens, previous discussions will be repeated or revisited with the same or different outcomes. The SPIKES model is limited in addressing only the initial encounter of a physician's confronting a patient with bad news. Yet a terminal diagnosis or equally upsetting medical news cannot be processed instantaneously by the patient/family. Patients and families need to digest the news incrementally and frequently in a non-linear fashion—with subsequent questions about treatment options and prognosis, which are often heard by nurses. This principle values family as a vehicle for reiterating the bad news to the patient if she/he resists the diagnosis initially (Wittenberg-Lyles, Goldsmith, Ragan, & Sanchez-Reilly, 2010). It champions adaptive communication based on the patient's/family's acceptance of information concerning disease, prognosis, and plan of care, and it emphasizes team-based family communication over dyadic communication between clinician and patient.

Relating involves prioritizing the relationship between the clinician and the patient/family and attending to the goal of relationship in order to facilitate instrumental (task) goals of nursing. Often this involves the ability of the nurse to be *radically adaptive*, that is, to take into account the patient's/family's experiences rather than rely on her own script for an encounter. Removing the clinician's habituated response to an interaction and adapting to the patient's/family's unique perspective means that the nurse values that perspective over her own. This underscores a primary tenet of narrative nursing and of the mutual influence model of communication discussed in this chapter: outcomes of clinician–patient interactions—and patients'/families' stories—are as dependent on patients/families as they are on clinicians.

Practice Example

A palliative care nurse must face a family that remains convinced that the patient's end-stage esophageal cancer can be cured; rather than opting for hospice, as the physician has encouraged, they are demanding to enroll in a clinical trial for which the patient is ineligible. In this instance, it will not be helpful for the nurse to simply repeat the clinical trial requirements (habituated response). Rather, the nurse needs to be radically adaptive, relating to the dynamics of the situation.

Communication Behaviors

The communication *task* is a challenging one, which involves careful repetition of the prognosis and care options to both patient and family. The nurse needs to exercise perceptive attentiveness, presence, and empathy (Pavlish & Ceronsky, 2009) at times when it will be tempting to become impatient with a resistant family that not only is in denial about impending death but, in refusing hospice, is denying the patient the quality-of-life benefits of hospice. Relating to their conflicting goals, talking about those goals, and working toward the goals are opportunities for nurses to be active in their engagement of relating. Caring is obviously the *relationship* message that must be communicated both verbally and nonverbally.

Team

A detailed discussion of this principle is found in Chapter 8. *Team* implies that a multidisciplinary group of individuals trained in various aspects of palliative care will ensure the highest standard of care for end-of-life patients. This also means that team members must communicate with each other about their patients in order to keep abreast of a patient's status, share information about her needs and concerns, and skillfully coordinate her care; thus, team meetings are an essential component of this principle. A team approach can also assure patients and family that they will not be abandoned by medical caregivers, either during or after a patient's illness and death. The collaborative efforts of team members can aid each other in optimizing care for both patient and family.

Practice Example

A palliative care nurse visits an elderly man dying of prostate cancer. While his pain and other symptoms are being satisfactorily managed, he is quite anxious about what will happen to his wife when he dies, as she suffers from severe diabetes and is unable to care for herself. The nurse also learns that he is a deeply devout Roman Catholic.

Communication Behaviors

This nurse must consult with palliative care team members, primarily a social worker and a chaplain but perhaps a psychologist as well, in order to address the patient's nonphysical suffering. The communication *task* is likely twofold: she must convince the patient, if he is resistant, that self-disclosing his concerns to other professional members of the team is potentially advantageous; likewise, she must influence her team members to visit and assist this patient. In doing so, she takes an active role in coordinating his care. Verbally and nonverbally, she must choose messages that manifest caring, advocacy, and confidence (*relationship*).

According to Wittenberg-Lyles, Goldsmith, and Ragan (2010), the COMFORT concept "is driven by narrative practice in nursing, the prioritization of family, early intervention of palliative care, and radically adaptive communication between and among patient/family/team members/clinicians" (p. 291). Its primary function is to assist palliative care nurses in implementing the paramount goal of their patient-centered care: preserving their patients' quality of life. We believe that the COMFORT model in its acknowledgment of the complex, multiparty, nonlinear, and repetitive nature of communication in the palliative care context promises a more effective and humane approach to patients and families than do traditional physician-derived communication protocols. We emphasize that the seven COMFORT principles be used "concurrently and reflectively" (p. 284) rather than sequentially or as an algorithm for communication. Rather than being mutually exclusive, the principles work collectively and in tandem to offer a model of palliative care communication that we believe affords the best chances for maximizing patient-centered care.

To summarize, this chapter has emphasized that communication between nurses and their patients/family members does not consist merely of disseminating information: instead, nurses must view communication as the mutual creation of meaning in that both nurse and patient mutually affect the other's communication.

Thus, both speaking *and* listening skills are pivotal to effective communication.

Every message has two levels of meaning: the content level, usually conveyed by the words themselves, and the relationship level, generally conveyed by nonverbals. Nonverbal communication (kinesics, haptics, proxemics, etc.) relays most of the meaning of a message and affects both the task (patient care) and the relationship (communication climate) between nurses and patients/families. For this reason, it is essential that verbal and nonverbal communication match each other: for example, you would not ask how a patient is feeling while focusing on her chart!

The five roles of nursing revealed in Pavlish & Cerosky's (2009) research include teaching, caring, coordinating, advocating, and mobilizing: each of these roles involves communication that conveys both task and relationship aspects of patient care. In addition, the verbal and nonverbal behaviors of patient-centered care outlined by Epstein & Street (2007) both facilitate the task of caring for patients as well as influence the nature of the relationship between them.

The chapter ends with a brief description of the communication model that undergirds the entire book, a new model of palliative care communication termed *the COMFORT model*. This model is based on seven components of effective end-of-life communication:

C—Communicate
O—Orientation and opportunity
M—Mindful presence
F—Family
O—Openings
R—Relating
T—Team

In the next chapter, we discuss more specifically the principle of *communication* in this model.

REFERENCES

Afifi, W. A. (2007). Nonverbal communication. In B. B. Whaley & W. Samter (Eds.), *Explaining Communication: Contemporary Theories and Exemplars* (pp. 39–60). Mahwah, NJ: Lawrence Erlbaum.

Baile, W. F., Buckman, R., Lenzi, R., Glober, G., Beale, E. A., & Kudelka, A. P. (2000). SPIKES—A six-step protocol for delivering bad news: Application to the patient with cancer. *Oncologist, 5*(4), 302–311.

Buckman, R. (2005). Breaking bad news: The S-P-I-K-E-S strategy. *Community Oncology, 2,* 138–142.

Burgoon, J. (1994). Nonverbal signals. In M. L. Knapp & G. R. Miller (Eds.), *Handbook of Interpersonal Communication* (pp. 229–285). Beverly Hills: Sage.

Charon, R. (2004). Narrative and medicine. *New England Journal of Medicine, 350*(9), 862–864.

End-of-Life Nursing Education Consortium. *Training Manual.* Washington, DC: American Association of Colleges of Nursing. Duarte, CA: City of Hope National Medical Center, 2010 [updated 2010]. http://www.aacn.nche.edu/elnec/. Accessed June 4, 2010.

Epstein, R. M., & Street, R. L. (2007). *Patient-Centered Communication in Cancer Care: Promoting and Reducing Suffering.* Bethesda, MD: National Cancer Institute.

Goldsmith, J., Wittenberg-Lyles, E., Rodriguez, D., & Sanchez-Reilly, S. (2010). Interdisciplinary geriatric and palliative care team narratives: Collaboration practices and barriers. *Qualitative Health Research, 20*(1), 93–104.

Mehrabian, A. (1981). *Silent Messages: Implicit Communication of Emotion and Attitudes* (2nd ed.). Belmont, CA: Wadsworth.

Pavlish, C., & Ceronsky, L. (2009). Oncology nurses' perceptions of nursing roles and professional attributes in palliative care. *Clinical Journal of Oncology Nursing, 13*(4), 404–412.

Ragan, S., & Goldsmith, J. (2008). End-of-life communication: The drama of pretense in the talk of dying patients and their M.D.s. In K. Wright & S. Moore (Eds.), *Applied Health Communication* (pp. 207–228). Cresskill, NJ: Hampton Press, Inc.

Ragan, S. L., Wittenberg, E., & Hall, H. T. (2003). The communication of palliative care for the elderly cancer patient. *Health Communication, 15*(2), 219–226.

Ragan, S., Wittenberg-Lyles, E., Goldsmith, J., & Sanchez-Reilly, S. (2008). *Communication as Comfort: Multiple Voices in Palliative Care.* New York: Routledge/Taylor & Francis.

Sanchez-Reilly, S. E., Wittenberg-Lyles, E. M., & Villagran, M. M. (2007). Using a pilot curriculum in geriatric palliative care to improve communication skills among medical students. *American Journal of Hospice and Palliative Care, 24*(2), 131–136.

Saunders, C. (1967). *The Management of Terminal Illness.* London: Hospital Medicine Publications.

Villagran, M., Goldsmith, J., Wittenberg-Lyles, E., & Baldwin, P. (2010). Communicating COMFORT: A communication-based model for breaking bad news in health care interactions. *Communication Education, 59,* 220–234.

Watzlawick, P., Beavin, J., & Jackson, D. D. (1967). *Pragmatics of Human Communication: A Study of Interactional Patterns, Pathologies, and Paradoxes.* New York: W.W. Norton.

Wittenberg-Lyles, E., Goldsmith, J., & Ragan, S. L. (2010). The COMFORT initiative: Palliative nursing and the centrality of communication. *Journal of Hospice & Palliative Nursing, 12*(5), 282–294.

Wittenberg-Lyles, E., Goldsmith, J., Ragan, S. L., & Sanchez-Reilly, S. (2010). *Dying with COMFORT: Family Illness Narratives and Early Palliative Care.* Cresskill, NJ: Hampton Press, Inc.

Wittenberg-Lyles, E., Greene, K., & Sanchez-Reilly, S. (2007). The palliative power of story-telling: Using published narratives as a teaching tool in end-of-life care. *Journal of Hospice and Palliative Nursing, 9*(4), 198–205.

Wittenberg-Lyles, E., & Thompson, S. (2006). Understanding enrollment conversations: The role of the hospice admissions representative. *American Journal of Hospice & Palliative Care, 23*(4), 317–322.

DISCUSSION QUESTIONS

1. How is the COMFORT model different from other models with communication?
2. What is meant by the phrase "We cannot not communicate"?

2

COMMUNICATE

Eileen is an oncology nurse employed in a women's cancer clinic. She previously worked on an inpatient medical surgical unit but decided to move to oncology as she felt it might be more meaningful work. She has enjoyed the change to oncology but admits feeling overwhelmed by the emotions of the patients. Eileen works with Dr. Martee, an excellent oncologist, but she has found that while his medical knowledge is excellent, his communication skills are lacking. Dr. Martee's clinic is always overbooked, and he often is in a position to inform patients of a new cancer diagnosis amidst a busy clinic, leaving Eileen alone to support the patient and answer their questions and witness their shock and distress after hearing the life-altering words "you have cancer."

A month ago Eileen had a very difficult encounter with a new patient, Mrs. Williams, who was newly diagnosed with Stage III ovarian cancer. Following Dr. Martee's brief explanation of the diagnosis and treatment options, Eileen was left to answer Mrs. Williams' many questions. Mrs. Williams cried intensely, and Eileen tried as best as she could to offer support, assuring her that Dr. Martee would provide the best treatment possible.

Mrs. Williams began a rigorous treatment regimen of weekly chemotherapy. Eileen noticed that Mrs. Williams always comes alone for treatment, and after the initial appointment she has been very stoic, rarely expressing any emotion. Eileen reacts to her stoicism by offering constant reassurance and "cheering her on" through each treatment.

As Eileen becomes more frustrated with her ability to communicate with the complex oncology patients, she seeks advice from the clinic social worker, Ronald. He offers support based on his many years in the clinic and advises Eileen on essential skills such as attentive listening and ways to illicit the patient's experience. Ronald agrees to continue meeting with Eileen as she gains experience in these skills.

Mrs. Williams completes her initial course of chemotherapy and returns to the clinic for an appointment following reevaluation of her tumor status. Unfortunately, Dr. Martee informs her that the tumor has not responded to the therapy as hoped and the latest scan reveals she has developed metastasis to the liver. Dr. Martee asks Eileen to spend a few minutes with Mrs. Williams. Eileen enters the room, sits quietly with Mrs. Williams, resisting the urge to offer reassurances and listens as she sobs. Eileen at first thinks of the best response she can offer but instead applies

Ronald's advice to seek to understand Mrs. William's experience. She asks Mrs. Williams to share what it felt like to hear that the treatment wasn't working. Mrs. Williams has spoken little about her family but she opens up to Eileen and with great distress says that her greatest concern is "abandoning her mother-in-law." Eileen listens as Mrs. Williams shares that when her husband died from colon cancer 5 years ago she promised him that she would care for his elderly mother. Her greatest concern is now feeling that she is abandoning her mother-in-law and the promise to her beloved husband.

Eileen experiences the struggles that many nurses face when it comes to communication. She is left with the responsibility of compensating for a physician's lack of communication skills, alone with a patient who is emotionally distraught from hearing bad news. Awkward communication situations like this come often in palliative care, and few nurses receive adequate preparation for what to do or say. Eileen's reaction to this problem is very common—she seeks help from coworkers or team members. She feels compelled to cheer her patient (and family, when applicable) through treatment, seeing this as a primary way of communicating patient support. But still, these attempts have left her feeling as if she has failed. She still continues to share in the suffering of patients and families, wanting to do more, say more.

Palliative care nurses do much more than simply provide presence when physicians break bad news by giving patients and families a serious or life-threatening prognosis. Nurses are there before this happens, while it happens, and after it happens. The ongoing presence of nurses affords an opportunity for both task-based and relational communication. This chapter presents the basic communication characteristics of these health care interactions. Communication is the cornerstone of palliative nursing. Awareness of the unique role of nurses in patient/family encounters guides this discussion so that we may illustrate specific ways to shape nurse communication practices.

This chapter will outline three foundational components for communication in palliative nursing. The first section will detail narrative clinical practice and describe how to approach patients/families so nurses have an understanding of the duality of task and relational communication in their every interaction. The next section focuses on verbal clarity and how to practice person-centered communication with patients, family, and team members. Finally, the last section will feature nonverbal immediacy and an awareness of the mistaken assumptions that can lead to miscommunication and conflict. These three principles will serve as tools to initiate and respond to difficult communication encounters. Throughout this chapter and the next, we will demonstrate how these principles overlap and offer specific strategies that can be used to achieve both relational and task-oriented goals.

WHAT IS MY ROLE IN COMMUNICATING IN PALLIATIVE CARE?

Nurse communication in palliative care is inaccurately depicted as a supportive role during breaking-bad-news exchanges between physicians, patients, and families

(Malloy, Paice, Virani, Ferrell, & Bednash, 2008). Although communication protocols and guidelines exist, there is no one protocol that explicitly focuses on the unique role of the nurse in this process (Price, McNeilly, & Surgenor, 2006). Instead, guidelines summarize four domains of action, beginning with preparation, message delivery, empathizing with emotional response, and summarizing the encounter; however, nurses do so much more (Dahlin, 2010). For the nurse, supporting patients and families receiving bad news is a process that happens before, during, and after the actual delivery of bad news (Warnock, Tod, Foster, & Soreny, 2010). The intimacy of nursing communication is the relationship a nurse shares with a family and patient during disease progression. The nurse is unable to control events surrounding bad news, as these disclosures often occur in "uncontrolled" and unplanned moments with patients and families (Warnock et al., 2010). The nurses' role requires flexibility and attention to the task and relational dimensions of communication during interactions that depart from the familiar or known path.

Task Communication in the Bad News Context

Simply put, task communication includes the nurse's role in confirming and explaining the bad news delivered by the physician. If faced with a situation where the physician does not do an adequate job conveying bad news, the nurse may find herself in Eileen's shoes attempting to compensate for a lack of information. In some instances, the nurse may be the one to deliver the bad news. For example, increasingly nurse practitioners (NPs) play a role as primary caregivers, and the NP may be giving the news of a biopsy or other diagnostic tests. Either way, nurses should be prepared to provide supplemental information and ongoing evaluation of the patient's condition (Price et al., 2006). Educating families enables them to engage in decision making (Pavlish & Ceronsky, 2009). The nurses' supportive role includes but is not limited to assessing informational needs, clarifying misunderstandings, and educating about medical information (Warnock et al., 2010). All of these tasks will be unpacked in the coming chapters.

To validate bad news, nurses must engage in extended discussions of prognosis and care options and when appropriate assist with planning end-of-life care (Radziewicz & Baile, 2001). Preparing to deliver bad news can often fall to the nurse who will facilitate selecting and arranging for a place of care and gathering patient/family information (Price et al., 2006). An additional and often overlooked communication task is to share information with the health care team and provide support to the physician (Price et al., 2006; Radziewicz & Baile, 2001). Reporting to the team helps the nurse coordinate multiple services in the delivery of a cohesive treatment plan and mobilization of needed resources (Pavlish & Ceronsky, 2009).

Relational Communication in the Bad News Context

As nurses work to confirm and explain bad news, these efforts must include comforting patients and families and attempting to reduce their uncertainty. During bad news encounters, patients and families need empathy and support (Price et al., 2006).

Nurses can extend their physical care tasks to include the psychosocial aspects of illness (Pavlish & Ceronsky, 2009). Relational communication is so much more than meeting with the patient/family for comfort (Radziewicz & Baile, 2001). It includes facilitating emotional reactions and providing opportunities to process the bad news (Warnock et al., 2010). For Eileen, this meant engaging in active listening and trying to elicit patient experiences. Teaching, caring, coordinating, and advocating are all enabled through a communication behavior called *narrative clinical practice.*

NARRATIVE CLINICAL PRACTICE

Narratives reveal who people are and where they are headed—or where they think they are headed (Aloi, 2009; Hess, 2003). In hospice and palliative care, these are typically stories of pain and suffering. A meaningful story no longer exists as illness produces incongruity—patients and families who do not understand or talk about this incongruity are still attempting to live a normal story without illness (Hess, 2003). Their stories remain general, and focus on a clinician's orders in order to live a longer life, rather than a patient-specific story of illness (Hess, 2003). A palliative story includes recognition of the turning point toward decline. This is important when attempting to gauge patient/family understanding about prognosis.

As people negotiate illness, struggle to make decisions, and experience pain, nurses bear witness to these struggles. To engage in narrative clinical practice, the nurse must allow herself to witness. Bearing **witness** involves "being with and relating to others" while at the same time honoring their voice, their lived experience (Naef, 2006, p. 147). One way to do this is to acknowledge the patient/family through listening, writing, and speaking about their story (Naef, 2006). Be open to others' judgments, beliefs, values, and actions (Hess, 2003). Narrative clinical practice involves helping patients and families rewrite or reauthor their story to focus on quality of life (Aloi, 2009).

Witnessing with patients and the family consists of three principles. First, the nurse must recognize their individuality (Kendall, 2007). A special form of active listening called **deconstruction** will help focus on gaps, ambiguities, and conflicting plots within the story (Aloi, 2009). This allows the nurse to notice the vulnerability of patients/family members and to recognize their profound difference. Each has a unique story. When sharing patient/family information with others, use adjectives to describe their uniqueness (this can also be helpful in remembering each patient/family!) For example, nurses can describe patients by the information they learn about their childhood or their personality.

Second, it is useful for nurses to get to know what the patient/family was like prior to the diagnosis and illness/prognosis (Kendall, 2007). Allowing patients and families to reflect on their personal lives helps to incorporate the psychosocial history in the diagnostic assessment. As the story is told, the nurse should solicit and employ **externalization**—or information the storyteller might include—for example, to express his or her self-blame about the illness or life regrets (Aloi, 2009). Acknowledging and responding to these moments of externalization with affirmation and acceptance will facilitate the patients' coping with the illness. Prior patient histories by the patient or by family members can reveal common forms of self-blame, including life decisions/actions that lead to illness, feelings of guilt for poor decisions, and the desire to cure at all costs. As nurses witness these stories, they address these feelings and work to help the patient rewrite the story to include quality of life as central in all decision making.

Finally, nurses need to go beyond the medical facts associated with each patient (Kendall, 2007). The nurse can work on **reauthoring** the story by seeing problems as care goals rather than cure goals. Reauthoring alters the patient/family narrative in a way that includes the total impact on the storyteller, and widens the lens beyond the borders of the illness alone (Aloi, 2009). This involves refocusing the story in order to redefine the person (i.e., patient/family). As the story unfolds, the nurse can gather an understanding of prior biomedical interventions to grasp an understanding of the present complaint. As the story emerges and the nurse begins to understand where the patient and family are in terms of understanding and acceptability, verbal clarity will help to communicate and process appropriate goals of care.

VERBAL CLARITY

While verbal clarity is an important feature of health literacy—to ensure that patients/ families receive information given to them by the nurse—it is important in hospice and palliative care as a communicative feature that conveys emotional support. We assume that there is a direct connection between communication behaviors and well-being, and that some forms of supportive communication are more effective than others (Burleson & MacGeorge, 2002). Supportive communication is in direct response to a need—and the variation of these responses is how we characterize verbal clarity.

Person-centered messages are one way to convey supportive communication. **Person-centeredness** is "the extent to which the perspectives and feelings of distressed others are acknowledged, elaborated and granted legitimacy," and has been empirically validated as a key dimension of emotion support skill (Burleson, 1994, p. 258). Comforting behaviors expressed through supportive messages termed *person-centered messages* (PCMs) have consistently been judged as more supportive and encouraging for those having difficulty addressing their feelings (Jones, 2004). PCM can draw out the thoughts and feelings of patient/families as they face a life-threatening illness, making their challenges, symptoms, and fears known by their nurse.

PCMs range from low emotional support to high emotional support (MacGeorge, Gillihan, Samter, & Clark, 2003). To achieve verbal clarity, the goal is to use PCMs that are high in emotional support. Low–emotional support messages include criticism, challenging legitimacy, and telling the patient/family how they feel. Low PCMs deny the patient and family's feelings. Middle-level emotional support messages explicitly recognize the patient/family's feelings albeit through distraction, offering sympathy, or explaining the situation. Highest forms of PCMs include explicitly recognizing and legitimating the patient/family's feelings by elaborating and articulating feelings.

Communicating social support during care allows the nurse to accomplish task goals and still be relational. Oncology nurses who provided chemotherapy to patients reported that they worried that they provided too much irrelevant information, didn't really answer patient/family questions, assumed instructions were easy, and did not provide enough opportunity for the patient/family to talk (O'Baugh, Wilkes, Sneesby, & George, 2009). A PCM allows the nurse to present a realistic picture for the patient/family, clarifying what the "silent" patient is experiencing and reminding families of all that is being done to the "person in the bed" (Robichaux & Clark, 2006). PCMs lead to: perceived communication competence of the nurse, improved coping skills for the patient, increased liking of the nurse, and increased relational satisfaction between the nurse and the patient (Jones & Guerrero, 2001). PCMs are used in conjunction with nonverbal immediacy.

NONVERBAL IMMEDIACY

In short, **nonverbal immediacy** communicates liking (Burgoon, Birk, & Pfau, 1990). Facial expressions, body movements, interactional distance, vocal tone—all of these behaviors communicate dimensions of the interpersonal relationship between nurses and patients and families (Haskard, Williams, DiMatteo, Heritage, & Rosenthal, 2008). Appropriate nonverbal behaviors for nurses who share in the delivery of bad news include maintaining eye contact with patients, leaning forward to show attentiveness, self-awareness of the body to avoid fidgeting or other distracting movements, and nodding to indicate agreement or understanding when the patient speaks. Nonverbal immediacy can improve the cognitive learning of patients and increase the perceived credibility of the nurse. Even though the verbal content of each bad news interaction will change based on the patient, family, and team, the need to mirror and model nonverbal immediacy proves to be the most beneficial for all parties in the interaction (Ragan, Wittenberg-Lyles, Goldsmith, & Sanchez-Reilly, 2008).

Particularly in breaking bad news interactions, the patient fears the nurse's message and the nurse fears the patient's response (McGuigan, 2009). While the patient fears that bad news is coming and then more uncertainty following bad news, nurses fear that their communication may evoke intense emotional reactions that they are unable to handle (McGuigan, 2009). According to **expectancy violations theory**, we all have expectations of how others will behave and react. We use these expectations to gauge our idea of "appropriate" and "normal" nonverbal responses. **General expectations** involve our expectations for behavior in certain environments. In hospice and palliative care, nurses expect patients and families to be respectful of their work by following directions and collaborating with them to reach goals of care. When expectancies are violated, individuals focus less on the conversation and more on the violation of expectations. Our focus shifts to the communicator, our relationship with him or her, and the context.

First, nurses reflect on communicator characteristics and consider the demographics of the patient/family member. Does the gender of the patient conjure up specific patient expectations? Does the nurse have different expectations for patients/family members with health care backgrounds (i.e., retired nurse, practicing physician)? Second, we reflect on our relationship to the patient/family member—do they have power over us? How long has the nurse known them? Is this a patient the nurse has cared for many times over the last year? Or is this a new patient? Power and intimacy compose relationship expectations. Finally, context characteristics concern our reflections on specific interactions, such as breaking bad news, and often involve third parties. It is in these instances that nurses are more apt to have preinteraction expectations.

Take, for example, Donald, a hospice nurse who goes to see a patient in the palliative care unit of a large metropolitan hospital to talk to the family about hospice. Upon entering the patient's room, he is greeted by a woman relative sitting by the bedside: "We're going to go out of town today. We've said our good-byes. I'm at peace with all of this. If he goes while I'm gone it will be okay. I just need to get the paperwork done today before I leave."

Immediately, this family member violates Donald's *general expectations*. Donald expects to be greeted by a family relative and allowed to provide his opening introduction of hospice as well as assessment. Since he has no prior relationship with this patient and knows nothing about the woman relative, he relies on his expectations for the interaction. He finds a seat directly across from her—instead of going directly to paperwork (a communication task that she expects), he violates her expectations by engaging in a conversation about the patient, saying in a quiet tone with his paperwork lying on his lap: "Okay, well can you catch me up on what's been going on?" His nonverbal communication (sitting down, neglecting paperwork) indicates to her that he is interested in what she has to say. The woman explains that she has cared for her father for 3 years, they have shared open communication about death and dying, that her father has a living will, and she is a medical assistant in the hospital who is familiar with hospice and palliative care services. Further into the conversation, Donald reveals his expectations for the interaction to her: "Typically in hospice we have to convince people that hospice is appropriate." She replies, "I'm just sorry it's taken this long. This was his fear—that this would happen and he would linger." Donald then inquires, "Even though your father has been ill a long time and you have prepared for his death, is this a difficult time for you?" After further conversation, hospice paperwork was completed. Donald's reaction to expectancy violation could have very easily have been to go straight to paperwork, speaking very little with this woman. Instead, he set his assumptions aside about why she was okay to leave her dying father and prioritized relational communication alongside communication tasks.

Violations of expectations associated with breaking bad news come when nurses judge whether or not emotional reactions are "normal" or "abnormal" (Radziewicz & Baile, 2001). When expectations aren't met, we socially evaluate the patient/family member and adjust our communication accordingly. This evaluation is perceived as either positive or negative, depending on many factors. Similarly, for patients, breaking bad news interactions violates expectations as they are incongruent with expectations for cure and thus increase uncertainty in communication (Afifi & Burgoon, 2000). Expectancy violations can exist for both parties and highly impact clinical communication from that point forward.

Patient/family members' emotional reactions to bad news can trigger violation expectations, a point at which nonverbal immediacy moves center stage. The nurse's reaction to how bad news is handled will impact his/her ability to communicate comfort and support. Patient sadness often elicits a relational communication response; however, patient/family anger is more likely to trigger task-related communication only (Sheldon, et al., 2009). Nurses should anticipate that they will experience many types of emotional reactions in their career. Proximity, eye contact, and demonstrated caring about what the patient is saying and feeling are key behaviors that help nurses express nonverbal immediacy (Andersen & Guerrero, 1998; Epstein & Street, 2007). Nonverbal immediacy communicates involvement and personal engagement—body language, gestures, and vocal tone are all related to patient satisfaction (Haskard et al., 2008).

Self-awareness is important. **Self-awareness** allows nurses to appreciate their own self-worth and care for themselves before caring for others (see Chapter 9 for self-care) (McGuigan, 2009). A nurse's opinions, values, and ideas about patients and their families impact how they approach the situation, and shape communicative choices and strategies. Nurses can practice humility by allowing themselves to be equal to the patient/family, by not presuming to be an expert in a story they have not even told, and have faith that other clinicians can also demonstrate this humility (Hess, 2003). Self-awareness about individual ideas and opinions can aid in the recognition of ideas that are separate or different from the patient/family.

DEVELOPING CLINICAL PRACTICE SKILLS

This chapter reviews communication in palliative nursing, identifying three overarching features for the nurse's involvement in breaking bad news communication. Considering the unique role of the nurse in bad news interactions and his or her unlimited and unprotected exposure to patients/families, we offer the following communication strategies to demonstrate specific communication concepts in each step of nursing practice.

Assessment

Earlier in the chapter, we described the process of witnessing as a way of listening and capturing the patient/family's story. In the case study that opened this chapter, Eileen was advised by Ronald, a social worker, to be an attentive listener and to elicit the patient's experiences. To accomplish this, nurses can engage in witnessing by using questions that capture meaningful aspects of the patient/family's life (Aloi, 2009). The following checklist (Table 2.1) can be used as a guide:

The nurse's goal is to listen to the story, share it with others, and record it.

Witnessing is so much more than prompting patients/families to share, and listening (task communication) is about incorporating comfort communication into feedback and interpretation (relational communication). The following vignette serves to illustrate the process of **witnessing**. A meeting with the adult son of a patient (S), the

Table 2.1 Checklist of Witnessing Skills

Principle	What to Listen for	What Questions to Ask
Recognize individuality	Identify vulnerabilities, uniqueness	• "Tell me about times when you aren't thinking about illness/your loved one's disease." • "How would you describe this illness/the shared experience of illness?" • "Is there anything else that could explain your/his/her illness?" • "I'm wondering if there is more to this than meets the eye." • "Who else is involved in your/his/her illness?"
Understand life prior to illness	Encourage sharing, address feelings	• "How has your illness (or his/her illness) affected your life and your relationships?" • "How do you think ignoring this will affect your life?" • "How does your illness (or his/her illness) reflect on you as a person?" • "How do you see the future?" • "How are you affected by others' opinions?" • "What do you think influences this experience?"
Go beyond medical information	Consider the mental health of patient/family caregiver	• "What people in your life are supporting you?" • "What do you think needs to happen in order for you to be able to care for your loved one/yourself?" • "What needs to change?" • "What does your success in solving problems related to care say about your abilities?" • "How is this experience affecting your life?" • "What do you see in yourself now that you didn't see before?"

Adapted from: Aloi, J. A. (2009). The nurse and the use of narrative: An approach to caring. *Journal of Psychiatric and Mental Health Nursing, 16*(8), 711–715.

patient's daughter-in-law (DIL), and a hospice nurse (RN) took place in a hospital family room:

> s: He's got terminal cancer. We've talked before he came into the hospital. He has a will. I'm just doing what he wants.
> DIL: He's gone blind now.
> s: It's like I told my brother. If two could go out and one could stay, I would …
> DIL: It's in his lungs, his liver, it's ate [*sic*] up everywhere. He took chemo 3 weeks ago today, and he's had two blood transfusions since then. I talked

to his cancer doctor, and now he's had three strokes. So, now with the strokes, it's time for you. Dr. [X] told me yesterday that he'd be better off in hospice, and with his will, he did not want to live like this.

RN: In hospice, we do what's needed. We do what we need to do. With his cancer, he must be in pain.

s: Well, he has no spleen, no kidney—he lost those to cancer. He's had heartattacks, a heartattack a month ago. That's how we found out he had cancer again. [Son further explains that this is a second type of cancer]. So when can we move him? How does this work? *(Note: Son is urgent to move the patient from hospital to hospice facility.)*

RN: We are guests here [referring to hospice in the hospital], but we could do the paperwork today and have him moved this afternoon to our inpatient facility.

s: I don't want him moved today. I need to get used to this. *(Note: Despite urgency, son does not want patient moved today. The nurse recognizes this gap inconsistency and addresses it through externalization.)*

RN: After this long haul, as you are approaching the end, you are afraid of what's next …

DIL: We don't know want to do. My husband lost his job and has been taking care of him. Then I lost my job, and we've just been taking care of dad.

s: My priority is my dad. They didn't understand why I kept having to leave work to take care of him, so they let me go.

DIL: [begins to cry] This has been our life for 2 years.

RN: I hope you find peace knowing that you did do it. Not many people do it. Do you feel like everything has been tried? *(Note: Family reveals life prior to hospice referral. Nurse responds by reauthoring, going beyond medical facts to understand prior interventions)*

DIL: Yes, everything has been tried.

RN: Hospice does not start with consents. It starts with a hospice evaluation [explains process]. As far as pain management, I would recommend a subcutaneous infusion. I did it for my own grandmother. It provides the relief needed for his extensive cancer pain [explains]. Once you stop artificial hydration, we can expect 7–10 days. But once you factor in extensive cancer, as he has, strokes which keep a person from taking in fluid, it will be shorter [explains]. And in hospice, we won't judge you if you aren't camping out and staying by his side. That's okay. *(Note: Nurse deconstructs any preconceived ideas about hospice—recognizes family's individuality.)*

s: Yeah, I won't be there. I don't deal well with this. I need some time alone.

RN: (to DIL) Just the fact that he's able to admit that to you, that's healthy. Well, we can move him tomorrow if that's what you'd like. *(Note: Nurse recognizes his individuality, uses positive adjective to reauthor.)*

Plan

As the nurse moves from listening and responding to patients/families through witnessing, the next step is to determine what to do with the information. This was most problematic for Eileen—she knew to prompt Mrs. Williams to share her feelings but did not know what to do when Mrs. Williams began sharing. For Eileen, the emotional reaction shared by Mrs. Williams felt uncomfortable, yet understandable. The intimacy of nursing creates opportunities where patients and nurses are vulnerable to witnessing the reciprocal suffering of patients and families. Nurses can prepare themselves by learning to listen for key patient/family features as well as how to negotiate problematic situations.

It is helpful to sort and organize the patient/family story according to the four quality-of-life dimensions (Table 2.2) that comprise palliative nursing. Use the checklists provided in Table 2.2 for each of these dimensions.

Sorting the story's content according to physical, social, spiritual, and/or psychological care will naturally help the nurse to identify specific assessments, resources, and additional involvement from interdisciplinary team members (for more on this, see Chapter 8). For example, Eileen's patient, Mrs. Williams, reported that she worried about "abandoning her mother-in-law." Eileen learns that Mrs. Williams is a widow, responsible for providing care for another family member. This is how Mrs. Williams defines the priorities in her life and thus her quality of life—and the nurse's job is to develop a plan of care that recognizes this. The precedence for care planning should be

Table 2.2 Overview of Quality-of-Life Dimensions

✓ Checklist	
✓ Physical Well-Being and Symptoms	✓ Psychological Well-Being
▪ Fatigue	▪ Anxiety
▪ Sleep disruption	▪ Depression
▪ Function	▪ Helplessness
▪ Nausea	▪ Difficulty coping
▪ Appetite	▪ Fear
▪ Constipation	▪ Uselessness
▪ Aches/Pain	▪ Concentration
	▪ Control
	▪ Distress
✓ Social Well-Being	✓ Spiritual Well-Being
▪ Isolation	▪ Meaning
▪ Role adjustment	▪ Uncertainty
▪ Financial burden	▪ Hope
▪ Roles/Relationships	▪ Religiosity
▪ Affection/Sexual function	▪ Transcendence
▪ Leisure activities	▪ Positive change
▪ Burden	
▪ Employment	

Used with permission from: Ferrell, B., & Grant, M. (2011). Quality of life: 1525 voices of cancer. *Oncology Nursing Forum*, 23(6), 907–916.

Table 2.3 Overview of Breaking Bad News Scenarios and Suggested Communication

Barriers to Breaking Bad News	*How to Handle/What to Say*
Lack of privacy	• "I know this is not ideal, but let's try to find as much privacy as possible to talk. We will have more opportunity later for a quieter space, but this is an important time to talk together."
	• "It would be good if you talked with each other [family] and decided if all of you want to be included in decisions of care discussions. Can we talk again this afternoon after you have had time to visit together?"
Over the phone	• "I know this not ideal, but I can talk to you now over the phone about your health and we can meet together tomorrow to talk more."
	• "Is it alright with you if I visit with you about your recent test? I know that a phone call discussion is not my favorite, but this way I can get you the information now and we can meet face to face when it works with your schedule."
Unable to contact family until after medical event	• [by phone]: "I am so glad to reach you. I am Karen, a clinical nurse from Memorial Hospital. I have been with your Dad this afternoon and I need to talk to you about what we have been going through here. Your father is very ill. Can I explain more details now about your Dad?"
	• [in person]: "I am so glad you are here. Can I talk to you about what we have been facing with your Dad today?"
Lack of time to explain	• "Let me apologize up front for being short on time in this moment, but I do want to you give you a sense of what we know about your blood levels. I promise to come back by this afternoon and talk more with you about your questions and concerns."
	• "I have just a few minutes to update you on your blood work. I know this is not enough time to process any questions or concerns you might have, so I will be back by to talk more with you and your family after lunch. Is that a good time for you?"
Cognitive impairment	• "Julie, I want to talk to you about how you are doing, and what the tests we have been running are telling us. In case you need help understanding what we know, I think it would be helpful to share this information with your family, too."
	• "Because Julie's having a hard time understanding what we are learning about her kidney function, I am glad I can share the information with you [family]. Can you talk with me about Julie?"
Interpreter required	• Explain to patient/family that you are using the help of an interpreter to take the best care of the patient/make the best decisions.
	• When the interpreter translates, look at the patient/family.
	• Confirm that the patient/family have asked the questions that they have.

(continued)

Table 2.3 (*continued*)

Barriers to Breaking Bad News	How to Handle/What to Say
Cultural differences	• "Are there any care needs that your family would specifically like to see happen?" • "What can we do to better support your family's traditions? There is a lot we can do, even in this environment, as long as we know what you would like." • "How does your family want to be included in care decisions? We want to be as attentive as we can to the needs of your family."
Lack of knowledge about patient/ family	• "It is so good to meet you. Can you help me understand who else is in your family?" • "I have been helping Ken this evening on my shift. Who is part of his family here?" • "I think we have learned this evening that Ken has been struggling with some of the medications he has been taking."
Lack of knowledge of events	• "I understand you are concerned about the changes you see from this morning. I will absolutely check with the nurses' station as well as call his physician. I will get back to visit more with you." • "Let me repeat to you what I hear are your questions … and then I will go seek out the answers. Since I am new to your brother's situation, this will help me learn about him and your family as well."
Concerns about own clinical knowledge	• "The most important thing for me is to understand your concerns and questions. I will work diligently to get you the answers you need to make the best care choices for your family/self." • "This is the news I do know and can share with you. If there is something I am unfamiliar with, I will find out the answers. We can make a list of questions together." • (Note—In this instance ask your colleagues and team members about the patients status.)
Family is not present	• "I am glad we have an opportunity to discuss your Mom's health. She did want us to give her the assessment from the tests this morning, despite your absence. Now that we are all here together, how can I help you [family] as we understand that surgery will not be possible?" • "I understand you [patient] had a visit with Dr. X about your CT scan. I know you would like your family to have been here for that conversation. Would it be helpful to have Dr. X meet with you and your family and me to talk more about how you are feeling in light of this news?"
You are not present	• "Since I was not here for the news, can you tell me how the conversation with the team went? [response] Now, as I listened to you these are the questions I think you still have [relay patient questions discerned], is that right? I will be sure to get these answers and come talk with you."

(continued)

Table 2.3 (*continued*)

Barriers to Breaking Bad News	How to Handle/What to Say
	• [to team member] "Can you help me understand the care decisions that Dr. X proposed? How do you think the patient understood this conversation and is feeling about it?"
Own doctor not present	• [to family] "I will pass on your concerns and questions to your primary doctor and seek some response about these issues. I know it is important after you have spent so much time with a physician and be placed with a new doctor."
	• "I am sorry you are upset. We will do all we can to provide information and comfort that will help you through this. And we will be with you in this struggle."
Dying without relatives present	• "There is some very difficult news I need to share with you about Joe. Can you come with me to the family room to visit about the events of this afternoon?"
	• "I want to ensure your privacy. Can we go together to a quiet place and talk about Joe?"
	• "You are part of our care effort. Let's go to my office so we can have some time to process the events of the day in a quiet place."
Providing information in difficult circumstances	• "I know this information is not at all congruent with what we knew earlier in the day about your brother. I am so sorry for the sudden change in things."
	• [family members feuding violently] "I wanted to share information about Joan with you. We are also talking with your mother in another room about the very same information. What else can we do to help you manage this information in the midst of your difficult family dynamics?"
Family unprepared	• [phone] "We have been caring for Steve during the last hour. He is not responding well, and we are worried that he is really declining quickly. I am so sorry to give you this news. I want you to know what we know and give you the chance to get here if that is important to you."
	• "I need to try and prepare you that Steve is not doing well. We are surprised and saddened by his turn this evening. This is your opportunity to spend time with him. He is declining."
Patient not told at relative's request	• [to a 9-year-old unaware of impending death] "We are all working to take the very best care of you we can. We want you to feel as good as you can so make sure you tell us about your pain, or any worries so we can help you."
	• [to a 90-year-old Latina woman] "You have a loving family. We are going to take the best care of you we can and help you feel as good as possible."

(*continued*)

Table 2.3 (*continued*)

Barriers to Breaking Bad News	How to Handle/What to Say
Patient told despite family request Patient doesn't want to know	• [to family] "What are the positive aspects of [patient] knowing the news about his health?" • "Tell me why you don't want to know about your health and the problem you have had with your leg?" • "Where do you eventually want to be to face the rest of this illness? At home? In the hospital?"
Relatives not being honest	• [with patient and family] "Can we come together and think about the pros and cons of moving Jade home for the rest of her illness? I think it would be important to think about these things together to ensure that Jade gets all the care she needs, and that [family member] can be a caregiver in the way that he really can." • [among family members] "Could we talk about who can provide the care at home if that is really what [patient] wants? This is a great opportunity to come together and make the best decision for [patient]."
Patient/relatives poorly informed	• "Let me go over the news about your blood work and fill in the blanks that might exist. I know this can seem very frustrating to not have all the information at once to process the overall situation. As we talk, keep your questions coming." • "I am here just to process this with you and make sure you feel like you understand the information and this procedure. Stop me at any point and ask questions if you need to."
Not understanding the implications of the information	• "Ben, I want to revisit this news with you and make sure you understand these developments. Can you describe to me what you understand to be the news so I can see if we are on the same page?" • "I am worried that you might not understand the gravity of this information. Let me try to explain in different words, and please stop me at any point and we can go over this until it makes sense."
Emotionally significant events	• "Beth, I know this is the hardest news you could hear. I want to help you process this in any way that would be helpful. I know there are things we need to think about regarding your family. What is your biggest concern or fear?" • "I know this is very difficult. Do you think it would be helpful if we all met with [social worker] to process the impact of this news on your husband?"
Challenging deaths	• "We can never know when death really will come. I still cannot predict as well as you might imagine I could. So, we need to continue to provide support for [patient], but especially for you [family]. Can you think of a few things that we can help you manage as we continue to support [patient]?"

(continued)

Table 2.3 (*continued*)

Barriers to Breaking Bad News	*How to Handle/What to Say*
	• "I can tell you that [patient] is receiving the best comfort care there is. She is not showing any signs of pain or distress. Letting go of life can be long work, longer than we would like or expect sometimes. But that is why we are here, to make her comfortable."

Adapted from Warnock, C., Tod, A., Foster, J., & Soreny, C. (2010). Breaking bad news in inpatient clinical settings: Role of the nurse. *Journal of Advanced Nursing, 66*(7), 1548–1549.

psychological well-being, as Mrs. Williams describes stress, anxiety, and helplessness. Eileen's plan of care and communication with Mrs. Williams should first address psychological burden, followed by the other dimensions of care.

Patient and family stories are loaded with emotional weight, and a multitude of reactions and scenarios may exist—especially surrounding bad news. Reactions to bad news can include verbal abuse, anger, hysteria, threatening, and physical aggression. Dealing with the emotions of patients and family members is routine in palliative settings; interactions that involve bad news are especially problematic in hospital settings where information barriers are abundant and relationships are complex. Even though nurses are well trained and knowledgeable about palliative care, there will be daily events and situations that are uncomfortable and awkward when it comes to communicating. As nurses work to soothe and comfort during these interactions, they must also acknowledge the barriers present. Table 2.3 identifies some of the barriers found in palliative care nursing and examples of how to work within these constraints.

INTERVENE

By recognizing the defining features of the patient/family's story and identifying their own definition of quality of life, nurses can tailor their own supportive communication while providing primary care. In our opening case study, Eileen learns that the most devastating aspect of bad news for Mrs. Williams is the psychological burden associated with her obligation to oversee care for her mother-in-law. As Eileen negotiates care-planning needs in terms of coordination of care and possibly referral to hospice care for Mrs. Williams, she must acknowledge this burden (relational communication) while at the same time work to ensure that Mrs. Williams understands her prognosis and transition to palliative/hospice care (task). To accomplish comfort care and communication, nurses must recognize their own assumptions and emotional involvement as well as practice person-centered messages.

How we feel about others impacts how we communicate—how much attention we give to patients/family members varies based on how we feel about them. Some get more attention, and others get limited time and effort. It is important to recognize our

Table 2.4 ✓ Checklist

✓ How do you feel about the patient?
✓ Will your feelings make the discussion more difficult?
✓ How will you react if the patient gets more upset?
✓ Do you and the patient/family share the same values?
✓ Are you critical of the life choices this patient/family member has made?
✓ Do you find their lifestyle to be appropriate based on your standards?

Adapted from Radziewicz, R., & Baile, W. F. (2001). Communication skills: Breaking bad news in the clinical setting. *Oncology Nursing Forum, 28*(6), 951–953.

own assumptions about patients/family members, especially when we haven't worked closely with them and don't know their story well. Use the above checklist (Table 2.4) to help discern assumptions from facts.

Practicing self-awareness helps nurses realize how emotionally involved they are with patients/family members and whether or not they are able to provide objective primary care. Does the nurse answer the call button immediately for their favorite patient? The one who reminds them of their own parent or the patient they have known throughout 4 years of treatment? Is it easier for the nurse to return calls to family members whose lives are similar to their own and who have a similar family structure? The answer is probably "yes" because their communication style is familiar. But what about patients/family members who are dissimilar to the nurse? Is the nurse slow to answer these patients' and families' requests? The yardstick for determining whether or not patients/families meet communication expectations, verbally and nonverbally, is based on the nurse's assumptions of them. Nurses need to be mindful of how they assess the stories that they hear—and recognize when and where their thoughts and feelings are separate from the story they are being told. For more on this topic, see Chapter 9 on self-care.

As we noted earlier in the chapter, practicing person-centered messages is one way to communicate relational support. Table 2.5 provides examples to demonstrate the variation and types of supportive messages that can be offered to patients and families following bad news.

Keep in mind that these messages are examples and the real power of a message is in the nurse's ability to match the patient/family member's quality-of-life issues with an appropriate response and feedback. For more on this, see Chapter 7. The goal is to recognize that some messages are more powerful than others, and the incorporation of I-Thou statements, as discussed in detail in Chapter 4, will prove powerful in letting patients and family members know that their nurse cares.

Person-centered messages are just one way of practicing verbal clarity. The role of the palliative nurse is to teach, advocate, mobilize, and care for patients and their families. The nurse's ability to talk about death and dying compassionately requires verbal acknowledgment of dying and mortality in order to educate about hospice care and

Table 2.5 Variation of Person-Centered Messages Following Bad News

Low–Emotional Support Messages
> *Messages that do not acknowledge the patient/family's feelings*

Communicative Behavior	Example Message
Nurse condemns patient's feelings.	"You knew this was coming. I don't know why you are so shocked."
Nurse challenges the legitimacy of the patient's feelings or actions following from those feelings.	"You should not feel bad because this is not your fault."
Nurse ignores the patient's feelings.	"Let's talk about your treatment from this point forward."

Moderate–Emotional Support Messages
> *Messages that explicitly recognize the patient/family's feelings*

Communicative Behavior	Example Message
Nurse attempts to reframe the situation in a positive way by diverting the patient's attention away from the event, smoothing over the negative feelings, or offering some sort of consolation, or suggested method to deal with the bad news.	"You should at least be happy that you know for sure now and can deal with the situation."
Nurse acknowledges the patients' feelings but does not attempt to help the patient understand how to cope with them.	"I can see why you are upset."
Nurse provides a non-feeling-centered explanation of the situation intended to reduce the patient's distressed emotional state. This explanation offers some principle for interpreting the situation.	"It is very normal to be upset. I see people get upset like this all the time when they have to deal with a diagnosis like this."

High–Emotional Support Messages
> *Messages that recognize and legitimize the patient/family's feelings*

Communicative Behavior	Example Message
Nurse explicitly recognizes and acknowledges the patients feelings but does not elaborate on those feelings.	"I'm so sorry this has happened. Did you think this was coming? I realize it's frustrating, especially since you've been sick for so long. Please talk to me about how you feel."
Nurse provides an elaborated acknowledgment and explanation of the patient's feelings	"You may not be ready to talk about this now, but I want you to know that I am here for you. I will continue to be your nurse. I am going to do my best to make

(*continued*)

Table 2.5 (*continued*)

	you comfortable. I want you to know that this is nothing that you did, that this is not your fault. I don't want you to second-guess the decisions that you have made. You've done everything that you could."
Nurse helps the patient to gain a perspective on his or her feelings. Feelings about the bad news are explicitly elaborated and legitimized. Nurse attempts to help the patient see how his or her feelings fit into a broader context.	"I'm so sorry. I know how much you wanted to beat this disease and how hard you have fought. And I know that you would do anything you could to feel better. You must be thinking so many things right now. You must feel hurt and anger and question why this is happening to you. I know that you have seen many specialists and that there have been many mixed messages—which makes this hard to believe. I'm going to make sure that you are comfortable. We have a team here to help you with anything that you need. It is important to take advantage of this time that you have to talk with your family, friends, and those that you love."

Adapted from: MacGeorge, E. L., Gillihan, S. J., Samter, W., & Clark, R. A. (2003). Skill deficit or differential motivation: Testing alternative explanations of gender differences in the provision of emotional support. *Communication Research, 30*(3), 272–303.

philosophy and the dying process. Remember, many of these patients and families have only thought about cure until the nurse, the physician, or a member of the health care team begins to talk about palliative care.

The following example illustrates how a nurse can be both verbally clear, yet eloquent in these discussions:

An initial hospice visit to the emergency room of the local hospital reveals that the patient is an elderly woman recently placed on a bi-pap machine. Two sons and one daughter (D) are present, and another daughter who serves as the primary caregiver is absent. The hospice nurse (RN) enters the patient's room and sees that the patient is sitting up in bed and is communicating—however, the family quickly escorts him out of the room into a private family meeting room:

D: They called us yesterday and said she probably wouldn't make it through the day. We did comfort only. Today we are just waiting.

RN: So today she has a little rally, a little more "umph." So today you are wondering: am I doing the right thing by talking to hospice? *(Note: Although family has been told that patient is dying, they are reluctant to elect for hospice care. The nurse summarizes this experience.)*

D: Yes, we are confused.

RN: When you have a person who is elderly and you have the day-to-day care and events, it changes. Today is an "up" day and a good day. But, could tomorrow be a down day? So you need to step back and look at things globally. What can we fix? What is her quality of life? What are the things in life she's been losing that we can get back? [pause] Is there no fixing? Then it's time for hospice. *(Note: The nurse begins to educate about hospice philosophy by focusing attention on quality of life and helps the family recognize how quality of life is compromised.)*

Yesterday was a bad day. Today is a good day. I saw that she is on a bi-pap machine. Can she be without the bi-pap?

SON-1: Only for about an hour.

D: And she told me she doesn't want that machine but that she doesn't want to die. *(Note: The family is first to bring up death and dying. The nurse acknowledges and educates.)*

RN: Yes, well no one really wants to die. [lowered voice] Even a terminal person doesn't want to die.

SON-2: She hasn't slept in 3 days.

RN: That could be part of the medications.

SON-2: I don't think so. She told me that she won't go to sleep because she's afraid she won't wake up.

RN: That tells me that she's pretty aware of what's in front of her. That she knows she's dying. *(Note: The nurse vocalizes a conclusion for this family.)*

Educating patients and families can be accomplished by using storytelling, metaphors, and analogies to describe physical decline. For example, the body can be described in terms of a system, an assembly line, a machine, or a car to illustrate the process of decline and loss of function. Compassionate education is about teaching the patient and family what is normal and then helping them to identify what is abnormal. The goal is to help patients/families become aware of abnormalities that represent disease progression and loss of quality of life. This approach conveys sensitivity to the situation and is less abrupt than structured education. The following excerpt is from a palliative care nurse (RN) sitting bedside with a family member (FM):

RN: I am watching his breathing.

FM: Yes, it's changed since Tuesday. Yesterday he was breathing a lot and hard. Now he goes 2 seconds and then breathes.

RN: It's not that....Is he breathing? It's about the quality and effort of the breathing. He is now working to breathe and doing it less often. *(Note: The nurse uses the patient's breathing to teach about dying.)*

EVALUATE

Encouraging patients and families in sharing their stories, listening and sorting pertinent information relative to the quality-of-life domains, and practicing self-awareness and person-centered messages will collectively produce quality palliative communication. Still, the nurse's ability to reflect on his/her own communication choices and its impact on delivery of care will reveal strengths and highlight areas in need of improvement. Essentially, best practices for communication are ones we learn in hindsight!

Evaluation is particularly important following emotionally charged interactions and upon a patient's death or discharge. Taking the time to understand our reactions and assess how well the situation met task and relational goals is important. Try using the following questions (Figure 2.1) to guide the reflective process:

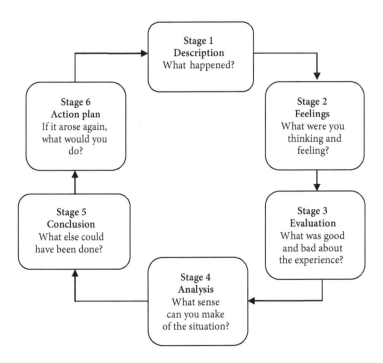

FIGURE 2.1 **Gibbs Reflective Cycle**
Used with permission from: Gibbs, G. (1988). *Learning by doing: A Guide to Teaching and Learning Methods.* Oxford, UK: Oxford Polytechnic.

Family and patient feedback is also important, as their thoughts and feelings may be different from those of the nurse. Patient and family feedback should be encouraged to determine if a communication goal was accomplished and whether or not verbal and nonverbal communication conveyed support. Use the following checklist (Table 2.6) to generate talking points with patients and families:

Table 2.6 Checklist

What happened in the effort to provide care?

What were you thinking and feeling in the course of care?

What was good about the experience?

What was bad about the experience?

What sense can you make of the experience now?

Could we have done something else, or done something differently?

If something similar happens again, what would you prefer us to do?

CHAPTER SUMMARY

Patients and families facing serious, chronic, or terminal illness have a story to tell. Most of them want to share their journey and talk about the trials and tribulations of illness. Most of them want to share it with their nurse. Learning to listen to these stories and capturing important information about what they value, what's important to them, and what is meaningful about their life can lead to comforting communication. Encouraging storytelling, listening to quality-of-life issues, and practicing person-centered communication are cornerstones of communication in palliative nursing. These principles work together to accomplish task and relational communication at the same time. Chapter 3 will illustrate how the nurse can tailor communication messages to meet the health literacy needs and cultural sensitivity of patients and families.

REFERENCES

Afifi, W. A., & Burgoon, J. K. (2000). Behavioral violations in interactions: The combined consequences of valence and change in uncertainty on interaction outcomes. *Human Communication Research, 26,* 203–233.

Aloi, J. A. (2009). The nurse and the use of narrative: An approach to caring. *Journal of Psychiatric and Mental Health Nursing, 16*(8), 711–715. doi: JPM1447 [pii]10.1111/j.1365–2850.2009.01447.x

Andersen, P., & Guerrero, L. (1998). The bright side of relational communication: Interpersonal warmth as social emotion. In P. Anderson & L. Guerrero (Eds.), *Handbook of Communication and Emotion* (pp. 305–324). Orlando, FL: Academic Press.

Burgoon, J. K., Birk, T., & Pfau, M. (1990). Nonverbal behaviors, persuasion, and credibility. *Human Communication Research, 17,* 140–169.

Burleson, B. R. (1994). Comforting messages: Significance, approaches, and effects. In B. Burleson, T. Albrecht, & I. Sarason (Eds.), *Communication of Social Support: Messages, Interactions, Relationships, and Community* (pp. 3–28). Thousand Oaks, CA: Sage.

Burleson, B. R., & MacGeorge, E. L. (2002). Supportive communication. In M. L. Knapp & J. A. Daly (Eds.), *Handbook of Interpersonal Communication* (3rd ed., pp. 374–424). Thousand Oaks, CA: Sage.

Byrnes, K., & Myers, S. A. (2010). Using group work to introduce students to affectionate communication. *Communication Teacher, 24*(3), 142–145.

Dahlin, C. (2010). Communication in palliative care: An essential competency for nurses. In B. Ferrell & N. Coyle (Eds.), *Oxford Textbook of Palliative Nursing* (3rd ed., pp. 107–136). New York: Oxford University Press.

Dias, L., Chabner, B. A., Lynch, T. J., Jr., & Penson, R. T. (2003). Breaking bad news: A patient's perspective. *Oncologist, 8*, 587–596.

Epstein, R., & Street, R. L. (2007). *Patient-Centered Communication in Cancer Care: Promoting Healing and Reducing Suffering.* Bethesda, MD: National Cancer Institute.

Ferrell, B., & Grant, M. (2011). Quality of life: 1525 voices of cancer. *Oncology Nursing Forum, 23*(6), 907–916.

Gibbs, G. (1988). *Learning by Doing: A Guide to Teaching and Learning Methods.* Oxford, UK: Oxford Polytechnic.

Haskard, K., Williams, S., DiMatteo, M. R., Heritage, J., & Rosenthal, R. (2008). The provider's voice: Patient satisfaction and the content-filtered speech of nurses and physicians in primary medical care. *Journal of Nonverbal Behavior, 32*, 1–20. doi: DOI 10.1007/s10919-007-0038-2

Hess, J. D. (2003). Gadow's relational narrative: An elaboration. *Nursing Philosophy, 4*(2), 137–148. doi: 126 [pii]

Jones, S. (2004). Putting the person into person-centered and immediate emotional support. *Communication Research, 31*(3), 338–360.

Jones, S. M., & Guerrero, L. (2001). The effects of nonverbal immediacy and verbal person centeredness in the emotional support process. *Human Communication Research, 27*, 567–596.

Keady, J., Ashcroft-Simpson, S., Halligan, K., & Williams, S. (2007). Admiral nursing and the family care of a parent with dementia: Using autobiographical narrative as grounding for negotiated clinical practice and decision-making. *Scandinavian Journal of Caring Sciences, 21*, 345–353.

Kendall, S. (2007). Witnessing tragedy: Nurses' perceptions of caring for patients with cancer. *International Journal of Nursing Practice, 13*(2), 111–120. doi: IJN615 [pii]10.1111/j.1440–172X.2007.00615.x

MacGeorge, E. L., Gillihan, S. J., Samter, W., & Clark, R. A. (2003). Skill deficit or differential motivation? Accounting for sex differences in the provision of emotional support. *Communication Research, 30*, 272–303.

Malloy, P., Paice, J., Virani, R., Ferrell, B., & Bednash, G. P. (2008). End-of-life nursing education consortium: 5 years of educating graduate nursing faculty in excellent palliative care. *Journal of Professional Nursing, 24*(6), 352–357. doi: S8755–7223(08)00094-X [pii]10.1016/j.profnurs.2008.06.001

McGuigan, D. (2009). Communicating bad news to patients: A reflective approach. *Nursing Standard, 23*(31), 51–56; quiz 57.

Naef, R. (2006). Bearing witness: A moral way of engaging in the nurse-person relationship. *Nursing Philosophy, 7*(3), 146–156. doi: NUP271 [pii]10.1111/j.1466–769X.2006.00271.x

O'Baugh, J., Wilkes, L. M., Sneesby, K., & George, A. (2009). Investigation into the communication that takes place between nurses and patients during chemotherapy. *Journal Psychosocial Oncology, 27*(4), 396–414. doi: 915716917 [pii]10.1080/07347330903182291

Pavlish, C., & Ceronsky, L. (2009). Oncology nurses' perceptions of nursing roles and professional attributes in palliative care. *Clinical Journal of Oncology Nursing, 13*(4), 404–412. doi: U247007J68225560 [pii]10.1188/09.CJON.404–412

Price, J., McNeilly, P., & Surgenor, M. (2006). Breaking bad news to parents: The children's nurse's role. *International Journal of Palliative Nursing, 12*(3), 115–120.

Radziewicz, R., & Baile, W. F. (2001). Communication skills: Breaking bad news in the clinical setting. *Oncology Nursing Forum, 28*(6), 951–953.

Ragan, S., Wittenberg-Lyles, E. M., Goldsmith, J., & Sanchez-Reilly, S. (2008). *Communication as Comfort: Multiple Voices in Palliative Care.* New York: Routledge.

Robichaux, C. M., & Clark, A. P. (2006). Practice of expert critical care nurses in situations of prognostic conflict at the end of life. *American Journal of Critical Care, 15*(5), 480–489; quiz 490. doi: 15/5/480 [pii]

Sheldon, L. K., Ellington, L., Barrett, R., Dudley, W. N., Clayton, M. F., & Rinaldi, K. (2009). Nurse responsiveness to cancer patient expressions of emotion. *Patient Education and Counseling, 76*(1), 63–70. doi: S0738–3991(08)00591–0 [pii]10.1016/j.pec.2008.11.010

Warnock, C., Tod, A., Foster, J., & Soreny, C. (2010). Breaking bad news in inpatient clinical settings: Role of the nurse. *Journal of Advance Nursing, 66*(7), 1543–1555. doi: JAN5325 [pii]10.1111/j.1365–2648.2010.05325.x

Additional References for Expectancy Violation Theory

Burgoon, J. K. (1978). A communication model of personal space violation: Explication and an initial test. *Human Communication Research, 4,* 129–142.

Burgoon, J. K. (1993). Interpersonal expectations, expectancy violations, and emotional communication. *Journal of Language and Social Psychology, 12,* 30–48. doi:10.1177/026192X93121003

Burgoon, J. K., Buller, D. B., & Woodall, W. G. (1994). *Nonverbal Communication: The Unspoken Dialogue.* New York: HarperCollins/Greyden Press.

Burgoon, J. K., & LePoire, B. A. (1993). Effects of communication expectancies, actual communication, and expectancy disconfirmation on evaluations of communicators and their communication behavior. *Human Communication Research, 20,* 67–96. doi:10.1111=j.1468–2958.1993.tb00316.x

Burgoon, J. K., Walther, J. B., & Baesler, E. J. (1992). Interpretations, evaluations, and consequences of interpersonal touch. *Human Communication Research, 19,* 237–263. doi:10.1111=j.1468–2958.1992.tb00301.x

Canary, D. J., & Dindia, K. (Eds.) (1998). *Sex Differences and Similarities in Communication: Critical Essays and Empirical Investigations of Sex and Gender in Interaction.* Mahwah, NJ: Lawrence Erlbaum and Associates.

Floyd, K., & Voloudakis, M. (1999). Affectionate behavior in adult platonic friendships: Interpreting and evaluating expectancy violations. *Human Communication Research, 25*(3), 341–369.

Additional References for Narrative and Nursing

Charon, R. (1993). Medical interpretation: Implications of literary theory of narrative for clinical work. *Journal of Narrative and Life History, 3,* 79–97.

DasGupta, S., Irvine, C., & Spiegel, M. (2009). The possibilities of narrative palliative care medicine: "Giving Sorry Words." In Y. Gunaratnam & D. Oliviere (Eds.), *Narrative Stories in Health Care: Illness, Dying and Bereavement* (pp. 33–46). New York: Oxford University Press.

Gadow, S. (1995). Narrative and exploration: Toward a poetics of knowledge in nursing. *Nursing Inquiry, 2*(4), 211–214.

Gadow, S. (1999). Relational narrative: The postmodern turn in nursing ethics. *Scholarly Inquiry for Nursing Practice, 13*(1), 57–70.

Gunaratnam, Y., & Oliviere, D. (2009). Introduction. In Y. Gunaratnam & D. Oliviere (Eds.), *Narrative and Stories in Health Care: Illness, Dying and Bereavement* (pp. 1–14). New York: Oxford University Press.

Hess, J. D. (2003). Gadow's relational narrative: An elaboration. *Nursing Philosophy, 4*(2), 137–148. doi: 126 [pii]

Marnocha, M. (2009). What truly matters: Relationships and primary care. *Annals of Family Medicine, 7*(3), 196–197. doi: 7/3/196 [pii]10.1370/afm.1004

Romyn, D. M. (2003). The relational narrative: Implications for nurse practice and education. *Nursing Philosophy, 4*(2), 149–154. doi: 134 [pii]

Skott, C. (2001). Caring narratives and the strategy of presence: Narrative communication in nursing practice and research. *Nursing Science Quarterly, 14*(3), 249–254.

Swenson, M. M., & Sims, S. L. (2000). Toward a narrative-centered curriculum for nurse practitioners. *Journal of Nursing Education, 39*(3), 109–115.

Young, A. J., & Rodriguez, K. L. (2006). The role of narrative in discussing end-of-life care: Eliciting values and goals from text, context, and subtext. *Health Communication, 19*(1), 49–59. doi: 10.1207/s15327027hc1901_6

Additional References for Person-Centeredness/Supportive Communication

Albrecht, T. L., & Goldsmith, D. J. (2003). Social support, social networks, and health. In T. L. Thompson, A. M. Dorsey, K. I. Miller, & R. Parrott (Eds.), *Handbook of Health Communication* (pp. 263–284). Mahwah, NJ: Lawrence Erlbaum Associates, Inc.

Burleson, B. R. (1994). Comforting messages: Significance, approaches, and effects. In B. R. Burleson, T. L. Albrecht, & I. G. Sarason (Eds.), *Communication of Social Support: Messages, Interactions, Relationships, and Community* (pp. 3–28). Thousand Oaks, CA: Sage.

Burleson, B. R., & Goldsmith, D. J. (1998). How the comforting process works: Alleviating emotional distress through conversationally induced reappraisals. In P. A. Andersen & L. K. Guerrero (Eds.), *Communication and Emotion* (pp. 246–275). Orlando, FL: Academic Press.

Burleson, B. R., & MacGeorge, E. L. (2002). Supportive communication. In M. L. Knapp, J. A. Daly, & G. K. Miller (Eds.), *Handbook of Interpersonal Communication* (3rd ed., pp. 374–424). Thousand Oaks, CA: Sage.

Burleson, B. R., & Samter, W. (1985). Consistencies in theoretical and naïve evaluations of comforting messages. *Communication Monographs, 52*, 103–123.

Jones, S. M. (2004). Putting the person into person-centered and immediate emotional support: Emotional change and perceived helper competence as outcomes of comforting in helping situations. *Communication Research, 31*(3), 338–360.

Jones, S. M., & Guerrero, L. K. (2001). The effects of nonverbal immediacy and verbal person centeredness in the emotional support process. *Human Communication Research, 27*, 567–596.

Jones, S. M., & Wirtz, J. G. (2006). How does the comforting process work? An empirical test of an appraisal-based model of comforting. *Human Communication Research, 32*, 217–243.

MacGeorge, E. L., Gillihan, S. J., Samter, W., & Clark, R. A. (2003). Skill deficit or differential motivation: Testing alternative explanations of gender differences in the provision of emotional support. *Communication Research, 30*(3), 272–303.

DISCUSSION QUESTIONS

1. How are task and relational communication provided in palliative nursing?
2. What are some implications of patient/family stories? What can they tell you?
3. In what ways can you encourage patients and families to share their stories?
4. What are the varying levels of person-centered messages?
5. What nonverbal behavior can be used to convey that you like someone?
6. Describe *your* general expectations when working with patients who are given bad news. What are the implications for their reactions on the way *you* communicate with them?
7. When expectations are violated, what are the three characteristics we rely on to evaluate a positive or negative reaction?
8. How can self-awareness be beneficial when using nonverbal behavior to convey empathy and support?
9. How does witnessing work? In what ways does witnessing appeal to you?
10. What are the four domains of quality of life? Do you see evidence of these in the patients and families you care for?
11. From the list of barriers to breaking bad news, which is the most problematic for you? Why? What nonverbal behavior will you employ to help handle the situation?
12. What are the effects of how you feel about others? How does this impact your emotional involvement with patients and family members?
13. How can person-centered messages be used to educate patients and families?

TEACHING RESOURCES AND MATERIALS

EXERCISE #1

Adult Family Member, sitting at bedside:

> My father has been living with us for about 3 years. A week ago he fell and broke his hip. They found bleeding in his stomach; he's had a hernia for over 40 years. They went in and put the g-tube in, pulled his stomach down, and anchored it (g-tube) to the stomach. During this time he crashed and was intubated. He came out and for 5 days he sat here; his hip was still not fixed and he was in so much pain. After they did hip surgery, they were never able to extubate. We removed the tube because we knew that's what he wanted. Everything is now failing—and I said "stop"—his arms are so swollen from blood clots and they wanted to do tests. I said "no"—he didn't want that.

Discussion Questions

1. What was the turning point that shifted this patient's *general story* to a *palliative story*?
2. Identify the gap in this story as identified by this family member. What does this tell you about her acceptance of the situation?
3. Practice externalization and provide an example of how you would respond to this family member.

EXERCISE #2

Kath's narrative—Adult daughter, primary family caregiver:

> Let me introduce myself. I am Kath and by day I work as a customer service supervisor for one of the major high street banks. I have a partner, Simon, and a brother, and in my spare time I am a competitive archer. I am a good organizer, caring and born on my father's birthday more years ago than I care to reveal!
>
> Four years ago my mother began to disturb her neighbors by saying there was a "strange man" in her home, a man who was my father and her husband of over 40 years. This fear and problem with recognition was so out of character for my Mom that I took her to the doctors who arranged for "tests" to be carried out, mainly memory and blood tests, and a brain scan. When the results came back,

49

they said that Mom had Alzheimer's disease, Vascular dementia and Lewy Body dementia. Each of us, my mother, father, brother and me, absorbed the multiple diagnoses the best we could and vowed to carry on, although it was my father who shouldered most of the responsibility for my Mom's daily support. Dad would tell us: "you've got your own lives to lead" and would only accept help, reluctantly, when things became too difficult for him to manage. He had such strength of character and he was my anchor. We all respected his pride and independence.

On a cold, crisp December's day, Dad was on his way to collect Mom from the local Day Center when he had a car accident. At first all seemed ok, but he was admitted as a precautionary measure to the hospital where he was found to have a severe chest infection. Initially, Dad responded well to treatment, but then he lost his sight. Funnily enough, he did not make a fuss about that, it was only when he kept looking at a non-existent wristwatch that I became suspicious and challenged him; it was then that he admitted he could no longer see. I visited Dad each day before breakfast so I could feed him and only left after supper time, but after a short period of time his kidneys started to fail. Dad needed an operation to survive but, as we were told, would not survive the operation. The most cruel paradox, with the only tangible outcome being one we did not want to face. But we had to confront it and honor Dad's dignity and quality of life. Eventually, the monitors giving him life support were unplugged and the morphine increased and I watched until Dad closed his eyes and died. I had to let him go, the father who had given me so much unconditional love during his lifetime. It was then that Susan (nurse) entered my world.

With help I tried looking after Mom, staying with her in her home, but it was too difficult and confusing for her. So, after a lot of thought, discussion and soul searching, Mom agreed to go into residential care. Although I knew, on balance, it was the right thing to happen, when the day came for her to "go there" I was heartbroken, a feeling of loss as great as when my Dad died. Well-meaning friends say how relieved I must feel now that Mom was in residential care: how wrong they were! Such feelings of guilt, in letting Dad down, and of sadness, in seeing someone you love struggle to make sense of their life and new surroundings.

Mom has insight for short periods—windows on the world as I call it—and at these times she has such clarity. During one of her "windows" Mom may ask me a number of questions, such as: "Has my mental state got worse?" and: "Will I get better?" You learn to think on your feet, asking her for her telephone number, knowing that she will remember it, and then you can say: "Can't be so bad can it Mom? … of course you will get better"—all the time knowing that is not going to happen, but at least it gives her hope. Mom also asks about Dad. Invariably, when I go and see her, Mom will jump up, glad to see me, take my hand, and ask: "Where's Dad?" I try and fight back the tears explaining that Dad, her husband, has died. Mom has no recollection of the day of his funeral when she said she felt like crying, but couldn't. I smile, glad that my mother does not feel the pain as I do.

Each visit to the residential home is challenging, as you do not know what you will find or what questions you will be asked. Sometimes friends and colleagues at work ask me how I am doing: "Fine" I will reply, but I am not fine, feeling that every waking moment is consumed by the sheer effort of coping and locking my emotions away.

Exercise Discussion

1. Recognize individuality—What unique vulnerabilities exist for this family member?
2. Understand life prior to illness—What was Kath's like life prior to her mother's illness and father's death? What is it like now?
3. How would you describe/educate Kath about her mother's condition (mental health)?
4. How does Kath define quality of life? Which domain is important when providing a plan of care for her mother?

Used with permission from: Keady, J., Ashcroft-Simpson, S., Halligan, K., & Williams, S. (2007). Admiral nursing and the family care of a parent with dementia: Using auto-biographical narrative as grounding for negotiated clinical practice and decision-making. *Scandinavian Journal of Caring Sciences, 21,* 345–353.

EXERCISES FOR VERBAL CLARITY

EXERCISE #1

Review the opening case study scenario for this chapter.

1. What communication barriers are present for Eileen?
2. Imagine you are in Eileen's shoes and write down exactly what you would say to Mrs. Williams after she tells you that she is worried about "abandoning her mother-in-law."
3. Refer to Table 2.5 of person-centered messages and evaluate your own message. Is it at the top of the hierarchy? If not, rewrite your message so that is supportive.

EXERCISE #2

Divide students into four groups. Assign each group one of the four domains of quality of life (physical, psychological, social, and spiritual). Working in groups, have students write an example statement for each aspect listed in their assigned domain (e.g., for physical well-being, students would write example statements for fatigue, sleep disruption, etc.). Statements can be made up or can be examples that they have heard from their practice. Once statements have been written, have groups identify specific resources available or care plan actions that would be supportive for the patient/family member.

EXERCISE #3

Have students write a verbal analogy and detail verbal directness statements to describe a disease or illness (e.g., cancer, dementia, COPD). Below is an example:

Table 2.7 Communicating the Diagnosis of Congestive Heart Failure

Verbal analogy	For example, congestive heart failure could be described as a traffic jam. Just like when the electricity goes out and traffic lights don't work, drivers don't know what to do, so they slow down or hesitate. The same is true for the body when the heart can longer pump blood: blood supply and blood flow slow down.
Verbal directness	You have what we call congestive heart failure. This is a long illness. Your heart is not like it once was. It has a harder time squeezing the blood through your body— and all of the veins and arteries that run throughout your body.

Once students have drafted an analogy and verbal directness statement, pair them up with a classmate and have students share their work, choose and refine the best one for each, and then have pairs share with the larger group as a whole. Instructors may want to assign specific diseases to certain parts of the classroom or as appropriate given coursework curriculum.

EXERCISES FOR NONVERBAL IMMEDIACY

EXERCISE #1

Patient: Let me take you back to the start. I was completely well. I was toodling along with two little kids and a husband. He is a physician. I was teaching school, and one day I found a football-sized mass in my abdomen. It frightened me, but because it was so huge, I felt it had to be benign. After all, something that big could not possibly be a cancer, and the word cancer just never even entered my mind. I was too young, I thought. Anyway, I went into surgery not having a clue. The doctors really did not prepare me for it except to say I had a mass. I remember exactly what he said. I woke up from surgery to hear my surgeon say, "I have good news and bad news. I didn't have to remove any of your organs, but (pause) you do have cancer." It just blew me away...

1. Identify the barriers present in the delivery of bad news.
2. How would you change the delivery of bad news to this patient? What would you say? What would you do?

3. What quality-of-life domains should have been prioritized?
4. What are your general expectations of this scenario? What would you expect to happen?
5. List three adjectives that you would use to describe this patient/family member.
6. List your perception of their living arrangements (e.g., type of housing, area in your community, school district, extracurricular activities).
7. What is the relational history (positive or negative) between the patient and doctor?
8. Are task and relational communication goals accomplished in this scenario?

Used with permission from: Dias, L., Chabner, B. A., Lynch, T. J., Jr., & Penson, R. T. (2003). Breaking bad news: A patient's perspective. *Oncologist, 8,* 587–596.

EXERCISE #2

Put students in pairs. Have them each share a funny story or their most embarrassing moment. During the story, students who are listening should provide no feedback (e.g., they should not laugh or smile, which is a violation of expectations). Then ask students:

1. Was it hard for you to continue communicating/sharing when you received no feedback? Did you alter your story because of it? If so, how?
2. Alternatively, how did it feel to mask your emotions?

COMPREHENSIVE EXERCISES FOR CHAPTER MATERIAL

RESPONDING TO DENIAL

Show students a clip from a film (see the table below) and ask them to write how they would respond to the patient (verbally and nonverbally).
Optional: Scene/dialogue can be role-played between two students.

FOLLOWING BAD NEWS

The following is an excerpt from the 1983 film *Terms of Endearment*, where Debra Winger's character is given the following prognosis by her doctor:

"The response to the drugs we tried isn't what we hoped. But there are investigatory drugs which we are willing to utilize. However if you become incapacitated

Table 2.8 Recommended Movie Examples

Examples	
Movie	*Scene/Dialogue*
Stepmom (1998)	Susan Sarandon's character reacts to the news of more cancer: "But you said the last time that you got it all. So if you were wrong the last time then there's a good chance you're wrong this time because the last time you … but people … you … we … we can beat it. I mean people beat it all the time right?"
My Life (1993)	Michael Keaton's character reacts to news that he has 3–4 months to live: "Come on. I'm still in the game here man. There are a lot of other therapies … treatments." The next scene shows him and his wife walking to their car when suddenly he stops and runs back to confront the doctor: "Who the hell do you think you are? To take away my hope like that. That's all I have."
Brian's Song (1971, 2001)	After more surgery Brian awaits news from the doctor. Agitated, he turns to his friend: "I want them to check me out and get me out. There's too many sick people around here.… Everyone's talking to me like I'm a child." When the doctor comes in and tells him that the cancer has spread to his lungs, Brian responds by yelling and throwing things across his hospital room.
Beaches (1988)	Toward the end of the film, Barbara Hershey's character stops taking phone calls. When confronted with this, she responds: "I don't care what they (her friends) think." An argument ensues, and Bette Midler's character comments that she hasn't changed clothes in a week. Hillary: "Just leave me alone. Okay. That's all I want is to be left fucking alone … You don't know what this feels like at all. I'm the one who won't live to see my daughter grow into a woman. I hate it. I don't want it to be over with yet.… So you don't understand what this feels like. Alright. You're still in the land of the living."

or it becomes unreasonable for you to handle your affairs for a block of time, it might be wise to make some decisions now. Any questions?" Emma responds: "No. I know what you are saying. I have to figure out what to do with my kids."

1. What barriers are present in this delivery of bad news?
2. Rewrite this dialogue so that it is more person centered and conveys comfort.
3. If left alone with this patient following this scene, what would you say to her? What could you do for this patient?

USING GROUP WORK TO INTRODUCE STUDENTS TO AFFECTIONATE COMMUNICATION

The Activity

Before beginning this activity, instructors should read Morman and Floyd (1998). In it, the authors define affectionate communication as "an individual's intentional and overt enactment or expression of feelings of closeness, care, and fondness for another" (p. 145). Additionally, the three dimensions of affectionate communication (i.e., verbal, nonverbal, and supportive communication) are identified.

This activity allows students to create their own examples of affectionate expression by placing them in one of two roles: that of the healthcare provider who works with patients or that of a family member. As healthcare providers, students are to create a list of behaviors they should use to demonstrate their fondness and positive regard for their patient. Meanwhile, the other students, working as family members, should also create a list of behaviors they should use to demonstrate their fondness and positive regard for their loved one. This activity lasts approximately 15 minutes, with an additional 45 minutes needed for discussion and debriefing.

First, divide students into two groups, with each group congregating on opposite sides of the classroom. Once divided into two groups, each group should then be subdivided into smaller groups of three members each. Once in these groups, begin this activity by telling one half of the students that they are to imagine they are colleagues working at a local hospital. The other half should then be told they are family members with a loved one at a local hospital. An example script is listed below.

Health Care Provider Script Sample:

> You are a healthcare provider who works with patients at a local hospital. Over time, you and your colleagues notice your patients, while successful at their exercises, are suffering from low morale. After conversing with each other, you and your fellow healthcare providers decide to take a more active role in communicating feelings of liking and fondness to your patients. Collectively, you decide that by sharing your liking and fondness, your patients will experience an increase in morale and feel more positive. A meeting is arranged for all the healthcare providers at the local hospital. At the meeting you and your colleagues brainstorm a list of behaviors that should be used with your patients.

Those working in the healthcare provider condition should then generate as many examples as possible of nonverbal, verbal, and supportive affectionate communication behaviors to use with their patients. The other students, working as family members, should receive the following prompt.

Family Member Script Sample:

> A member of your family is staying in a local hospital for cancer care. Over time, you and the other members of your family notice that your loved one is suffering

from low morale. After conversing with each other, you and your family decide to take a more active role in communicating feelings of liking and fondness to your loved one. Collectively, you decide that by sharing your liking and fondness, your loved one will experience an increase in morale and feel more positive. The entire family decides to meet and discuss what types of behaviors they could use with their loved one to express liking and fondness.

Those acting as family members should create examples of verbal, nonverbal, and supportive affectionate expressions. All students should receive 15 minutes to identify as many behaviors as possible. Instructors might consider providing groups with a definition of verbal, nonverbal, and supportive affectionate expressions. Floyd (2006b) identifies verbal affectionate communication as phrases such as "I like you," nonverbal affectionate communication includes behaviors such as hugging, kissing, or holding hands, and supportive affectionate communication includes actions of social and instrumental support such as helping with a favor or loaning materials. Once the 15 minutes has expired, the groups should share their lists orally.

Used with permission from: Byrnes, K., & Myers, S. A. (2010). Using group work to introduce students to affectionate communication. *Communication Teacher*, 24(3), 142–145.

DEBRIEFING

The debriefing consists of two steps. The first step is to address the groups' examples. The following questions can be used to facilitate the discussion:

1. What examples did your group create for expressions of verbal, nonverbal, and supportive affectionate communication?
2. As a health care provider, what type of affectionate expression was the easiest to create examples of?
3. As a family member, what type of affectionate expression was the easiest to create examples of?
4. What are the similarities/differences between the health care provider examples and the family examples?

The second step is to explain the implications of affectionate communication and changes in the family and healthcare provider–patient interaction:

5. How would you expect the relationship between the patient and the health care provider to change if patients received more affectionate communication?
6. How would you expect the relationship between the patient and family member to change if patients received more affectionate communication?

7. What benefits could the patient experience from receiving more affectionate communication?
8. What benefits would the health care providers or family members receive from giving affectionate communication?

Once this in-class debriefing is completed, students should be given the opportunity to raise any additional issues or questions. After all issues and questions have been addressed, the instructor should conclude class by reminding the students the purpose of the activity, which was to identify and create examples of affectionate communication, and examine the effect affectionate communication can have on individual's well-being.

REFERENCES AND SUGGESTED READINGS

Floyd, K. (2006a). Human affection exchange: XIII. Affectionate communication is associated with diurnal variation in salivary free cortisol. *Western Journal of Communication, 70,* 47–63.

Floyd, K. (2006b). *Communicating affection: Interpersonal Behavior and Social Context.* New York: Cambridge University Press.

Floyd, K., Hess, J. A., Miczo, L. A., Halone, K. K., Mikkelson, A. C., & Tusing, K. J. (2005). Human affection exchange: VIII. Further evidence of the benefits of expressed affection. *Communication Quarterly, 53,* 285–303.

Floyd, K., Mikkelson, A. C., Tafoya, M. A., Farinelli, L., La Valley, A. G., Judd, J., et al. (2007). Human affection exchange: XIII. Affectionate communication accelerates neuroendocrine stress recovery. *Health Communication, 22,* 123–132.

Morman, M. T., & Floyd, K. (1998). The measurement of affectionate communication. *Communication Quarterly, 46,* 144–162.

3

ORIENTATION AND OPPORTUNITY

George is a nurse practitioner in a large outpatient renal dialysis center where he has practiced over the past 10 years. He and his colleagues are proud of the excellent care provided to their dialysis patients, although George has begun to recognize deficiencies in care provided to patients at the end of life. His colleagues have dismissed his concerns, but a new nurse, Sheila, who has joined the clinic, has made similar observations. George and Sheila have discussed the problem of patients who continue on dialysis despite the enormous burdens—even as it is evident they will die soon. Recently, one of George's favorite patients, an elderly World War II Veteran and first-generation Italian-American, Lanz (who has always reminded George of this own grandfather), developed serious complications, and George felt that perhaps a team conference should be convened to reevaluate the goals of care. Though Lanz was always a man of few words and difficult to talk to, George felt a great respect for him as well as a deep concern for his declining quality of life. At his last visit, Lanz was accompanied by his sister and a niece. All of them seemed weary, and Lanz embraced George when leaving, thanking him for his years of care. The clinic was very busy, and George had little time to spare, but he asked Lanz how he was "holding up." Lanz simply replied that he was "tired" and not so sure how much longer he could "fight."

Unfortunately, no such team communication occurred about his declining status, and a few days later Lanz developed acute cardiac failure, was resuscitated at home by emergency technicians and admitted to a hospital CCU where he underwent 4 days of aggressive care and mechanical ventilation and two additional resuscitations, and died amid a third cardiac arrest. George learned of Lanz's death only when he failed to appear for his dialysis treatment. The following day George phoned his home and was told by Lanz's niece that his funeral was being held that very day.

Sheila, sensing George's grief, offered to relieve him at the center and give George some time alone. He thanked Sheila, saying, "There must be a better way to care for these patients at the end of life."

George is now left to wonder about Lanz and his family as they endured high levels of invasive intervention too near the end of life—potentially because of low health literacy and little communication about care options and disease trajectory. As a nurse present for so many dialysis treatments with Lanz, George had seen his dwindling health and increasing tiredness. Many nurses have observed and been distressed over similar ethical dilemmas of patient treatment and its futility. George shared a connection with Lanz and is haunted by the care decisions that were never intentionally planned for this patient. George feared what was ahead for Lanz but was unsure about how to engage him in challenging subjects about withdrawing dialysis, advance directives, his family concerns. These issues followed George in his care for Lanz and turned into anxieties and regrets in light of the intensive period of resuscitations that punctuated the final days of Lanz's life.

Palliative care is a philosophy of care that penetrates every area and specialty of nursing. Palliative care is a fundamental element of nursing that transcends practice areas and roles (Dahlin, 2010). For advanced-practice nurses specializing in palliative care, coordinating communication with the patient and family about the illness and treatment options is central to care. However, the communication traps and frustrations in providing this care are many. Identifying influencing factors such as low health literacy and cultural differences will facilitate the work of educating the patient and family about the illness and their options for care.

The "O" in COMFORT, the matter of interest for this chapter, deals with orientation and opportunity for a patient and family facing serious, chronic, or terminal illness. An overarching concept in this chapter is that of accommodation, and ideas from communication accommodation theory will help explain accommodation in clinical practice. The first idea introduced in this chapter is health literacy and how this determines the kind of care, cost of care, experience of care, quality of care, choice of care, and the nurse's experience of providing that care. Second, the chapter presents cultural theory and how this colludes intractably with health literacy—for any patient and family.

The ideas of communication accommodation, health literacy, and culture come together to help identify nursing skills to better understand patients and families and facilitate shared understanding with them about care choices and treatment in light of their values.

CONVERGENCE AND THE PALLIATIVE CARE NURSE

Communicating the entire story of the patient's status and options for care—and ensuring this happens in an understandable way—is the essence of **orientation** to life-limiting illness. The palliative care nurse is central to making true orientation possible, as well as appreciating and articulating what **opportunities** for treatment and care exist for a patient/family. Without this information, far fewer desirable decisions, choices, and ultimately outcomes will happen for a patient and family in the face of treatment and dying.

Communication Accommodation Theory

Communication accommodation theory (CAT) grounds the themes in this chapter, and therefore is a very useful foundation to use as we think of the culture of patients and families and dealing with health literacy challenges. CAT establishes that all people communicate in similar and dissimilar ways and that the way in which we *understand* the speech and behavior of another will determine what we think of the interaction. Using this communication idea (Figure 3.1), we can see that nurses communicating with patients and families will practice **convergence** (i.e., adapting and aligning with their communication), **divergence** (i.e., increasing the differences between them), or **overaccomodation** (i.e., overdoing efforts to regulate, modify, or respond to others) (Giles, 2008).

As we address the concept of low health literacy and cultural difference throughout this chapter, we will offer practice suggestions that will help palliative care nurses converge with their patients and families rather than diverge or overaccommodate.

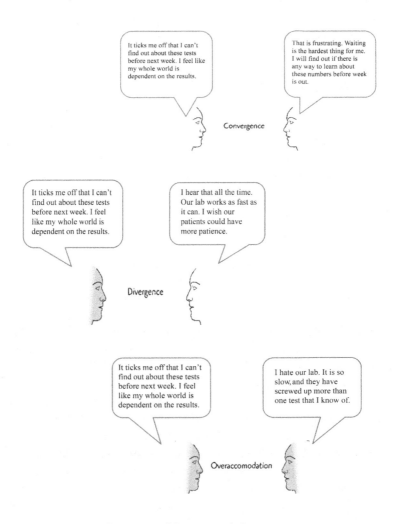

FIGURE 3.1. Convergence, Divergence, and Overaccomodation

Images adapted from West, R., & Turner, L. (2010). *Introduction to Communication Theory: Analysis and Application*. New York: McGraw-Hill.

Health literacy is about receiving or acquiring information, understanding that information, and then using that information in decision making about health-related issues. Limited health literacy affects people of all ages, races, incomes, and education levels, but the impact of limited health literacy disproportionately affects low-socioeconomic and minority groups. It affects peoples' ability to search for and use health information, practice healthy behaviors, and use important public health warnings.

The National Action Plan to Improve Health Literacy was released in 2010 from the Department of Health and Human Services Office of Disease Prevention and Health Promotion. This study prioritizes needed change in our society that will provide: (1) health information that people can use to make decisions, (2) person-centered information and services, and (3) a support of lifelong learning to promote good health (U.S. Department of Health and Human Services, 2010). The nurse is at the nucleus of each tenet. Also at the center of these goals is the idea of increasing the health literacy of patients and families who face the complex issues of the medical world.

Limited health literacy is associated with worse health outcomes and higher costs (U.S. Department of Health and Human Services, 2010). Researchers estimate the cost of limited health literacy to the nation's economy to be from $106 to $236 billion each year, while the future costs of low health literacy might be as high as 1.6–3.6 trillion dollars. Substantial indirect costs related to low health literacy have not even been calculated in this figure, and this would include additional chronic illness, disability, lost wages, and poorer quality of life (Vernon, Trujillo, Rosenbaum, & DeBuono, 2007). An earlier study identified an increased cost of $7798 per hospitalization for those navigating illness with low health literacy (Weiss & Palmer, 2004). These figures are staggering and distressing, but further research is needed to discover exactly where and why these costs are incurred.

Nurses have the chance to improve orientation and opportunity for patients and families in profound ways. But currently, there is no standard for a particular depth of health literacy content to be included in undergraduate nursing education, and nursing education programs in general do not address the complexities of health literacy when covering patient education. Nurses need support and direction in finding ways to improve health literacy for patients and families in light of all that is at stake—not just the patient and family experience, but also dimensions of ethical dilemmas and the emotional impact of these clinical issues on burnout and professional error.

A close partner to health literacy in improving patient and family communication in palliative nursing is an awareness of cultural theory. Though at first the two might seems like two separate concepts, their links and mutual effects become inextricably linked upon further examination. **Cultural theory** is rooted in two basic claims about culture and power. First, culture pervades and invades all parts of human behavior. And secondly, people are part of a hierarchical structure. To a large extent, cultural practices and institutions permeate the way people think about and behave in life—impacting communication, family structure and involvement, and health care decision making. Additionally, cultural studies explain that there is power in every part of society, and this power combines with meaning to guide people in their communications and decisions (West & Turner, 2010).

Nursing is not a stranger to the realization of the profound cultural impact in practice. Cultural competencies and transcultural nursing are not only concepts that have been valued in the nursing profession, but they also have been increasingly emphasized in nursing education given the growing diversity of our population. Using the framework of convergence in the communication accommodation theory, the already existing cultural competency discussion is extended here to include health literacy improvement. Attention to these concepts is essential to improving patient and family understanding of disease and treatment choices.

Health Literacy and Palliative Care Nursing

All populations and geographic locations seem to be affected by disparities in health knowledge. Many studies demonstrate extreme disparities for those people with lower incomes, lower levels of education, and older age—most specifically adults over 65, nonwhites, those with less than a high school degree, those at or below the poverty level, and nonnative or non-English speakers (U.S. Department of Health and Human Services, 2010). The Department of Education offers a taxonomy of health literacy levels that many scholars and clinicians use in designing tools and interventions to evaluate patients and families. We simplify those categories here (Table 3.1).

It is not surprising that 30 million Americans are unable to perform even the simplest everyday literacy tasks, many of whom are not literate in English. "Most of the

Table 3.1 Health Literacy and Task Competency

Health Literacy Level	Task Competency
Below basic	- Can identify health care activity to perform a simple set of instructions - Can read text with simple words - Graphics are useful
Basic	- Can read text using simple words and declarative statements - Can extract major points - Middle school reading level - Graphics are useful.
Intermediate	- Can accurately read prescription label and follow directions - Can apply information on a scale to locate answers - Can interpret information presented in narrative or graphics
Proficient	- Can compare and contrast from different sources - Can understand difficult abstract concepts pertaining to medical information - Able to figure costs pertaining to health insurance plan

Kutner et al. (2007). *Literacy in Everyday Life: From the 2003 National Assessment of Adult Literacy (NCES 2007–480)*. Washington, DC: US Department of Education, National Center for Education Statistics.

adults with *Below Basic* health literacy skills would have difficulty reading a chart or simple instructions. These same adults are more likely to report their health as poor (42%) and are more likely to lack health insurance (28%) than adults with *Proficient* health literacy" (U.S. Department of Health and Human Services, 2010, p. 9). These numbers are at once troubling, but not a complete shock. The majority of the literature intended to guide nurses through the low–health literacy maze focuses heavily on written materials and how to determine if a patient/family can really understand those materials. But as we have already noted, health literacy is not entirely straightforward in terms of reading and comprehension. Health literacy includes more than word reorganization, reading comprehension, and numeracy skills. Understanding health literacy in its fullness includes language, context, culture, communication skills levels, and technology (Mancuso, 2009). Only by understanding these additional elements can we help people acquire and apply information in the best way.

The general assumption in the literature is that patients and families with language barriers and social determinants are likely candidates for low health literacy. What is unique to palliative care is the reality that *all* patients and families experience compromise in health literacy. Impeded communication, emotional stability, thought processing, listening, and information processing all serve to lower health literacy. Though we recognize studied and proven populations operating in below-basic and basic health literacy levels, we also propose that any patient and family receiving palliative care—despite their ethnicity, background, and appearance—be cared for as though they are operating with lower levels of health literacy until the contrary is demonstrated.

Imagine a physician who herself was suffering from stage IV non–small cell lung cancer. She is emotionally compromised. Her family is emotionally compromised. Their health literacy is then compromised and lowered. So we suggest that the nurse clinician move beyond essentialized ideas about those with low health literacy and always work to gain an understanding of how a patient/family is processing health information and the ways they are using information to make decisions.

Cultural Humility

Concerns about cultural insensitivity and inadequate training for patient/family communication with people of diverse backgrounds draw attention to inconsistencies between the idea of **cultural competency** and the reality of the practice of intercultural nursing in palliative care (Gunaratnam, 2007). Gunaratnam notes that cultural awareness in the palliative care setting is unique in that it depends on the "non-rational and visceral components" of care (Gunaratnam, 2007, p. 470). Because cultural competency exists as a movement, it has been reflected in palliative care education and training. For palliative care, this often takes the form of lists that identify different cultural and religious groups, death-related beliefs, practices, and rituals (Jones, Cason, & Bond, 2004). Palliative care recognizes that death and dying can intensify the profundity of culture and ritual. Rethinking the suggested characteristics of cultural competency, nurses could instead question the basic assumption that cultural knowledge is something that can be "mastered."

Cultural knowledge can be presented in a way that brings nurses and patients/families together, rather than something that separates and differentiates. As with many protocols and required skill sets for nurses, the "retreat behind a technique" can protect the nursing clinician from demonstrating humility in the face of difference (Saunders & Bains, 1983).

From a communication standpoint, which is what we offer in this volume, the basic goal of communicating with patients and families—as well as a team and staff—is to create shared understanding. We advocate that this is best accomplished by privileging the narrative and the relationship with the patient/family first. In other words, valuing the patient and family experience with time and communication in the clinical setting heralds their journey as important and credible and necessary to moving forward in achieving good care.

In nursing literature, **cultural awareness** addresses the clinician's consciousness about a nurse's own reactions to individuals who are different from the clinician. **Cultural attitude** is based on a clinician's own thinking about cultural differences. And **cultural skills** include the practice of culturally competent communication (Nyatanga, 2008). Communication skills and an open dialogue are developed and supported by a willingness to attain cultural knowledge and sensitivity (Flaskerud, 2007). Joining these cultural competency categories with patient/family interaction, nurse communication might fall into the **successful** category, in which the message intentionally sent was interpreted accurately. Then again, the message might not be interpreted with accuracy. A message might result in **miscommunication**—in which a message was intentionally sent but was not interpreted accurately (i.e., a patient/family member does not understand dosage of pain medication due to their low health literacy surrounding numeracy). **Accidental communication** is sent without intent but interpreted accurately (i.e., a nurse checking her phone, her watch, and the clock on the wall during a short bedside encounter is presumed by the visiting family member to be prioritizing time and task over relationship with patient). **Attempted communication** includes messages that were sent but not received (For example, a notation to provide a social work consult is added to a chart and inadvertently deleted. The family, expecting the consult to occur the following day is distressed and confused when this visit does not materialize.). **Accidental and miscommunicated** messages can be the most destructive to clinician/patient/family relationships. In this fifth category of communication, a message is sent unintentionally and interpreted inaccurately (for example, a NP frowns and grimaces as she enters a room with a patient/family; this is interpreted as her dislike toward the patient/family, when in fact she is frustrated by a previous staff interaction about a different matter altogether) (Guerrero & Floyd, 2006). This simple framework is helpful in considering the complex impact of culture on intended and unintended messages while a nurse is attempting to make patients and families aware of their health situation and possible care options.

The idea of potential low health literacy for every patient and family is in concert with a need to practice cultural humility with all patients and families. Consider first the culture of health care, nursing, and medicine. Those working/training/operating in this culture have been medically socialized to this culture (DuPre, 2010). This socialization has taken thousands of hours, exposures, and personal sacrifices. Those outside of the health care culture simply do not share in this socialization experience. A base assumption, with the exception of patients who also live in the health care culture, can be that a cultural divide exists between nurses and all of their care receivers.

Cultural competency requirements can systematically support a static and "brass tacks" conception of culture. As various programs in cultural competency have matured, voices in health care have issued warnings about a too essentialized conception of culture. Scholars and health care professionals note that "culture" is always moving and morphing as people make use of their cultural resources in creative ways, and increase the possible blend of cultural factors as populations grow and cross paths (Santiago-Irizarry, 1996). If we accept the definition of culture to essentially get at the idea of competing discourses within situations characterized by an unequal distribution of power, then we must also accept health care as its own cultural context.

We are in agreement with other writers who propose that the term **cultural humility** can supersede the idea of cultural competence (Tervalon & Murray-Garcia, 1998). Traditional family configurations are blurred, multiple generations of intercultural marriages have created too many cross-fertilized cultural patterns to contain, and so the dominant pattern in nursing to adopt standardized cultural competencies may now be much less beneficial to the patient. Cultural humility asks nurses to adopt a "clean slate and assess the patient regardless of their cultural orientation" (Nyatanga, 2008, p. 315). This approach to cultural sensitivity and communication asks the nurse to mindfully respect each patient/family member, their dignity, and their need—regardless of an ethnic origin, religious belief, or personal attribute that might label them. Consider this example of cultural humility. *A 75-year-old woman from a large Korean family was admitted with end-stage heart disease to the cardiology unit. The woman had a large family including her spouse, five children, many grandchildren, siblings, and a 95-year-old mother. The family and patient were highly anxious, speaking only in Korean to each other. The patient's elderly mother created an altar in the room, bringing daily offerings of fruit and incense. A major conflict ensued when a nurse informed the patient's mother that incense could not be lit due to fire codes. The patient unfortunately declined and her heart failure worsened. The family became very agitated, and the hospital patient advocate representative was called in as the family became very distraught and dissatisfied. One of the specific complaints was that while their mother had been hospitalized for 2 weeks and was now dying, they had never seen a chaplain. When the patient advocate met with the nurses, they admitted that they assumed the patient and family were Buddhist and would not want a chaplain. The family explained that they were a family very strong in their Korean heritage and Buddhism as a life philosophy; they also were "born-again" Christians and were offended by the lack of spiritual care, especially since they had seen chaplains visiting other patients, and thus they felt excluded.*

The current curriculum in cultural competency does not and cannot accurately and completely reflect the cultural world in which nurses practice. True cultural competence is not a discrete end point, but rather an ongoing and active engagement in a lifelong process. This process requires humility as nurses will continually reflect and consider their practice, and their interaction with patients/families/staff, and ultimately this reflection will result in better ways to communicate (Tervalon & Murray-Garcia, 1998). Cultural humility does not suggest disposing of valuable knowledge about the health care practices of particular communities; rather, it adds flexibility to the mix that will allow for humbleness: an opportunity for nurses to seek out and locate the best resources for their patients and families.

LIFEWORLD IN PALLIATIVE CARE NURSING

The idea of **Lifeworld** is used in many areas of study and thinking, including health care. Jurgen Habermas extended the idea of Lifeworld, making our application to the world of the palliative care nurse useful. In short, the Lifeworld includes the entire backdrop of a patient/family life including their communication, their culturally based understanding, and their language patterns (Habermas, 1987). These are the elements of everyday life that define their reality and create their horizon. This is what they know. This is a patient's or family's specific spin on what is likely a *blend* of cultural competencies.

It makes sense that patients understand their health according to the context of life most familiar to them—*their* everyday life. By extreme contrast, and another way of thinking of the culture of health care, is what Mishler identifies as the Voice of Medicine (Mishler, 1981,1984). Patients and families speak the Voice of the Lifeworld and relate end of life to ways in which this will affect their day-to-day life. In terms of practical differences, patients cite feelings more often than precise empirical data and experience the global impact of illness on their life instead of identifying specific and measured segments of poor health impact. The fallout from illness on day-to-day living is how patients experience loss and stress. For example, a patient who learns that he can no longer drive as a result of amyotrophic lateral sclerosis (ALS) is concerned with the loss in no longer driving his teenage children to soccer meets and fishing tournaments.

Processing loss of a healthy body must include the contagion of life experiences and people who are affected, not just the patient's own practical loss of function. Diffusion becomes a way of processing changes in the Lifeworld for a patient. While it can be frustrating for a clinician who has a great need to impart specific information in order to maintain a particular treatment plan, a patient's losses are many times indirect and less obvious to someone approaching the illness from the Medicalworld lens.

Valuing the Lifeworld of the patient/family better positions the nurse to support integrated patient participation, as well as the humanizing focus central to palliative care. The nurse is positioned uniquely to straddle the two Voices of the Lifeworld and Medicine. One voice interprets the disease in its broadest context, while the other is a voice of reduction. The nurse can weave these two voices together to accomplish what we describe in Chapters 2 and 3 as the coexistence of task and relational communication.

DEVELOPING CLINICAL PRACTICE SKILLS

In this chapter we describe the role the nurse plays in helping patients/families gain access to information and making care decisions. We offer a variety of tools in the clinical context while employing the ideas of assumed low health literacy and cultural humility in the practice of palliative nursing care. The following section will be organized using the primary categories for nursing intervention: assessing, planning, intervening, and evaluating. The materials included here should useful as nurses expand their skill set to include the convergent components of orientation and opportunity.

ASSESS

George, from our opening case study, has troubling concerns that patients in his center might be engaging in a cycle of treatment that will ultimately lower their quality of life at the end of life. At the heart of his angst is the realization that communicating about treatment options and care plans are not a regular part of care for the majority of patients on dialysis. In the case we share, he worries for Lanz. George has not identified the time or the manner in which to talk with Lanz about his care options, or how he and his family might feel about those options in light of their cultural orientation and family structure. Even more difficult, George does not know what Lanz understands about his current dialysis care and his overall disease trajectory. He is sensitive to Lanz's age, his rich Italian-American culture, and their shared patient–nurse relationship.

Multiple assessment tools for patients currently exist. It is important to keep in mind that the palliative care setting is unique in terms of the potential for patient weakness and even unconsciousness. For this reason, the family must be considered central not only in health literacy matters but also cultural humility practice. Interactions to secure health literacy will more often than not include family and might well include patients who cannot respond. Though several tools now exists to assess health literacy, few are available in multiple languages, are simple to employ, facilitate the workload of nurses, or increase satisfaction for the nurse and the client(s) (Wallace, 2004).

Remember, health literacy is not limited to reading alone, but also writing, listening, speaking, numeracy skills, critical thinking, decision making, and cultural sensitivity abilities (i.e., crossing over to the world of medicine/health care) (Singleton & Krause, 2009). The connection between literacy and culture is inextricable. What patients/families face in the Voice of Medicine explains a great deal of the health literacy load in addition to cultural barriers that can reduce success in care. Often there is a simple overestimation of patient/family ability to absorb terminology (i.e., aural literacy demand), make sense of rare words, or stay focused in the midst of words and ideas that invite worry and anxiety (i.e., "The doctor noted a new mass on your skull. Had you felt any headaches or other new symptoms?") (Koch-Weser, Rudd, & DeJong, 2010).

Many assessment tests are geared for English speakers and readers, which already assumes too much about a patient/family. In a recent study of English-speaking Americans who predominantly possessed their high school diplomas, nearly half of them indicated discomfort in taking either the REALM (Rapid Estimate of Adult Literacy in Medicine) or the s-TOHFLA (short Test of Functional Health Literacy in

Table 3.2 Checklist of Observable Cues Indicating a Need for Health Literacy and/or Cultural Accommodation

Does patient/family display a disinterest in reading a form/instructions? "I'm too tired for this." "I need my glasses for this."	y/n
Is it hard for the patient/family to locate a central focus on the text?	y/n
Have answers such as "no" been provided to questions asking for more information or a description?	y/n
Is there a general state of withdraw from the interaction? High nervousness? Confusion?	y/n
Have there been errors in medication, appointment times, treatment understanding?	y/n
In a shame-free environment that encourages the patient/family to share information, is the patient/family difficult to engage? Offended? Irritable?	y/n
Behavior from patient/family demonstrates that information is being withheld.	y/n

Adults) (Ferguson, Lowman, & DeWalt, 2011). Many scholars warn of the stigmatizing effect of a literacy test for patients when they are already facing frightening news, changing circumstances, and a culture of medicine that is foreign to their Lifeworld. There is fair evidence that suggests the possible harm of literacy testing outweighs the benefits of such testing (Paasche-Orlow & Wolf, 2007). Shame and alienation can take the place of the best intentions to converge, or find common ground with a patient. An additional challenge lies in the sometimes expert ability of patients and families to conceal their confusion or lack of understanding so that it can be impossible to know there is a lack of health literacy, or perhaps this occurs quite unintentionally as this has been a survival technique (Cornett, 2009). And so for these complex reasons, the clinical skills practice recommendations we make to support orientation and opportunity showcase accommodation in communication through cultural humility and low–health literacy assumptions.

Simple observations can tell the practitioner something about patient/family health literacy. Even if observations do not specify the communication challenge to be one of culture or health literacy, it suggests that further investigation is needed. Table 3.2 is a basic list of *clues* that might indicate an existing barrier in communication.

Targeted questions about communication are a good way to assess how the patient/family are processing information, the environment, and their treatment choices. Table 3.3 presents researched questions, or prompts, that can quickly identify comprehension and engagement (to a degree) between patient and nurse, but could also be used between family and nurse.

COMFORT advocates for narrative care, in which the nurse is mindful of the patient/family, and privileges their experience and concern. While the previous two assessment items are proven to identify language deficits in health literacy, the following tools also attend to the special challenges of cultural humility and Lifeworld discernment in palliative care.

Table 3.3 Suggested Communication Strategies

Clinical Communication	Study	Benefits	Drawbacks
- How often do you have someone help you read hospital materials? - How confident are you filling out our forms alone? - How often do you have problems learning about your illness because of difficulty understanding information about it?	Chew, L., Bradley, K., & Boyko, E. (2004). Brief questions to identify patients with inadequate health literacy. *Family Medicine, 36,* 588–594.	- Rapid collection of feedback - Practitioner administered—can lead to more communication about accommodation	- Questions are worded at a high level of literacy.
- How often do you need to have someone help you when you read instructions, pamphlets, or other written material from us?	Morris, N., MacLean, C., Chew, L., and Littenberg, B. (2006). The Single Item Literacy Screener: Evaluation of a brief instrument to identify limited reading ability. *BMC Family Practice, 7*(21). doi:10.1186/1471–2296-7-21 http://www.biomedcentral.com/content/pdf/1471–2296-7-21.pdf	- Rapid collection of feedback - Practitioner administered—can lead to more communication about accommodation	- Questions are worded at a high level of literacy.

Table 3.4 Questions Specific to Palliative Care Topic for Patient and/or Family

- How can we help you live in the best way possible for you?
- How would you like to spend your time together?
- What experiences are most important or meaningful for you?
- What fears or worries do you have about this illness?
- Do you have other worries or fears?
- What do you hope for your family?
- What kinds of needs does your family have?
- What is the hardest thing in your life right now?
- What religious or spiritual beliefs are important to you?
- What would make this time in your life (lives) meaningful?
- What makes life worthwhile?
- What kinds of medical care are unacceptable to you?

Excerpted and adapted from Dahlin, C. (2010). Communication in palliative care: An essential competency for nurses. In B. Ferrell, & N. Coyle (Eds.), *The Oxford Textbook of Palliative Nursing* (3rd ed., pp. 107–133). New York: Oxford University Press.

Table 3.5 Questions Specific to Cultural Difference

- Tell me more about you/your family.
- Where were you born and raised?
- What language would you prefer to speak?
- Where do you go for support (family, friends, church, etc.)?
- Would you like to have anyone else here with you/your family?
- Who do you want to know about your illness? Who is okay to talk with?
- How does your family make health decisions? Should I talk to you about decisions? Or someone else?
- We want to take the best care of you that we can. What do we need to know about any customs, practices, family rituals, etc., that are important to include in your care?
- Is spirituality or religion, or both, important to include in your care? What would that look like?
- We want to make sure we respect how you want to be addressed/named, including how we act when addressing you.
- Do you have a preference for a male or female caregiver?
- Do you have any foods you would especially enjoy, or that you especially like to avoid?
- Do you have any worries about how to pay for care or your medicine or care once you go home?

Culturally Sensitive Questions Specific to Dying

- Are there any ceremonies or rituals after death you would like us to know about and facilitate?
- What is your sense of what happens after death?
- Can we help in planning for anything you might need at death or after?
- In your family/background, do family members participate in the care of the body after death?
- Do we need to specify a man or a woman caring for you/yours after death?

Excerpted and adapted from Mazanec, P., & Panke, J., (2010). Cultural considerations in palliative care. In B. Ferrell, & N. Coyle (Eds.), *The Oxford Textbook of Palliative Nursing* (pp. 701–711). New York: Oxford University Press.

A culture-specific set of prompts that attends to ways in which a clinical team can accommodate difference is useful in achieving convergence with a patient/family and also builds shared meaning with them (Tables 3.4 & 3.5). These prompts also clarify if there will be a need for an interpreter to share the spoken word.

PLAN

Even one of the above assessment prompts could have been the opening to a conversation between George and Lanz. Based on information gathered, George could have identified a useful plan of action that would lead to the best care plan for Lanz at the end of his life. Once a nurse gains an understanding of the patient and family through observing cues and exploring their Lifeworld through specific questions, a fairly grounded sense of health literacy as well as cultural specificity can be discovered. Based on the nurse's interaction, which is most productive if it avoids a checklist of traits and invokes instead curious inquiry that facilitates storytelling and learning about the values important to a patient, she or he will be prepared to identify a basic plan to move forward in securing orientation and opportunity for this patient/family. Communication accommodation through convergence will be possible.

Identifying what to plan for a patient and family is the next step. Selecting areas of need on the checklist below (Table 3.6) will assist in determining what kinds of interventions might best suit a nurse and patient/family.

The nurse should anticipate multicultural identities, not simply a cultural code that aligns with a list of cultural group descriptors. A patient/family might appear to be the same ethnicity as the nurse—even from the same place. But expect the unknown, and the nurse should avail her or himself to this opportunity to be taught about these unique individuals. Because of this, inviting the patient/family into the planning process will be beneficial to the practice of palliative care. We suggest the following question as part of any planning process:

As I participate in your care, can you think of some specific things that would make you more comfortable with the information we are talking about? Or make the information more clear?

Identifying concerns that need to be addressed and how to plan for the best care as the nurse moves forward beyond assessment will help create the most useful intervention. These points of awareness will also advance the application of communication accommodation directly to and for the patient in palliative care by providing tailored and patient-specific convergence to increase nurse–patient message success.

Table 3.6 Planning for Low Health Literacy and Cultural Humility Intervention

✓ Reading or vision deficit	✓ Memory or cognitive deficit
- Clear speech	- Repeat and question
- Well-described examples	- Multiple message channels
- "Living room" language	
✓ Medical culture divide	✓ Hearing deficit
- Examples from Lifeworld	- Create visual message channels
- Elicit stories from Lifeworld	- Employ interpreter and family support
- Open-ended opportunities for talk	to clarify messages
✓ Language difference	✓ Pain (emotional/physician/social/spiritual)
- Translator	Compromise
- Language-appropriate materials	- Team members
	- Open-ended opportunities for talk

INTERVENE

A potential intervention for Lanz might have involved George arranging a time to talk with Lanz and his sister and niece during the last visit to the Dialysis Center. This conversation might have led to George's coordination efforts of care for Lanz, including a visit from a social worker, subsequent advance directive, and a more peaceful death with fewer extreme medical interventions in his last days of life. Lanz was clearly tired of his dialysis treatment the day of his last visit. George, in reflection, regrets their lack of discussion about quality of life. They shared trust and care over time, but never the planning conversations that could also have accompanied that close patient–nurse dynamic.

Table 3.7 Communication Interventions

Aspect of This Intervention	Goal of This Kind of Communication	Example
Partnership communication style	Build trust and openness.	*Let patient/family decide when teaching session should be—best time of day.*
Nurse values patient/family agenda.	Facilitate disclosure.	*"I want to hear about the concerns that are important to each one of you."*
Nurse values biopychosocial perspective.	Learn about Lifeworld of patient and family.	*Take a few minutes to ask about family outside of the hospital/clinic.*
Not a static notion of culture competence	Commit to learning about the specifics of this patient/family.	*Listen to/ask about a typical day in wellness. Ask more questions. And then more.*
Clear pathway created for patient telling/family telling of illness or wellness story	Create opportunities for narrative sharing.	*Listen. Take time. Be aware of the message you might send that indicates you don't have the time.*
Nurse relinquishes the role of expert, becoming student of the patient/family.	Establish person-centeredness and build a relationship.	*Learn from patient/family about what they think is important. This will guide your care.*
Expression that patient and family are full partners in care alliance	Empower patient and family.	- *"We are in this together."* - *"Thank you for teaching me."* - *"You help me understand."*

Aspects of intervention adapted from Tervalon, M., & Murray-Garcia, J. (1998). Cultural humility versus cultural competence: A critical distinction in defining physician-training outcomes in multicultural education. *Journal of Health Care for the Poor and Underserved, 9,* 117–125.

The clinical skill intervention we want to detail first in this section is one that might accompany or supersede other interventions simply because it is also a way of practicing that coincides with the primary concern of this chapter. **Person-centered** interviewing and care are an extension of the ideas we describe in Chapter 2. But here we also apply the idea of cultural humility to person-centeredness. Listed above are basic components of this kind of interviewing (Table 3.7). Communication is the kind of care that provides the comfort here.

Communicating comfort can be the intervention. As we describe in Chapter 2, person-centered messages are built verbally and nonverbally. Table 3.7 reflects this idea.

Table 3.8 presents a wide variety of interventions that the nurse might pursue depending on the needs noted during assessment and planning.

Failing to communicate with a patient/family because of low health literacy and/or cultural differences is costly and contributes to burnout and high time costs later in the course of care (Geller, Bernhardt, Carrese, Rushton, & Kolodner, 2008). By combining basic interventions with person-centered communication, palliative care nurses *can* break through barriers of low health literacy and cultural unfamiliarity and perform meaningful care on behalf of their patients.

Consider the following example:

Mr. Gomez was a 60-year-old, very stoic man who was diagnosed with late-stage pancreatic cancer. Unfortunately, Mr. Gomez had extensive disease including liver and renal involvement at diagnosis. He and his family were presented options for chemotherapy, but they have declined treatment. His wife and children are also very stoic and private. A social worker has now discussed discharge and has suggested referral to hospice. Mr. Gomez and his family adamantly decline hospice. His wife is silent but shakes her head "no," a daughter utters "no way," Mr. Gomez becomes tearful, and his eldest son speaks up to say, "No thank you. No hospice. We can take care of our father." The social worker shares this information with the primary nurse, who is very concerned about this patient and family going home alone as Mr. Gomez has extensive pain and other symptoms and she expects he will decline rapidly. The nurse goes to the patient's room and asks if she can talk with the family.

She begins the conversation by saying; "I wanted to talk with you all as we plan to get you home tomorrow, Mr. Gomez. The social worker shared with me that you were not interested in having Hospice come out to see you. I have noticed what a wonderful caring family you are and that you all want to provide the best care for your father. We have found that hospice can be so helpful to patients and families like yours. I am wondering if you can tell me more about why you are reluctant to have hospice come to visit you at home?"

Note that in this nurse intervention, the nurse shows convergence by communicating her observations of their family. Additionally, this nurse provides understanding of who can be helped by hospice. In order to show humility toward this family and understand their concerns and needs, the nurse asks them about their reluctance.

Table 3.8 Communication Strategies

Need	Intervention	Example
Message accommodation	Living room language - Speak simply. - Remove medicalization of description. - Keep content practical but not so oversimplified that patient is bored or offended.	*"If your legs swell, we need to check for a blockage in the deep veins of your legs."* As opposed to: *"There is a possibility of deep vein thrombosis. If we suspect this, we will perform a doplar."*
	Repetition - Describe idea a second and third time. - Use a different example if first one seems to fail.	*"It would be important for the three of you to talk about where you want Jill to spend the last part of her life."* *"Today is the right time to make some decisions about where you would like Jill to be."* *"Would it help to have the social worker come around this afternoon to talk with the three of you about deciding where Jill will go for the rest of her care"?*
	Appropriately gauged examples - Consider what you know about the patient as you provide information. - Make examples patient specific, patient relevant, and gauged to their social structure. - Use ideas and words that are familiar.	For a person that loves to cook: *"The amount that Dr. X has prescribed is about as much as 2 tablespoons a day."*
Improving patient/family education	Question - Allow time for follow-up questions. - Facilitate patient/family question asking.	*"What do you think about this? I'd like to hear your questions. I know this can be a foreign idea."*
	Codemonstrations - Go through a care process together with the patient or family member. - Do it together, with nurse playing a part in the process.	*"I will sterilize the catheter first. Now you take over and try the next part. If you get stuck I am right here."*
	Return demonstrations - A volley - Nurse shows, then patient or family shows how to accomplish something.	*"Do you feel like you can show me the first step now that I have shown you?"* *"Once we are all feeling confident, we can go on to the next part."*

(continued)

Table 3.8 (*continued*)

Need	Intervention	Example
	Patient/family teaches nurse. - Once the process is shown and explained, the nurse plays the role of the student. - Let the family or patient teach nurse the process and execution.	*Now, can you teach me to organize these three medications for the day? Pretend you are the nurse and I am trying to learn about these medications."*
	Images - Visuals should represent this population in a positive way. - Avoid stereotypic drawings or situations that are not relevant. - Images are always best accompanied with the spoken word for reinforcement.	*Create simple images on site, or find some already created art to help the patient/family that is struggling for clarity with complicated instructions or a substantial language barrier.* *For example, an African American family who is very hesitant to accept hospice may be best supported by a video or brochure illustrating examples of other African American families who have received hospice care.*
	Watch video recording together. - A tape can be intermittently stopped to clarify or elaborate. - A video recording can be intermittently stopped by patient/family to ask questions or talk about concerns.	*A film on advance directive or the story of ALS outcomes can help a patient/family understand what is ahead for them.* *Watching it together will help them to process it with the nurse, as well as create an additional connection with the nurse.*
	Send video recording home. - Patient/family will process information differently. - Access to this visual/audio is immensely helpful to patient/family in navigating new ideas.	*Patient and family might find it useful to share this with others to help them communicate about their illness, or to simply revisit some ideas that are hard to face or understand.*
	Audio record your meeting. - This can serve as a record for the patient/family to consult for reminders/clarity. - Varying levels of information processing make this a helpful tool in patient education.	*Family members hear and retain information differently. This record of a visit with a nurse can be of support in making home care decisions.*

(*continued*)

Table 3.8 (*continued*)

Need	Intervention	Example
Support needed	Interpreter - Request a team member who can facilitate communication between languages. - Look at the patient or family member when talking, not the interpreter.	*Use for patient communication or family communication.* *Shared fluency can create immediate allegiance.*
	Chaplain - Rely on chaplaincy support to help with religious and spiritual questions and concerns.	*"I can talk to you about my own religious experiences, but I think that our chaplain might be of great help as you work through these questions."* *"It is perfectly normal to have these questions, by the way."*
	Social Worker - Rely on social work support to help with navigating place of care, family conflict, and difficult transitions.	*"We have a palliative care team here to address your concerns. The team is wonderful in addressing symptoms and emotions common for patients and families facing similar problems. I work with them every day."*
	Psychologist - Rely on psychology support to help patient/family with depression, anxiety, and general emotional distress in palliative care.	*"I can see you are so anxious about your Dad. Would you be willing to talk with Steve? He works with the palliative care team. He is a psychologist."*
	Organ donor coordinator (ODC) - Rely on ODC, and talk to patient and family with ODC about donor concerns and questions. - Nurse can facilitate this conversation concerning cultural knowledge.	*"This is a really wonderful thing you are thinking about. Bill is our organ donor coordinator. He can answer some questions—much better than I can. And then you will better positioned to make a decision."* *"I can talk with Bill to help him get a sense of your family."*
	Billing specialist - Rely on a clinic or hospital financial specialist to help patient/family navigate cost and coverage. - Nurse can facilitate this conversation concerning cultural and literacy knowledge.	*"These worries about money are large and looming for you. I know. Can I invite Jane to come talk with you two and myself this afternoon about your Medicare coverage? She will know things I don't know, and I can help her get a sense of your family."*

(*continued*)

Table 3.8 (*continued*)

Need	Intervention	Example
Message processing	Teach back - Intermittently have patient participate in paraphrasing ideas that were discussed - Request that patient recall the highpoints of conversation. - Ask patient to summarize the goals of the talk	*"I wonder if you could relay the basic schedule of dosage for your Mom?"* *"What are the main things you will want to do in talking with your sister about the advance directive?"*
	Printed material clarity - Reinforcement in text - Large print - High contrast between text color and paper color - List format/bullets	*Specific directions, concrete terms, direct examples, visually clear (see plain language resources for printed material at end of chapter)*

Principally, whatever intervention a nurse selects, the patient and then family should be considered. Patient/family anxiety, stressors, embarrassment, shame, language, eyesight, hearing, mental health, and confusion should be your guide. Timing for these interventions is also important. If the morning is harder for this family, work with them at a different time. Or if a patient is too sick, unresponsive, or has just been given very bad news, gauge what information must be passed on to his or her family.

EVALUATE

Without any intervention, George is left with the heavy emotional toll of regret and worry. What about his other patients? What can he do for them? What should he do for them? Palliative care nursing is communication heavy in its task/relational load. Patients and families as well as professional teammates are the best barometer for evaluation of intervention and care. Without reflecting on care and communication, clinicians will learn little and grow less in their ability to deal with difficult cases and cultural specificities that have not been experienced before. Reflection is the most valuable part of evaluation in palliative care. Cultural humility, mindfulness (Chapter 4), teamwork (Chapter 8), and self-care (Chapter 9) are accomplished, in part, through reflection.

Each nurse will have his or her own experience with the care of a patient and family and will learn from that unique relationship. It is important to find out from patients and families about their experiences accessing information and treatment options. To

Table 3.9 Prompts to Elicit Feedback

Tool	Given to ...	In What Form?
"Let me know in your own words if I am doing an okay job."	- Patient - Family - Team	- Spoken
"How would you explain your treatment (or care) to your friends?"	- Patient - Family	- Spoken - Written
"How would you explain your (this) illness to your friends?"	- Patient - Family	- Spoken - Written

gain this information, ask questions at any point in their care, or even once patient/family care is complete. Table 3.9 provides some specific prompts that can provide palliative care nursing feedback.

CHAPTER SUMMARY

Orientation and opportunity are provisions of care that a nurse can provide and impact, primarily through successfully created and sent messages. It is difficult to be successful in sending messages to a patient and family if they remain unstudied to the nurse. Our position in this chapter is that all patient/family health literacy levels and cultural differences must not be essentialized or assumed based on appearance or ethnicity.

Communication accommodation theory (CAT) grounds the themes in this chapter and therefore is a very useful foundation as nurses consider all patients and families unique in their (1) cultural specificity, and (2) health literacy challenges. CAT includes three categories of accommodation that occur in all interactions. Convergence is accommodation characterized by aligning and adapting communication acts that are beneficial to the interaction and relationship.

The unique world of health care establishes a culture of medicalization that any patient must navigate. We present the Voice of the patient's everyday Lifeworld in juxtaposition to the Voice of the Medicalworld. Both Voices represent radically different perspectives on a topic, or description of a problem. This difference in Voices is a cultural challenge in and of itself.

So how can nurses communicate using convergence in the face of these unique patient/family needs? This chapter advocates that person-centered interaction that privileges the narrative of the patient/family is the primary tool to accomplish convergence. We include several assessment, planning, intervention, and evaluation tools that will facilitate nurses to reach that narrative and employ its contents in reaching the patient/family where they are in the health literacy levels and cultural understanding. Reflection plays a helpful role for the nurse in building patient/family-centered communication. This idea will be further explored in Chapter 4—"Mindful Presence."

REFERENCES

Aronson, E., Blaney, N., Stephin, C., Sikes, J., & Snapp, M. (1978). *The Jigsaw Classroom.* Beverly Hills, CA: Sage Publishing Company.

Chew, L., Bradley, K., & Boyko, E. (2004). Brief questions to identify patients with inadequate health literacy. *Family Medicine, 36,* 588–594.

Cornett, S. (2009). Assessing and addressing health literacy. *Online Journal of Issues in Nursing, 14*(3), Manuscript 2.

Dahlin, C. (2010). Communication in palliative care: An essential competency for nurses. In B. Ferrell & N. Coyle (Eds.), *Oxford Textbook of Palliative Nursing* (3rd ed., pp. 107–133). New York: Oxford University Press.

DuPre, A. (2010). *Communicating About Health: Current Issues and Perspectives* (3rd ed.). New York: Oxford University Press.

Ferguson, B., Lowman, S., & DeWalt, D. (2011). Assessing ltieracy in clinical and community settings: The patient perspective. *Journal of Health Communication, 16,* 124–134. doi: 10.1080/10810730.2010.535113

Flaskerud, J. (2007). Cultural competency: What is it? *Issues in Mental Health Nursing, 28,* 121–123. doi: 10.1080/01612840600998154

Geller, G., Bernhardt, B., Carrese, J., Rushton, C., & Kolodner, K. (2008). What do clinicians derive from partnering with their patients? Reliable and valid measures of "personal meaning in patient care." *Patient Education and Counseling, 72,* 293–300.

Giles, H. (2008). Communication accommodation theory. In L. A. Baxter & D. O. Braithwaite (Eds.), *Engaging Theories in Interpersonal Communication* (pp. 161–174). Los Angeles: Sage.

Guerrero, L., & Floyd, K. (2006). *Nonverbal Communication in Relationships.* Mahwah, NJ: Lawrence Erlbaum.

Gunaratnam, Y. (2007). Intercultural palliative care: Do we need cultural competence? *International Journal of Palliative Nursing, 13,* 470–477.

Habermas, J. (1987). *The Theory of Communicative Action: Lifeworld and System. A Critique of Functionalism and Reason* (T. McCarthy, Trans., Vol. 2). Boston: Beacon Press.

Jones, M., Cason, C., & Bond, M. (2004). Cultural attitudes, knowledge, and skill of a health workforce. *Journal of Transcultural Nursing, 15,* 283–290.

Koch-Weser, S., Rudd, R., & DeJong, W. (2010). Quantifiying word use to study health literacy in doctor-patient communication. *Journal of Health Communication, 15,* 590–602. doi: 10.1080/10810730.2010.499592

Kutner, M., Greenberg, E., Jin, Y., Boyle, B., Hsu, Y., & Dunleavy, E. (2007). *Literacy in Everyday Life: Results From the 2003 National Assessment of Adult Literacy (NCES 2007–480).* Washington, DC: US Department of Education, National Center for Education Statistics.

Mancuso, J. (2009). Assessment and measurement of health literacy: An integrative review of the literature. *Nursing Health and Science, 11,* 77–89. doi: 10.1111/j.1442-2018.2008.00408

Mazanec, P., & Panke, J., (2010). Cultural considerations in palliative care. In B. Ferrell, & N. Coyle (Eds.), *The Oxford Textbook of Palliative Nursing* (pp. 701–711). New York: Oxford University Press.

Mishler, E. (1981). The social construction of illness. In S. D. Osherson, S. T. Hauser, & R. Leim (Eds.), *Social Contexts of Health, Illness, and Patient Care* (pp. 141–168). Cambridge, UK: Cambridge University Press.

Mishler, E. (1984). *The Discourse of Medicine: Dialectics of Medical Interviews.* Norwood, NJ: Ablex.

Morris, N. S., MacLean, C. D., Chew, L. D., & Littenberg, B. (2006). The Single Item Literacy Screener: Evaluation of a brief instrument to identify limited reading ability. *BMC Family Practice, 7*(21). doi:10.1186/1471–2296–7-21 http://www.biomedcentral.com/content/pdf/1471–2296–7-21.pdf

Nyatanga, B. (2008). Cultural competence: A noble idea in a changing world. *International Journal of Palliative Nursing, 14,* 315.

Paasche-Orlow, M., & Wolf, M. (2007). Evidence does not support clinical screening of literacy. *Journal of General Internal Medicine, 23,* 100–102.

Ruccione, K. (2004). Coming to terms with language. *Oncology Nursing Forum, 31,* 913–925.

Santiago-Irizarry, V. (1996). Culture as cure. *Cultural Anthropology, 11,* 3–24.

Saunders, C., & Bains, M. (1983). *Living With Dying: The Management of Terminal Disease.* Oxford: Oxford University Press.

Singleton, K., & Krause, E. (2009). Understanding cultural and linguistic barriers to health literacy. *Online Journal of Issues in Nursing, 14*(3), Manuscript 4.

Slade, D., Thomas-Connor, I., & Tsao, T. (2008). When nursing meets English: Using a pathography to develop nursing students' culturally competent selves. *Nursing Education Perspectives, 29,* 151–155.

Speros, C. (2009). More than words: Promoting health literacy in older adults. *Online Journal of Issues in Nursing, 14,* Manuscript 5.

Tervalon, M., & Murray-Garcia, J. (1998). Cultural humility versus cultural competence: A critical distinction in defining physician training outcomes in multicultural education. *Journal of Health Care for the Poor and Underserved, 9,* 117–125.

U.S. Department of Health and Human Services, Office of Disease Prevention and Health. (2010). *National Action Plan to Improve Health Literacy.* Washington, DC: Author.

Vernon, J. A., Trujillo, A., Rosenbaum, S., & DeBuono, B. (2007). *Low health literacy: Implications for national policy.* Retrieved November 30, 2008, from http://www.gwumc.edu/sphhs/departments/healthpolicy/chpr/downloads/LowHealthLiteracyReport10_4_07.pdf

Wallace, M. (2004). An application of health literacy research. *Applied Nursing Journal, 17,* 61–64.

Weiss, B., & Palmer, R. (2004). Relationship between health care costs and very low literacy skills in the medically needy and indigent Medicaid population. *Journal of the American Board of Family Practice, 17,* 44–47.

West, R., & Turner, L. (2010). *Introduction to Communication Theory: Analysis and Application.* Boston: McGraw-Hill.

Additional Supplemental References

Berkman, N., Davis, T., & McCormack, L. (2010). Health literacy: What is it? *Journal of Health Communication, 15,* 9–19. doi: 10.1080/10810730.2010.499985

Clayman, M., Pandit, A., Bergeron, A., Cameron, K., Ross, E. & Wolf, M. (2010). Ask, understand, remember: A brief measure of patient communication self-efficacy within clinical encounters. *Journal of Health Communication, 15,* 72–79. doi: 10.1080/10810730.2010.500349

Doak, C., Doak, L., & Root, J. (1996). *Teaching Patients With Low Literacy Skills* (2nd ed.). New York: Lippincott, Williams, & Wilkins.

Huang, Y., Yates, P., & Prior, D. (2009). Factors influencing oncology nurses' approaches to accommodating cultural needs in palliative care. *Journal of Clinical Nursing, 18,* 3421–3429. doi:10.1111/j.1365–2702.2009.02938.x

Mancuso, J. (2008). Health literacy: A concept/dimensional analysis. *Nursing and Health Sciences, 10,* 248–255. doi: 10.1111/j.1442–2-18.2008.00394.x

Mayer, G., & Villaire, M. (2007). *Health Literacy in Primary Care: A Clinician's Guide.* New York: Springer.

Tervalon, M. (2003). Components of culture in health for medical students' education. *Academic Medicine, 76,* 570–576.

Wynia, M., & Osborn, C. (2010). Health literacy and communication quality in health care organizations. *Journal of Health Communication, 15,* 102–115. doi: 10.1080.10810730.2010.499981.

DISCUSSION QUESTIONS

1. Name a negative communication outcome in the clinic/hospital that could have been prevented if culture had been approached with humility.
2. Share an example of the dueling discourses of the Lifeworld and Medicalworld from a patient/family interaction.
3. If a patient met with a nurse alone (no family) about what symptoms to expect in a very aggressive round of chemotherapy for Stage IV liver cancer and appeared not to be engaging any patient education material about preparation and side effects, what could a nurse do to ensure the messages being sent are actually successful?
4. What is the difference between cultural competency and cultural humility?
5. Share an example of overaccommodation from the clinical setting.
6. How can divergent messages alienate a patient and family receiving care?
7. How could the ideas of orientation and opportunity be central to quality of life in a patient/family receiving palliative care?
8. What is the role of reflection in gathering a patient/family narrative?
9. What are some ways in which nurses could teach nurses about cultural humility?
10. How is it possible that an individual who does not fit the low–health literacy profile (socioeconomic/minority/age) could experience low health literacy in the palliative care context?

TEACHING RESOURCES AND MATERIALS

Each day nurses practice in an increasingly diverse patient population in which they will encounter language, culture, and health literacy challenges. The literature in nursing care indicates that cultural and low-literacy challenges are joined inextricably, yet nursing education and training provide minimal assistance for nurses to navigate these challenges (Singleton & Krause, 2009). There is no other practitioner as well positioned as the nurse to understand the interconnections between culture differences and low health literacy to improve health outcomes.

What we also observe in the literature is a gap in any resource or research that explores the family role in culture difference and low health literacy as it affects palliative care communication. In this section we provide some materials to use with nurses in training that will address these issues and others identified in the chapter.

EXERCISE 1: COMMUNICATION ACCOMMODATION THEORY ROLE PLAY

The goal of the role play is to practice **convergence** with this patient and family and avoid **divergence** or **overaccomodation**.

Setting: A Mexican-American family. Three daughters in their 60s. The father is deceased. The mother is dwindling and failing to thrive. She is 82 with increased frailty and weighs 78 pounds. There is no advance directive. The patient's physician has said that she is declining rapidly, and he anticipates she likely has a few months to live. She has been at the eldest daughter's home until the night previous to this meeting and is now hospitalized due to dehydration. The other two daughters are also local. All three daughters are bilingual. The two younger daughters have large families. The oldest daughter cannot care for her mother any longer due to financial strain and exhaustion. The two younger daughters have not been active in her care and have not seen her very often during the last 3 months. The youngest daughter, in particular, believes the oldest daughter has not been feeding their mother well and that this illness is short-term and can be rectified with proper nutrition. The mother, Rosa, is not an active participant in making decisions about her own care and is now becoming increasingly withdrawn with little verbal interaction.

Pat, an NP, comes by in the morning to see Rosa. She finds all three daughters in the room and is the first practitioner to encounter the full family on site. Pat speaks very little Spanish. The NP and social worker are hoping to help the family make discharge plans.

Roles: Pat—NP
Lou—Oldest Daughter

Ella—Middle Daughter
CiCi—Youngest Daughter

Discussion Questions

1. What are some cultural assumptions about the Mexican-American family that this family did not possess or demonstrate?
2. How did our NP go about gaining information about their specific story and potential health literacy levels?
3. How did our NP demonstrate convergence? Divergence? Overaccomodation?

EXERCISE 2: LOW–HEALTH LITERACY SOLUTIONS

In the following case, nurses can connect the dots from the preceding pages/topics as they understand specific patient experience within the domain of navigating clinical health literacy in palliative care.

Boka, a 30-year-old Cambodian woman who had just come to the United States, and her husband Leng, a 40-year-old Cambodian refugee who had been living in the United States for 15 years, were expecting their first child. The obstetrician informed them that their baby's heart rate was very irregular, and he suspected possible problems. Boka went into early labor and delivered at 25 weeks.

Boka and Leng's baby was placed in the NICU (neonatal intensive care unit) and they were told that the infant would not survive. A NICU nurse drew a picture of the heart with its chambers and valves to try to explain the cardiac defect to the couple. Leng was shocked, stating that he could not believe the heart could not be repaired in such a major hospital in America.

Boka and Leng did not request an interpreter and were reluctant to ask questions of their care providers. Boka and Leng were semiliterate in their country and had been raised in a family-oriented culture and were not familiar with a health care system in which families participated in care decisions. They struggled to understand their child's serious heart problem and early arrival. Their exposure to physicians and nurses in Cambodia had been limited. The felt truly lost without their family around to help them make these impossible health decisions.

Discussion Questions

1. Do Boka and Leng understand what is happening to their child?
2. What sorts of assessments should have been gathered early on in the care of Boka?
3. What kinds of planning and intervention might have been effective with this family?
4. At what point might a nurse request a palliative care team consult or other support for this family?

EXERCISE 3: MORE THAN A CASE: PATHOGRAPHY IN THE NURSING CLASSROOM

This project uses literature and the *story of illness* to teach the practice of palliative nursing as well as navigate the challenges of low health literacy and/or cultural challenges. The use of fictional and autobiographical literature is proven to be meaningful in nursing training in helping nurses identify and develop self-esteem, critical thinking, reflective skills, and competence in dealing with situations of low health literacy and cultural difference (Slade, Thomas-Connor, & Tsao, 2008).

This pathography is best used if it follows combination learning on health literacy/ low health literacy that employs role play, lecture, and a group research paper.

We suggest the following works to locate pathographies for this class project:

Davis, C., & Shaefer, J (1995). *Between the Heartbeats: Poetry and Prose by Nurses*. Iowa City: University of Iowa Press.

Sergi, P., & Gorman, G. (2009). A *Call to Nursing: Nurses' Stories About Challenge and Commitment*. New York: Kaplan Publishing.

Shalof, T. (2004). *A Nurse's Story*. Toronto: The Canadian Publishers.

Romm, R. (2010). *The Mercy Papers: A Memoir of Three Weeks*. New York: Scribner.

The stages of this assignment are as follows. First, students will read the story assigned and individually identify literacy and/or cultural issues at work in the text. Second, students will gather in small groups and engage the study questions that the educator should tailor for the piece read. These small groups then should join into one body for a group discussion of themes identified in the smaller groups. Third and finally, students will select one of the study questions and develop a short patient/family assessment essay.

Sample study questions for More Than a Case:

1. Who tells the story? Who tells the story of the protagonist? To whom is the story told? What insights, biases, and limits does the narrator have?
2. How do you as a nurse assess the main character?
3. Your assessment should address the following:
a. Language
b. The characters' self-esteem during care
c. Strengths and weaknesses in advocating for care
d. If you were the nurse in the story, would you do anything differently to address the needs of _____? To better intervene between the family and the doctor? What would be your difficulties?

More than a Case concept adapted from Slade, D., Thomas-Connor, I., & Tsao, T. (2008). Using pathography to develop nursing students' culturally competent selves. *Nursing Education Perspective*, *19*, 151–155.

EXERCISE 4: UNFOLDING CASE REFLECTION

This classroom project is a rich reflective practice opportunity for nurses to consider how the impact of low health literacy shapes patient/family realization of treatment options. In brief, this family engages in overtreatment of end-stage cancer days from death as a result of low health literacy, though their profile might not readily indicate low health literacy. This is a white family from West Oklahoma. Both husband and wife are college educated and very wealthy owners of power companies in this part of rural America. If tested on basic reading and language literacy, both spouses would likely rate as highly literate. But their *health literacy* requires information processing and decision making far beyond language use and comprehension. This family exemplifies the low health literacy that many families exhibit when navigating a terminal diagnosis.

This unfolding case can be used in many pedagogical ways. The more that participants are with one another and with their own thoughts, the more useful. Arranging students in dyads or triads per segment of the case and then regrouping to share their discoveries in the sequence of the story might be the most powerful use of this classroom tool.

July 10, 2009—Steve, a resident of rural West Oklahoma, thinks he has pneumonia and sees a local family doctor with his wife. His symptoms include labored breathing and exhaustion. Steve's physician diagnoses him with gall bladder inflammation and sends him on to a local surgeon, Dr. A. At the end of this appointment, Steve and his wife Amy talk casually with the nurse about the nuisance of surgery in a busy life.

July 11, 2009—Dr. A. indicates that he is not sure the difficulty is gall bladder. After the meeting with Dr. A., the nurse meets with Steve and Amy and tells them that Dr. A. is sending Steve to the local hospital to arrange for tests. They press her on the change of plans and why a CT scan and blood tests were ordered. They wonder if they should be worried. The nurse assures them that this is likely routine, a "bump in the road."

The wife, present in the technician's booth during the CT exam, notes white spots throughout the scan and converses with the technician about the test. The technician inquired, "Is he really supposed to have gall bladder surgery tomorrow?" That evening Dr. A. called Steve's home and notifies his wife that there are spots on Steve's liver and summons them both to the hospital ER immediately.

Assume that you are Dr. A.'s nurse and you must disclose that gall bladder surgery will not be performed in lieu of further testing. How you would communicate this information? How would you respond to Steve and Amy's concern? What you say to Dr. A. in preparation for your task and following this disclosure to patient/spouse?

July 12, 2002—A scope of Steve's lower colon is positive for tumor activity. Dr. A. diagnoses Steve with colon cancer. A liver biopsy is positive for cancerous tissue as well. Dr. A. suggests to Amy that they do not pursue surgery, chemotherapy, or any further treatment. Dr. A. does not tell Steve this. He has this conversation with the wife in front of several people in a hospital hallway. Steve is left alone in a hospital room unaware of his condition, Amy stops a nurse who has only been on the floor for an hour that day. Amy is sobbing and hysterical. She begs the nurse to explain the diagnosis and what they can do. Knowing that Amy is in crisis and having little information about Steve's case, what would you include in your conversation with Amy? How could you move forward from this moment?

July 14–20, 2009—The family goes on to a cancer center in Oklahoma for care. Oncologists perform additional testing and alter the diagnosis from colon cancer to adenocarcinoma of unknown primary site and suggest the family travel to MD Anderson Cancer Center. An advanced practice nurse meets with Steve and Amy to arrange referral plans, and Steve and Amy ask her if this is "good news?" They believe the doctors' referral to MD Anderson to be an indication of a possible cure.

Knowing that Steve is suffering from metastatic adenocarcinoma of unknown primary, how would you talk to him about his care, how to proceed, and issues to consider in his decision making?

July 20–August 10, 2009—Steve and Amy wait for an appointment at MD Anderson. In this interim Steve becomes jaundiced; his urine is brown and reduced in quantity. Steve receives IV fluids from the local Cancer Center and is then transported to Houston.

August 11–12, 2009—MD Anderson repeats CT and MRI scans; tumor activity in Steve's body is accelerating. These tests are compared with the tests from Oklahoma taken a few weeks before. The liver has become mostly cancerous in a matter of 3 weeks.

Assume you are the intake nurse meeting with Steve and Amy. What would you do next in assessing their understanding of his diagnosis and his care options?

The fellow for the GI (gastrointestinal) clinic meets with Steve's wife. Steve is too ill to participate in the conversation and is being admitted to the hospital. A Fellow tells Amy that Steve will die and that there is no hope. Amy demands to see the lead doctor and insists they receive chemotherapy. A nurse asks Amy to wait and locates Dr. C., who explains the prognosis to the wife and why treatments do not work but says he will try chemotherapy. He explains this therapy will probably not help Steve and will make him sicker. The nurse returns to arrange chemotherapy at the clinic later that day.

Steve receives chemotherapy that evening and becomes more ill with severe nausea and vomiting and worsening pain.

Put yourself in the position of the GI clinic nurse. What opportunities could you take to engage Amy and Steve in orientation and opportunity talk? What strategies could be employed in talking with Dr. C. or the Fellow about Steve and Amy's acceptability and plan of care?

August 13, 2009—Steve becomes very ill in their hotel room. Dr. C. recommends Steve go to MD Anderson ER. Steve waits for several hours until he can receive fluids.

August 14, 2009—Steve needs fluids again but is too ill to go and wait for them. Dr. C. sends a nurse to their hotel with fluids. Steve stays in bed vomiting. He has not urinated in 24 hours.

Put yourself in the visiting nurse position; what are some ways the nurse could engage Amy in considering options for care at this point in Steve's illness?

August 15, 2009—Amy sends for private plane to fly Steve home from Texas to Oklahoma as Steve is too ill to travel by car or commercial air. Steve and Amy return home.

August 16–30, 2009—Steve never leaves his bedroom again. He stops eating and eventually stops talking. He becomes confined to bed and his pain increases exponentially. Steve's original GP, diagnosing him with gall bladder problems, visits and prescribes pain medication in the last week of Steve's life, but soon Steve is unable to swallow the pill form of the medication that has been prescribed.

What do you see as the most crucial opportunity for a nurse to have made a more positive impact on the outcome of this case in terms of orientation and communication with the patient/family about care options?

EXERCISE 5: JIGSAW SOLUTIONS FOR LOW LITERACY AND CULTURAL CHALLENGES

Jigsaw learning is a strategy of small group self-teaching that has been practiced and researched for over three decades. If each student's part is essential, then each student is essential; that is precisely what makes this strategy so effective.

Here is how it works: nursing students are divided into small *learning* groups of five or six students each. Their task is to learn about ways to improve communication problems revolving around low health literacy and cultural differences in a variety of palliative care contexts. Each jigsaw group is assigned an *expert* on a particular topic of palliative care communication as it relates to orientation and opportunity.

The situation is specifically structured so that the only access any member has to the other five assignments is by listening closely to the report of the person reporting.

To increase the chances that each report will be critically thoughtful and useful, the students first meet with students who have the identical assignment in their *expert* groups (one from each jigsaw group). For example, students assigned to reducing medical language meet as a team of *experts*, gathering information, becoming experts on their topic, and rehearsing their presentations. It is particularly useful for students who might have initial difficulty learning or organizing their part of the assignment; it allows them to hear and rehearse with other "experts."

Once each presenter is up to speed, the jigsaw groups reconvene in their initial heterogeneous *learning group* configuration. Each student in a group educates the whole group about her or his specialty.

What is the benefit of the jigsaw classroom? First and foremost, it is a remarkably efficient way to learn the material. But even more important, the jigsaw process encourages listening, engagement, and empathy by giving each member of the group an essential part to play in the academic activity.

We include a sampling of communication challenges that bedside nurses from the Georgia Nurse Leaders Organization reported in the summer of 2010. These descriptions can be used as contexts and situations for learning group problems. Expert group topics will follow these nurse descriptions.

- Patients/families do not understand what I am saying or what the doctor is saying. Generally, they act like they understand, and when the MD leaves the room they ask me what he/she meant. The MD is usually in a hurry. The units are so busy that the staff does not have enough time to sit down and really talk/listen to the patient/family.

- I don't have the ability to predict the best method of information delivery with patients of all different educational and socioeconomic backgrounds.
- It is challenging to communicate how a patient/family can perform self-care, or manage himself or herself at home with a new permanent ostomy or new diagnosis that needs lifelong intervention.
- A brain-dead patient's family did not understand that body circulation does not equate to the possibility of survival/recovery after explanations from the physician that the brain was not working. After prolonged lack of oxygen, there was no chance of brain function getting better.

Expert group topics:

- Voice of Lifeworld versus Voice of MedicalWorld
- Practicing Cultural Humility
- Assuming Low Health Literacy
- Communication Accommodation Theory's Convergence
- Plain Language

This concept is adapted from Aronson, E., Blaney, N., Stephin, C., Sikes, J., & Snapp, M. (1978). *The Jigsaw Classroom*. Beverly Hills, CA: Sage Publishing Company.

EXERCISE 6: PLAIN LANGUAGE GAME

The plain language game can be administered in many different ways. The goal of this classroom project is to remind nurses of their role and ability to communicate difficult information to patients and families, especially in end-of-life situations.

In groups of six or seven, students are charged with making a difficult piece of information understandable and comprehensible for a variety of health literacy levels and cultural backgrounds. For instance, one group could be given the issue of explaining feeding tubes versus withholding nutrition. The group then determines four or five ways in which this message can be communicated and goes to work building those messages. Communication channels include using language that is not steeped in medicalese. For others, a set of pictures might accomplish an alternative message. Especially for this sort of medical decision, the anxiety and concern surrounding the absence of the nutrition is of most concern to families, as Western culture is bound to the idea of food as a signifier of care/love. So, each group is charged with identifying what the message will consist of, or how the message will be delivered. The goal is to introduce variety and creativity to increase the tools in the nursing toolbox.

Groups should be given a week to build/design their series of messages, and then a class session should be devoted to the delivery and discussion of these presentations.

ADDITIONAL SUPPLEMENTAL MATERIALS

Table 3.10 Communication Adaptations for the Deaf or Hearing Impaired Patient/Family

- Find out how your patient/family would prefer to communicate.
- Communicate with intended party, even if you are using a translator or signer.
- Inquire about patient/family interest in an American Sign Language translator.
- Let the entire staff know about hearing compromise.
- Keep writing material accessible for anyone to use.
- Use instructional videos with captions.
- Use relay service telephone calls or videophone.

Adapted from Ruccione, K. (2004). Coming to terms with language. *Oncology Nursing Forum, 31,* 913–925.

Table 3.11 Strategies to Facilitate Health Literacy in Older Adults

- Meet when patient/family is rested.
- Build in additional time to meeting.
- Provide the best lighting possible.
- Reduce background noise as possible.
- Minimize nurse distractions.
- Adjust room temperature to suit patient/family.
- Accommodate for physical needs/limitations with wall railings, straight-backed chairs, cushions.

Adapted from Speros, C. (2009). More than words: Promoting health literacy in older adults. *Online Journal of Issues in Nursing, 14,* Manuscript 5.

WEBSITES FOR CULTURAL HUMILITY MATERIALS

CROSS CULTURAL HEALTH CARE PROGRAM

www.xculture.org
- CCHCP addresses broad cultural issues that impact the health of individuals and families in ethnic minority communities.

EthnoMed
http://ethnomed.org

- The EthnoMed site contains information about cultural beliefs, medical issues, and other matters pertinent to health care of recent immigrants to the United States.

Harvard School of Public Health: Health Literacy Studies
www.hsph.harvard.edu/healthliteracy
- A research group providing current data and studies on the correlation of culture and low health literacy

ADDITIONAL WEBSITES FOR HEALTH LITERACY MATERIALS

Below is a government health literacy LISTSERV including posts on many different aspects of health literacy and communication. To subscribe and find the archives, go to
http://lincs.ed.gov/mailman/listinfo/Healthliteracy/.

American Medical Association Foundation Health Literacy
http://www.ama-assn.org/ama/pub/category/8115.html
- Toolkits including online videos, manuals, and tips in clinical practice

Ask Me 3
http://www.npsf.org/for-healthcare-professionals/programs/ask-me-3/ask-me-3-resources
- A site dedicated to improve communication between providers and patients. Includes toolkits, fact sheets, reproducible brochures, guidelines, and more

Doak, C., Doak, L., & Root, J. (1996). *Teaching Patients With Low Literacy Skills.*
http://www.hsph.harvard.edu/healthliteracy/resources/doak-book/
- Book included in supplemental section is available on the Harvard site in pdf

Health Literacy: A Prescription to End Confusion
http://www.nap.edu/openbook.php?isbn=0309091179
- A comprehensive article vital to every health care practitioner is the Institute of Medicine's report.

Health Literacy Month
http://healthliteracymonth.org
- Articles, links, logos, and promotion suggestions to advertise October as Health Literacy Month

Health Literacy Universal Precautions Toolkit
http://www.ahrq.gov/qual/literacy/ (also available at http://nchealthliteracy.org/index.html)
- Sponsored by AHRQ and created by Dr. Darren DeWalt's team at University of North Carolina Chapel Hill School of Medicine

LINCS Health Care Provider/Health Educator Resources
http://lincs.ed.gov/lincs/resourcecollections/healthliteracy
- Easy-to-read materials, information in languages other than English, cultural
  issues solutions, and activities

Literacy and Health Outcomes
http://www.ahrq.gov/downloads/pub/evidence/pdf/literacy/literacyup.pdf
- This report analyzes the effects of low health literacy on health outcomes.

North Carolina Program on Health Literacy
http://nchealthliteracy.org/index.html

Understanding Health Literacy and Its Barriers
http://www.nlm.nih.gov/pubs/cbm/healthliteracybarriers.html
- Current bibliography on the topic of health literacy

The Virginia Adult Education Health Literacy Toolkit
http://www.valrc.org/publications/healthlit/
- A one-stop resource for health literacy education needs

RESOURCES FOR DEVELOPING EASY-TO-READ MATERIAL

Clear Language Group
http://www.clearlanguagegroup.com
- Professionals doing work in health communication and particularly focusing on
  the needs of the people that have low health literacy

Clear and Simple: Developing Effective Print Materials for Low Literate Readers
http://cancer.gov/cancerinformation/clearandsimple
- An outline for procedures to develop publications for people with limited
  literacy skills

How to Write Easy to Read Materials
http://www.nlm.nih.gov/medlineplus/etr.html
- Four steps of development for the creation of easy-to-read material

Patient Education: An Author's Guide
http://www.med.utah.edu/pated/authors
- A useful guide on all aspects of writing for patients/families

The Plain Language Institute
http://www.plainlanguage.gov/
- The Plain Language initiative including examples, guidelines for content and
  layout, and numerous resources to support the creation of materials

4

MINDFUL PRESENCE

Elizabeth is a night shift nurse in the surgical ICU in a large teaching hospital. She has been a nurse for 5 years and chose the ICU as the setting for her work as she was intrigued by the fast pace, patient acuity, and complexity of the patients and their families. She loves the opportunity to care for the sickest patients and feels fortunate to work in an academic center where she is a part of a team and there are always opportunities to learn.

Over the past year, the ICU has been receiving more cancer cases as the hospital has expanded its surgical oncology program. Patients travel long distances to seek care even when they have often been told surgery is not possible for their advanced tumors. Elizabeth has felt increasingly frustrated in the care of these patients, often distressed in cases where very aggressive care is provided with very invasive surgeries. Sometimes the surgeries are successful but there is tremendous suffering involved; other times, these desperate patients and families become very difficult to care for when the surgery fails. Elizabeth had begun to feel like a "senior" ICU nurse, but now she has become uncertain about her work and ability to provide care.

For the past 2 weeks, Elizabeth has been caring for Mr. Chun, a 70-year-old Chinese man who underwent surgery for an advanced gastric malignancy. Mr. Chun was a successful businessman and a very stoic, serious man. Unfortunately, Mr. Chun developed several postoperative complications including a GI bleed, liver failure, and respiratory failure. He is no longer verbally responsive and his prognosis is poor. His wife, brother, 90-year-old father, and three children have refused a family meeting, and each has insisted that the hospital keep focused on Mr. Chun's survival. Mr. Chun's oldest son is serving as the family spokesperson and proxy decision maker. He has become hostile and very angry, especially if there is any mention of his father's poor prognosis.

Elizabeth is caring for Mr. Chun on the night shift, and his oldest daughter, Chin Lee, returns late at night and asks if she can sit with her father. She has always been very quiet, deferring all decisions to her brother. Elizabeth begins her routine care for Mr. Chun, checking his ventilator and drains and administering his many IV medications. She notices that Chin Lee is quietly weeping, and she senses her extreme anguish and grief as she watches her father, a vulnerable and weak man now with a ravaged and debilitated body burdened by the many high-tech treatments. Elizabeth continues her patient care as she considers how best to respond to Chin Lee and what she can possibly offer to this daughter.

In the case study above, Elizabeth finds herself in a position that palliative care nurses face continually in their work: uncertainty in dealing with patients and families in the face of failed surgeries or other treatments and poor prognoses, particularly when the patient is no longer verbally responsive, and his family members refuse to meet to discuss care plans. This case is complicated in particular by the patient's Chinese culture, whose traditions mandate that oldest sons speak for their families—Mr. Chun's son, angry and hostile because of his father's condition after surgery, only wants to focus on his father's survival. And yet Elizabeth discovers Mr. Chun's oldest daughter, Chin Lee, weeping in anguish in her father's hospital room. In the absence of a family meeting at which the palliative care team might help the family to discuss their possibly conflicting views concerning the care plan for Mr. Chun, Elizabeth must discover other means of ministering to this mute patient and his family, particularly at this time focusing on his distressed daughter.

This chapter introduces the "M" concept in the COMFORT model, *mindful presence*. It details the concepts of **mindfulness** and **presence**, two nonverbal behaviors that nurses can bring to patients/families when verbal behavior is necessarily limited (as with Mr. Chun), but that also can be practiced in any patient/family interaction. Drawing on the research in both mindfulness and presence (often called **compassionate or healing presence** in the nursing literature), we have combined these concepts into an essential nonverbal communication skill, *mindful presence*. The discussion will also deal with **empathy** and **active listening** and will point out how essential these competencies are for palliative care nurses and for the practice of **narrative nursing**. The chapter then will discuss the importance of a nurse's **intercultural sensitivity** in the care setting. It will conclude with a brief look at the philosophical underpinning of our notion of **mindful presence—Martin Buber's I-It/I-Thou dialectic.**

MINDFULNESS

The term "mindfulness," which originated in Buddhist philosophy, has been appropriated by a multitude of disciplines, including clinical psychology, social work, psychotherapy, medicine, and other helping professions. This section will look briefly at the tenets of mindfulness and will provide a rationale for what we believe is a more accurate descriptor of the communication behavior required for palliative care nurses—**mindful presence.**

In its classic sense, mindfulness describes an aspect of Buddhism that has been in existence more than 2,500 years, only gaining acceptance in the Western world for about the past 25 years (Day & Horton-Deutsch, 2004) as we began to recognize the relationships between our emotions and our physical and mental health. Essentially, mindfulness "is a state of being purposefully attentive to one's moment-by-moment experience," (Day & Horton-Deutsch, 2004, p. 165), but this attentiveness also includes an awareness of one's own maladaptive cognitive habits that impede personal growth and understanding (Goleman, 1997; Kabat-Zinn, 1990). Hirst (2003) describes mindfulness as "an awareness of being aware" (p. 360) that requires concentration and attention to being present in the current moment. Discussing mindfulness as it pertains to learning, Langer (1992, 2000) states that mindfulness entails a flexible state of mind and an active engagement in the present, a noticing of new things and a sensitivity to context. He contrasts it with *mindlessness*, which is linked to habitual behaviors performed without attention: for example, predictable emotional responses, fantasizing, worrying about the future, living with anger and hate, and indulging in addictive behavior.

Importantly for our discussion, however, mindfulness in its truest sense is a skill that is highly disciplined and whose cultivation and therapeutic usefulness mandate training and daily meditation (Day & Horton-Deutsch, 2004; Kabat-Zinn, 1990; Kabat-Zinn, Lipworth, & Burney, 1985). In fact, the skill of mindfulness is developed through meditation (Hirst, 2003), and its therapeutic usefulness frequently involves the teaching of Buddhist meditative practices. **Mindfulness as meditation** has been empirically investigated in a number of therapeutic settings, most frequently as a stress reduction technique in cognitive therapy and as a supportive therapy in the treatment of cancer patients. For example, mindfulness-based therapeutic interventions have been successfully utilized in psychiatric nursing (Day & Horton-Deutsch, 2004) and in cognitive therapy (Davis, 2007); mindfulness meditation has been taught to dementia caregivers (Oken et al., 2010); mindfulness-based stress reduction techniques have been utilized for both patients and health professionals (Cohen-Katz, 2004; Praissman, 2008), and mindfulness skills training has been utilized in clinical social work (Turner, 2009). In oncology nursing, mindfulness meditation has also been a potentially beneficial intervention for cancer patients (Matchim & Armer, 2007; Ott, Norris, & Bauer-Wu, 2006). Smith, Richardson, Hoffman, & Pilkington (2005) found that mindfulness-based stress reduction is a potentially valuable intervention for improving mood and sleep quality and for reducing stress in cancer patients. Ott (2002) utilized mindfulness meditation successfully in pediatric clinical practice. Keep in mind that all of these studies have involved the teaching of Buddhist meditation, a requisite skill for the practice of mindfulness.

Thus, while our communication tenet for palliative care nursing, *mindful presence*, adopts many of the concepts entailing Buddhist mindfulness, it does not advocate meditation as a requisite skill in the practice of being mindful. Rather, *mindful presence* involves a nurse's being nonverbally present for a patient/family while also being attentive, in the moment, nonjudgmental, and empathic. These ideas will be unpacked in the following section.

MINDFUL PRESENCE

Rapgay and Bystrisky (2009), in an article that differentiates classical mindfulness from the popular use of the word, state that popularized versions of mindfulness consider the formal practice of daily training and meditation too demanding; the Buddhist model of mindfulness has been altered to a "more general concept of being mindful, i.e. attentive to present moment experience" (p. 149). In particular, being mindful requires a nonjudgmental awareness of the present moment, being experientially open and accepting (Rapgay & Bystrisky, 2009).

Anthony and Vidal (2010) discuss *mindful communication* as a way of improving delegation and increasing patient safety; they define mindfulness as "a state in which there is keen awareness of the situation; it is being 'in the moment,' and a way of directing or focusing attention of everyday tasks to the present moment" (p. 8) It is this adaptation of mindfulness as *mindful communication* that we find most engaging as a skill in the practice of palliative care.

PRESENCE

Mindfulness and presence are frequently discussed in tandem in the clinical psychology literature. Childs (2007), for example, cites Kabat-Zinn's (1991) seven attitudinal foundations of mindfulness as conveying "an attentive, unprejudiced present" (p. 369): acceptance, patience, trust (in one's own intuition), nonjudging, nonstriving, letting go, and beginner's mind (seeing everything as if for the first time). Personal preference and critical thought are suspended when one is mindful. "The word 'presence' is a useful summary of this account as it conveys both present time and person present, a 'now' and an awareness attentive in it. Presence requires practice and emphasizes personal experience. You have to be there" (Childs, 2007, p. 369).

In the nursing literature, the word "presence" is more typically used to convey many of the attitudes of mindfulness that Kabat-Zinn espoused. Often this presence is referred to as "compassionate presence" or "healing presence," both terms referring to the nonverbal attentiveness and the attitudes that a mindful communicator employs. Simon, Ramsenthaler, Bausewein, Krischke, and Geiss (2009) interviewed palliative care professionals who described the **core attitudes of professionals in palliative care.** Interviewees listed the personal characteristics of authenticity, personal presence, honesty and truthfulness, openness, unconditional positive regard, and mindfulness as part of these core attitudes. Authenticity is seen as being present and accessible rather than behaving in a specific role; personal presence is described as a feeling of "completely being in the here and now" (p. 408), of focusing on the other person. Mindfulness is seen by the interviewees as cautiousness, attentiveness, humility, and acceptance. It also means nonacting, appreciating the other in his being. As one interviewee put it, "You know deep inside what is right and I am allowed to be the person that reminds and supports you…again this inner awareness and concentration on the uniqueness of this person, looking at what is happening" (p. 409). All of the attitudes described in the Simon et al. (2009) study are relational competencies that palliative care professionals exhibit with their patients—these competencies in care can be seen in Table 4.1 (Simon et al., 2009, Table 3, p. 408).

Table 4.1 Concept of Core Attitude in Palliative Care

Personal Characteristics	Experience of Core Attitude	Competence in Care
Authenticity	In relationship	Perception
Honesty	Dialogue	Active listening
Mindfulness	Companionship	Getting involved
Esteem/appreciation	Systemic approach	Creating space
Openness	Letting go	
Personal presence	Closeness/distance	
Responsibility		

Used with permission from: Simon, T., Ramsenthaler, C., Bausewein, C., Krischke, N., & Geiss, G. (2009). Core attitudes of professionals in palliative care: A qualitative study. *International Journal of Palliative Nursing, 15*(8), 408, Table 3: Concept of Core Attitude in Palliative Care.

HEALING PRESENCE

The core attitudes above help to describe the concept of "healing presence" discussed by McDonough-Means, Kreitzer, and Bell (2004), who state that, while the nursing literature since the early 1960s has attempted to define presence and its therapeutic importance, the emerging literature has been more conceptual than empirical. Citing Gilje (1992) and Gardner (1985), McDonough-Means et al. discuss two dimensions of presence: physical or "being there" and psychological or "being with." Physical presence involves actual proximity to the other—"seeing, examining, touching, doing, hearing, and hugging or holding" (McDonough-Means et al., p. S-25) whereas psychological presence entails the skills of "listening, attending to, caring, empathy, being nonjudgmental, and accepting" (p. S-25). Ferrell and Coyle (2008) cite Benner's (1984) work on the significance of presence: expert nurses come to realize that their "being" is as valuable as their "doing." Ferrell and Coyle (2008) further state that "presence is far more than being physically available or offering expert listening skills. True presence is a sacred act. It is transformative for the nurse as well as for the patient or family member" (Ferrell & Coyle, 2008, p. 85). We consider "being" and both types of nonverbal presence—physical and psychological—to be essential competencies for palliative care nurses.

COMPASSIONATE PRESENCE AND EMPATHY

McDonough-Means et al. (2004) further describe the characteristics of a healer that contribute to her ability to be fully present: *empathy*, compassion, charisma, and spirituality. One of the core attributes of a healing presence is empathy. Numerous studies show that the ability to exhibit empathy and focused attention are a part of effective communication in any therapeutic relationship (McDonough-Means et al., 2004). Williams & Stickley (2010) concur that patients desire empathic nurses and discuss the implications for teaching empathy for nurse educators.

Eide et al. (2004) explain that patients are hesitant to articulate their emotions directly and spontaneously, presenting indirect cues to indicate emotion. In a study in which they coded verbal transcripts of doctor–patient interaction for both explicit and implicit expressions of emotion, they defined implicit expressions of patient emotion as "a patient statement from which a clinician might infer underlying emotion that has not been explicitly expressed" (p. 292). This is shown in the following example in which a physician is talking with a patient about her hearing loss:

> PATIENT: Yes, of course you hear well, but I don't hear it at all, so that is my biggest handicap [The researchers coded this utterance as a "potential empathic opportunity"—PEO—that expressed concern.]
>
> DOCTOR: Yes, it may be that it will get a bit better. I don't know if it will return to normal, but I think it's a bit early to say, so soon after the operation that I…(pp. 292–293).

In this study, the authors concluded that there were four times more implicit than explicit expressions of patient emotion and that many opportunities to express empathy are missed. They also note that despite the traditional approach to treat patients' emotions as secondary to their diagnosis and treatment, recent studies show patients' emotions as integral to their care.

They cite evidence for this in a study by Stewart et al. (1999) that showed that physician acknowledgment and response to patient emotion results in improved patient satisfaction, greater probability of adherence to physician recommendations, and measurable outcomes such as improved blood pressure and blood sugar.

Thus, *listening* for feelings becomes all important for the palliative care nurse. In the case study at the beginning of the chapter, Elizabeth relies on the nonverbal cues of her patient's daughter—Chin Lee's quiet weeping—to give her information about Chin Lee's emotional state and her possible disagreement with her brother concerning their father's care. Being present and empathic in the moment are paramount for Elizabeth.

A healing and *compassionate presence* is discussed by Ferrell and Coyle (2008, 2010) as a requisite for palliative care nurses. In studies dealing with the suffering of children and their parents, nurses realized that "the greatest relief they could offer was presence" (Ferrell & Coyle, 2008, p. 73). One nurse in describing her **witnessing** of suffering wrote:

> Sometimes we can only witness. We cannot fix or do the work of creating meaning. This family responds to support, to ideas, to reframing, but ultimately they have to wrestle with the guilt themselves. We can provide a container, a holding environment of safety so they don't have to do this in isolation. We can keep showing up, even when it's messy and ragged and uncomfortable. (Ferrell & Coyle, 2008, p. 74)

Referring again to the opening case study, Elizabeth may not be able to offer the Chun family any comfort other than "showing up," witnessing with empathy and a mindful presence of the suffering of another: "Nurses respond to suffering first and foremost through presence. As witnesses to suffering, they serve as a compassionate voice that recognizes the human response to illness amidst the chaos and depersonalization of the health-care environment" (Ferrell & Coyle, 2008, p. 109).

ACTIVE OR DEEP LISTENING

Across all contexts of patient/family suffering—critical care, pediatrics, oncology, geriatrics and other settings—Ferrell & Coyle (2008) point out the critical importance of nursing presence and attentive *listening*. "Through listening to their patients, nurses can help the person move beyond mute suffering to expressing their emotional distress...Nurses can ameliorate distress and help restore wholeness through this human connection" (Ferrell & Coyle, 2008, 110).

Relational communication scholar Julia Wood (2000) discusses the skill of *listening* as being at least as important as talking. She distinguishes listening from hearing: hearing is a purely physiological activity requiring no effort; listening, on the other hand, is far more complex and effortful. Listening is defined as: "a complex process of attending to, receiving, perceiving, organizing, interpreting, responding, and remembering messages" (Wood, 2000, p. 68). Seven activities comprise the listening process, as illustrated in Table 4.2.

Wood (2000) further notes that the basic foundation of listening is being *mindful*: this entails being fully attentive to the here and now, refusing to think about what you were doing a moment before you encountered this person and disciplining your mind not to wander to what you will be doing later. While our normal state of mind is *not* being mindful, according to Wood, the act of being mindful requires a conscious decision to attend fully to another person, refusing to focus on our own experiences and feelings, and giving ourselves completely to the moment. Ting-Toomey (2010) discusses mindful listening as "listening deeply with all our senses open and all our perceptual filters unclogged" (p. 160). She cites the Chinese character for "listening," *ting*, which means "listening with one-pointed attention with our ears, eyes, and a focused heart" (p. 160).

LISTENING, PRESENCE, AND BEARING WITNESS

Baird (2010), in discussing spiritual care interventions in palliative care, believes that nurses provide presence, *deep listening, bearing witness*, compassion, compassionate presence, and what she terms *"deep listening"* as critical skills. To be compassionately present involves more than being physically present in the patient's room; rather, the psychological message is given: "There is no where else I would rather be at this moment than here with you" (Baird, p. 665). This type of presence definitely takes more effort, energy, and intention than the mere act of being in physical proximity to

Table 4.2 The Listening Process

1. Becoming mindful	Focusing on another person and the present moment, giving full attention
2. Physically receiving messages	Receiving a message, either through audio signals and sound waves or through another means such as seeing nonverbal communication or American Sign Language
3. Selectively perceiving	Selecting aspects of noise or messages for focus, distinguishing what's important from what is not
4. Organizing what has been received	Grouping information together, noting connections among ideas, linking this message to previous knowledge
5. Interpreting	Assigning meaning to the selected and organized material; drawing conclusions about what the communication means
6. Responding	Demonstrating interest and attention through verbal and nonverbal feedback, asking questions, giving responses, encouraging elaboration
7. Remembering	Retaining what we consider the most important parts of messages and the meanings we've assigned to them

Used with permission from: Wood, J. T. (2000). *Relational Communication: Continuity and Change in Personal Relationships* (2nd ed., p. 69). Belmont, CA: Wadsworth Publishing.

the patient. Likewise, Baird believes that *deep listening* means "hearing what is being said and what is not being said and trying to understand the emotions and feelings behind the words" (p. 665). It is allowing the person to be vulnerable in our presence so that we share in their pain and suffering.

Dahlin (2010) posits four basic elements to communication in nurse–patient relationships: imparting information, listening, information gathering, and presence and sensitivity. All of these elements work concurrently for effective palliative care nursing. Listening requires both presence and attention so that both words and nonverbal gestures are "heard." Dahlin notes that it is frequently useful to ask for the patient's story with an open-ended question, such as "What brought you to the hospital?" or "Tell me what has been going on" (p. 114). This permits the nurse to listen actively to the story while also keenly observing and interpreting nonverbal behavior, particularly expressions of emotion that might be communicating psychological or spiritual distress. Dahlin further stresses that *silence* is a valuable tool for the nurse to utilize—it permits her to listen without interrupting the patient, to be present in the moment without mentally preparing answers or replies. Such silence also conveys empathy to the patient. Just sitting quietly may permit the patient to express a deeper level of concern, and in that silence comes an opportunity and permission to self-disclose.

Case Study

An example is the case of Mildred, a 44-year-old woman being treated in the oncology clinic for stage IV ovarian cancer. Mildred has opted for aggressive

chemotherapy, hoping to extend her life to be able to see the birth of her first grand-
child due in 3 months. Mildred's nurse Karen has watched her patient decline,
becoming more cachectic with many signs that the tumor is progressing and not
responding to treatment. Today as Karen is beginning the fourth chemotherapy
infusion in the outpatient clinic, the physician enters the room and reports that
the ultrasound and lab work have confirmed their worst fear and that the tumor
has now extended to the liver. The physician, a very kind, older oncologist who
is very fond of Mildred, quickly exits, telling Mildred he will be in touch once he
has time to consider other options. Karen finishes connecting the chemotherapy
but remains seated next to Mildred, gently touching her arm in silence, acknowl-
edging the weight of the information she has received. Mildred begins to cry, and
Karen avoids the urge to jump up and get a tissue or to provide false assurances,
and instead, she sits in silence. Moments pass, then Mildred begins to speak, tell-
ing Karen that she knew she was getting worse and how difficult it has been to try
to keep positive and protect her family. Karen remains silent, offering Mildred the
space and security to absorb the latest news and its meaning.

Particularly with a dying patient, Dahlin (2010) notes that "simple presence, listen-ing, and attending to the basic humanity of the dying patient may be one of the nurse's most powerful contributions" (p. 126). Being present for and witnessing the dying pro-cess is a healing affirmation, even a sacramental gesture. "The communication skills required include: being present with the patient in his or her state of vulnerability and decline; consciously and non-judgmentally listening and bearing witness to the patient; and encouraging the patient to express all feelings while resisting defensiveness if the patient voices anger or disappointment about dying" (Dahlin, 2010, p. 126).

PATIENTS' STORIES AND NARRATIVE NURSING

The communication skills of active, deep listening, presence, and bearing witness invite patients' stories as Dahlin (2010) describes above. Baird (2010) writes of "bear-ing witness" as being present and responsive to the stories patients and their families tell about their illness journeys: "We feel the need to share our experiences, and we feel compelled to hear other people's stories. To bear witness is to be present to the events and the emotions of another's life and experience. We find strength and comfort in knowing that other human beings bear witness to the significant events of our lives—the good and the bad" (Baird, 2010, p. 666). The telling of and the deep listening to stories is perhaps the hallmark of mindful presence. Being present in the moment is often rewarded by the trust of patients and their families as they disclose intense, often painful illness narratives. Baird (2010) warns that interrupting the process of sharing such stories can stop them and the emotions they release abruptly. Baird writes:

Something as simple as reaching over and touching a person while he/she is telling
the emotion-filled story can stop the flow and interrupt the process. When these

interruptions occur, there is a good chance that the story, which was so important to tell, might never again find the opportunity to be told. It takes time, experience, and thoughtful awareness to learn when to speak, or move, or get tissues. (Baird, 2010, p. 666)

Narrative nursing, the theoretical framework that undergirds the *comfort* model, means that nurses can learn to bear witness, to sit quietly, and not to run from another human who is suffering, even as we experience our own pain and suffering in the process. It bespeaks a compassionate presence that permits the time and emotional space for storytelling—that enterprise that is deeply rooted in our humanity and that connects us to each other as no other form of communication can.

INTERCULTURAL SENSITIVITY

Elizabeth's awareness of Chin Lee's suffering tells us that the attribute of *mindful presence* is brought to bear when a nurse attends specifically to the moment at hand, suspends all judgment about what she sees and hears, listens deeply for emotional expressions, and realizes that her nonverbal presence—both physically and psychologically—may be the most compassionate response she can give to her patients and their families. In our case study, Elizabeth may choose to sit in silence with Chin Lee, perhaps touching her shoulder. But she may also decide to verbally communicate with the grieving daughter by asking her to talk about her fears and concerns. "Please tell me what you are most concerned about with your father's care." "Have you and your brother discussed this?" These and other questions might elicit Chin Lee's story about how she is experiencing her father's poor prognosis and, possibly, about her culturally prescribed deference to her brother, which may be contributing to her anguish and grief. It is important to note, however, that Chin Lee might **not** be troubled by the cultural value of male dominance; nurses must be cautious to avoid imposing their own cultural values on those who are culturally different.

Whereas we cannot expect Elizabeth to be knowledgeable about all values and norms across a wide variety of cultures, a part of displaying *mindful presence* is being interculturally sensitive (this is also discussed as cultural humility in Chapter 3). Sherman (2010) discusses this sensitivity as *cultural competence*, which has four components in health care contexts:

cultural diversity—recognition of diverse populations with unique values, traditions, and beliefs

cultural awareness—knowledge of cultural variations with regard to health beliefs and practices

cultural sensitivity—recognition of individual attitudes and beliefs "and a refinement of communication skills related to active listening, use of silence and touch, conversational distance, language patterns, and the effective use of translators" (p. 10)

cultural competence—the ultimate goal, incorporating diversity, awareness, and sensitivity into everyday practice

MARTIN BUBER'S I-IT/I-THOU DIALECTIC

From a values perspective, the entire *comfort* model and **mindful presence** specifically can be said to derive from the philosophical roots of Jewish theologian Martin Buber's I-It/I-Thou dialectic on human relationships. The I-Thou is Buber's shorthand for his advocacy that others should be treated as sacred entities (Thou) rather than as objects (It). Buber believed that human life finds its meaningfulness in relationships, all of which ultimately bring us into relationship with God, the eternal Thou. Our experience of the world consists of two aspects: the aspect of experience, perceived by I-It, and the aspect of relation, perceived by I-Thou. I-Thou relationships stress the mutual, holistic existence of two beings who meet one another authentically—it is characterized by dialogue, mutuality, and exchange.

In an I-Thou relationship, you and others are seen as persons who cannot be reduced to a simple characterization: "Each person has important life experiences that warrant positive regard, even when the experience of others is different from your own" (Littlejohn & Foss, 2008, p. 216). The I-It relationship, on the other hand, means that the "It" is seen as an object to be manipulated and changed; the self is privileged over the other. There is no dialogue, only monologue, as other people are treated as objects to be used and experienced. In any therapeutic setting and certainly in the context of palliative care nursing, we believe that mindful presence entails dialogue—the treatment of other as Thou.

DEVELOPING CLINICAL PRACTICE SKILLS

This chapter discusses the M component of COMFORT, **mindful presence**. It details the usefulness of the Buddhist concept of **mindfulness** as it combines with the idea of **compassionate or healing presence** in the nursing literature. **Empathy** and **active listening** are discussed as essential components of mindful presence, which lead also to **narrative nursing**, the theoretical underpinning of the COMFORT model. Finally, **Buber's I-It/I-Thou dialectic** is offered as the philosophical root for the practice of mindful presence. This next section provides communication tools that are helpful in the development and utilization of mindful presence.

In the case study at the beginning of the chapter, Elizabeth must draw on her knowledge of the Chun family and her intercultural sensitivity in general in order to bring the attitude and behavior of mindful presence to the grieving daughter, Chin Lee. Most importantly, Elizabeth must complete her routine tasks of completing her physical exams, providing medications, and monitoring his IVs and ventilator for Mr. Chun, and turn her full attention to being there for Chin Lee. In this case, it is likely that her presence will be both physical and psychological. Elizabeth might choose to sit beside Chin Lee, to touch her shoulder lightly, and to gently inquire whether she might be of any help. But initially she also might choose to be only psychologically and nonverbally present—permitting Chin Lee to weep without interruption and without judgment, not attempting to console her but, rather, silently being with Chin Lee in her anguish. Elizabeth might wait until Chin Lee speaks before speaking herself—she will realize that her deep listening, empathy, and compassionate presence might be more comforting to the girl than anything a nurse could say.

In a study of the experience of mindfulness among hospice caregivers who regularly practice mindfulness meditation at a Zen Hospice (Bruce & Davies, 2005), the themes emerged shown in Table 4.3 as the caregivers practiced meditation-in-action.

Meditation-in-action: Hospice care providers practiced being in the moment by paying attention to ordinary activities, such as the sensations of giving a massage or bathing a resident. They experienced mindfulness not by holding onto the past or future "but relaxing into the immediacy of whatever was happening" (Bruce & Davies, 2005, p. 1335)—paying attention to the everyday routine of service, including

Table 4.3 Themes

Meditation-in-action
Anchoring awareness in ordinary activities
An approach to being present
Relaxing into the immediacy of what is happening
Setting an intention and being aware of intention
Abiding in liminal spaces
Sense of separation dissolves
An in-between space
Appreciating opposing tensions
Sense of in/separability between caregivers and residents
Integral to empathy and compassion
Seeing differently
Perceptions shifting
Vivid sense of appreciation and beauty
Seeing what needs to be done
Leaning into stillness of activities
Cultivating openness without agendas
Resting with groundlessness
Recognizing we are change
Letting go of wishing things were otherwise and fearing what might be
Becoming intimate with fear
Practicing abiding in the midst of emotions
Practicing continuously opening to experience

Used with permission from: Bruce, A., & Davies, B. (2005). Mindfulness in hospice care: Practicing meditation-in-action. *Qualitative Health Research, 15,* 1336.

feeding, sitting with, and listening to residents. They also focused intentionally on being open and present and on being aware of this intention.

Abiding in liminal spaces: Liminal spaces are those in which such dualities as self–other, work life–spiritual life, and living–dying dissolve. It is an in-between space—"a space in the hyphen within living-dying or presence-absence. In this space, opposites meet in-between, where one is both living yet dying, or present yet absent…An appreciation that opposing tensions of living while dying or being joyful while saddened can be held simultaneously without contradiction" (Bruce & Davies, p. 1336). Appreciation of liminal spaces also means that caregivers and residents, self and other, are seen as inseparable: this is integral to empathy and compassion, including self-compassion. Working for others' benefit also benefits the self, as described by one hospice caregiver:

> We go to the bedside…in an interesting way…to be supported. I go with generosity and kindness—but there is mutuality. Our lives are interconnected…your suffering is my suffering…you're dying and I'm going to die. I don't assume that I am independent from the person in the bed. Or in a peculiar way, I don't assume that I am better off.

Seeing differently: This is a shift in perception that allows one to notice what has not been seen before or to appreciate the beauty of the familiar. For example, one hospice caregiver noted: "Preparing elegant, simple meals; having bright, clean rooms, fresh flowers, and incense; paying attention to the vital, immaterial space; and catering to the wishes and whims of residents as much as it was possible contributed to an expansive environment that could accommodate suffering and peace" (Bruce & Davies, p. 1337). Mindfulness made hospice workers see what needed to get done in supporting residents. One hospice worker asserted:

> Mindfulness makes me alert to what is happening…I see things that I didn't see before; I begin to notice. For example, when there is a lot of chaos in the room…or, if the commode is sitting in the middle of the room in the eye-line of the person lying in bed—is that what she is seeing all day? Maybe it's a convenient location for the caregiver but maybe it's a terrible location for the person in the bed. (p. 1337)

As residents deteriorate and withdraw, requiring less doing from the caregivers, the lines blur between doing-nondoing: "Leaning into the stillness of whatever activity they were doing became a meditative aspect of doing" (p. 1337). Seeing differently also involved cultivating an open attitude, without fixed judgments and expectations, without a script.

Resting with groundlessness: This involves a realization that change is inevitable:

> By turning the lens of mindfulness on ourselves we start to see the truth of change…we all understand that everything is changing, you know, we can

intellectually grasp this...however when we turn the lens of mindfulness on ourselves we begin to understand that we are change...then I can't hold so tightly to this notion of solidity...then my whole relationship to death changes...it dramatically shifts...and death becomes less of a tragedy." (Bruce & Davies, 2005, p. 1338)

Of course, this realization also brings fear and sometimes holding onto hopes that residents will get better. Hospice workers practicing mindful meditation explored the question: Can caregivers be open to and witness another's suffering in the midst of fear, struggle, and resistance within? One hospice worker noted:

I was thinking of Aretha this morning; she was kind of scared. And I really think creating an atmosphere where we are not scared when she is scared [is important] where we are just there with her. And we don't necessarily do anything with the fear. We don't say, 'no, no, no' but we don't say, 'YES, you're dying, oh how horrible' but we just kind of embrace that—then, it's much easier for people, you know? And I think that in itself, to be mindful that somebody is afraid and not to reject it, not to sugar it over with something but also not to be freaked out. But to really be with that feeling and to embrace it and to feel from our heart...Then, it seems the person can usually...can relax." (Bruce & Davies, 2005, p. 1339)

Caregivers learned to be with fearful residents and not to turn away from their fear.

The emphasis was not on perfecting fearlessness but, rather, on practicing to open to one's experience continuously and be willing to shift, and be changed in the process. (Bruce & Davies, 2005, p. 1330)

CHAPTER SUMMARY

The "M" in the COMFORT model—mindful presence—is both an attitude and a nonverbal behavior that the palliative care nurse brings to patients and their families in hospice and palliative care. Based on the Buddhist notion of mindfulness, a mindful attitude is focused on the here and now, is "in the moment," and is undistracted by any stimuli other than the immediate. Presence is that quality of being there for the patient or family member, either physically or psychologically or both, and being nonjudgmental, unscripted, and spontaneous. Thus, a mindful presence means that the nurse is totally dedicated to the circumstances she finds in the here and now, regardless of what has gone before or what is predicted to follow. It is a valuing of "being" over "doing," in the belief that compassionately bearing witness to a patient's/family's suffering may be the greatest gift a caregiver can offer.

This type of healing or compassionate presence involves actively listening to the patient's/family member's emotional state and responding to their situation with empathy. It also entails listening to and eliciting the patient's/family's stories of the illness journey. The following chapter deals with family as an integral component of palliative care.

REFERENCES

Anthony, M. K., & Vidal, K. (2010). Mindful communication: A novel approach to improving delegation and increasing patient safety. *Online Journal of Issues in Nursing, 15*(2), 2, 1 p.

Baird, P. (2010). Spiritual care interventions. In B. R. Ferrell & N. Coyle (Eds.), *Oxford Textbook of Palliative Nursing* (3rd ed., pp. 663–671). New York: Oxford University Press.

Benner, P. (1984). *From Novice to Expert.* Redwood City, CA: Addison Wesley Publishing Company.

Bolton, R. (1979). *People Skills.* Englewood, NJ: Prentice-Hall.

Bruce, A., & Davies, B. (2005). Mindfulness in hospice care: Practicing meditation-in-action. *Qualitative Health Research, 15,* 1329–1344.

Burns, M. M. (2001). Exercises for empathy. *Communication Teacher, Summer, 13.*

Childs, D. (2007). Mindfulness and the psychology of presence. *Psychology and Psychotherapy: Theory, Research and Practice, 80,* 367–376.

Cichon, E. J. (2001). Practicing active listening. *Communication Teacher, Fall,* 11–14.

Cohen-Katz, J. (2004). Mindfulness-based stress reduction and family systems medicine: A natural fit. *Family Systems and Health, 22*(2), 204–206.

Cupach, W. R., Canary, D. J., & Spitzberg, B. H. (2010). *Competence in Interpersonal Conflict* (2nd ed.). Long Grove, IL: Waveland Press, Inc.

Dahlin, C. M. (2010). Communication in palliative care: An essential competency for nurses. In B. R. Ferrell & N. Coyle (Eds.), *Oxford Textbook of Palliative Nursing* (3rd ed., pp. 107–133). New York: Oxford University Press.

Davis, C. (2007). Lifting the spirit. *Nursing Standard, 21*(48), 22–23.

Day, P. H., & Horton-Deutsch, S. (2004). Using mindfulness-based therapeutic interventions in psychiatric nursing practice—Part I: Description and empirical support for mindfulness-based interventions. *Archives of Psychiatric Nursing, 18*(5), 164–169.

Eide, H., Frankel, R., Haaversen, A. C. B., Vaupel, K. A., Graugaard, P. K., & Finset, A. (2004). Listening for feelings: Identifying and coding empathic and potential empathic opportunities in medical dialogues. *Patient Education and Counseling, 54,* 291–297.

Ferrell, B. R., & Coyle, N. (2008). *The Nature of Suffering and the Goals of Nursing.* New York: Oxford University Press.

Ferrell, B. R., & Coyle, N. (Eds.). (2010). *Oxford Textbook of Palliative Nursing* (3rd ed.). New York: Oxford University Press.

Gardner, D. (1985). Presence. In G. Bulechek & J. McCloskey (Eds.), *Nursing Interventions: Treatments for Nursing Diagnoses* (pp. 316–324). Philadelphia: Saunders.

Gilje, F. (1992). Being there: An analysis of the concept of presence. In D. Gault (Ed.), *The Presence of Caring in Nursing* (pp. 53–67), New York: National League for Nursing

Goleman, D. (1997). *Healing Emotions: Conversations With the DALAI LAMA on Mindfulness, Emotions, and Health.* Boston: Shambhala Publications, Inc.

Hirst, I. S. (2003). Perspectives of mindfulness. *Journal of Psychiatric and Mental Health Nursing, 10,* 359–366.

Johns, C. (2008). Passing people by (why being a mindful practitioner matters). *Journal of Holistic Healthcare, 5*(2), 37–42.

Kabat-Zinn, J. (1990). *Full Catastrophe Living: Using the Wisdom of Your Body and Mind to Face Stress, Pain, and Illness*. New York: Dell Publishing.

Kabat-Zinn, J. (1991). *Full Catastrophe Living*. New York: Dell.

Kabat-Zinn, J., Lipworth, L., & Burney, R. (1985). The clinical use of mindfulness meditation for the self-regulation of chronic pain. *Journal of Behavioral Medicine, 8*(2), 163–190.

Langer, E. J. (1992). Matters of mind: Mindfulness/mindlessness in perspective. *Consciousness and Cognition, An International Journal, 14,* 289–305.

Langer, E. J. (2000). Mindful learning. *Current Directions in Psychological Science, 9*(6) 220–223.

Littlejohn, S. W., & Foss, K. A. (2008). *Theories of Human Communication* (9th ed.). Belmont, CA: Thomson Wadsworth

MacPhee, M. (1995). The family systems approach and pediatric nursing care. *Pediatric Nursing, 21*(5), 417–437.

Matchim, Y., & Armer, J. M. (2007). Measuring the psychological impact of mindfulness meditation on health among patients with cancer: A literature review. *Oncology Nursing Forum, 34*(5), 1059–1066.

McDonough-Means, S. I., Kreitzer, M. J., & Bell, I. R. (2004). Fostering a healing presence and investigating its mediators. *The Journal of Alternative and Complementary Medicine, 10*(1), S-25–S-41.

Morgan, W. D., & Morgan, S. T. (2005). Cultivating attention and empathy. In C. K. Germer, R. D. Siegel, & P. R. Fulton (Eds.), *Mindfulness and Psychotherapy* (pp. 73–90). New York: Guilford.

Oken, B. S., Fonareva, I., Haas, M., Wahbeh, H., Lane, J. B., Zajdel, D., et al. (2010). Pilot controlled trial of mindfulness meditation and education for dementia caregivers. *The Journal of Alternative and Complementary Medicine, 16*(10), 1031–1038.

O'Neal, J. S. (1997). Mindfulness: Treasuring the moments. *Creative Nursing, 3*(3), 8–9.

Ott, M. J. (2002). Mindfulness meditation in pediatric clinical practice. *Pediatric Nursing, 28*(5), 487–490.

Ott, M., Norris, R. L., & Bauer-Wu, S. M. (2006). Mindfulness meditation for oncology patients: A discussion and critical review. *Integrative Cancer Therapy, 5,* 98–108.

Praissman, S. (2008). Mindfulness-based stress reduction: A literature review and clinician's guide. *Journal of the American Academy of Nurse Practitioners, 20,* 212–216.

Rapgay, L., & Bystrisky, A. (2009). Classical mindfulness: An introduction to its theory and practice for clinical application. *Annals of the New York Academy of Sciences, 1172,* 148–162.

Scheick, D. (2011). Developing self-aware mindfulness to manage countertransference in the nurse-client relationship: An evaluation and developmental study. *Journal of Professional Nursing, 27*(2), 114–123.

Sherman, D. W. (2010). Culture and spirituality as domains of quality palliative care. In M. Matzo & D. W. Sherman (Eds.), *Palliative Care Nursing: Quality Care to the End of Life* (pp. 3–38). New York: Springer.

Simon, S. T., Ramsenthaler, C. B., Bausewein, C., Krischke, N., & Geiss, G. (2009). Core attitudes of professionals in palliative care: A qualitative study. *International Journal of Palliative Nursing, 15*(8), 405–411.

Smith, J. E., Richardson, J., Hoffman, C., & Pilkington, K. (2005). Mindfulness-based stress reduction as supportive therapy in cancer care: Systematic review. *Journal of Advanced Nursing, 52*(3), 315–327.

Stewart, M., Brown, J. B., Boon, H., Galajda, J., Meredith, L., & Sangster, M. (1999). Evidence on patient-doctor communication. *Cancer Prevention and Control, 3,* 25–30.

Ting-Toomey, S. (2010). Intercultural conflict competence. In W. R. Cupach, D. J. Canary, & B. H. Spitzberg (Eds.), *Competence in Interpersonal Conflict* (2nd ed., pp. 139–162). Long Grove, IL: Waveland Press, Inc.

Turner, K. (2009). Mindfulness: The present moment in clinical social work. *Clinical Social Work Journal, 37,* 95–103.

Williams, J., & Stickley, T. (2010). Empathy and nurse education. *Nurse Education Today, 30*(8), 752–755.

Wood, J. T. (2000). *Relational Communication: Continuity and Change in Personal Relationships* (2nd ed.). Belmont, CA: Wadsworth.

DISCUSSION QUESTIONS

1. What is the main difference between the Buddhist concept of mindfulness and the attitude of being mindful?
2. How would you define the concept of mindful presence?
3. How is "being" valued more than "doing" in mindful presence?
4. How can presence be compassionate and healing?
5. What are some of the personal characteristics of the "core attitude" in palliative care?
6. What are Kabat-Zinn's seven attitudinal foundations of mindfulness?
7. How can mindful presence involve both a physical and/or a psychological presence?
8. Why are empathy and compassion considered key characteristics of a healer who is fully present?
9. How is active (or deep) listening linked to compassionate presence?
10. How does listening differ from hearing? (What are the seven activities that comprise the listening process?)
11. How is witnessing a part of mindful presence?
12. How and when is silence a valuable tool?
13. How does deep listening and bearing witness help elicit patients' and family members' stories?
14. How is intercultural sensitivity a part of mindful presence?
15. What are the four components of cultural competence in health care contexts?
16. How is Martin Buber's I-It/I-Thou dialectic an appropriate philosophical grounding for mindful presence?

EDUCATOR RESOURCES
AND MATERIALS

EXERCISES FOR LISTENING

Exercise 1—Practicing Active Listening

The objective of this activity is to provide nurses with the opportunity to practice active listening. This activity is based on Beebe & Masterson's (2000) six steps of active listening:

1. **Stop other activities.**
2. **Look at the speaker; focus on nonverbal cues.**
3. **Listen to the speaker, without interrupting.**
4. **Ask questions to determine the problem and clarify the speaker's feelings.**
5. **Paraphrase the problem and ask the speaker if you are correct.**
6. **If correct, speaker should empathize by paraphrasing feelings of the speaker.**

Place students into groups of three and have each student take turns playing the role of the nurse, patient, and family member. In the patient role, the student will possess information that he or she is reluctant to share. In the nurse role, the student will have to progress through the six steps of active listening before the patient can reveal the information. In the family member role, the student will be charged to prevent excuse making, judgments, or forms of defensive communication on the parts of the patient and nurse.

Role cards that provide the directions, a scenario, and the six steps of active listening are distributed to students. Students are told that the patient's role card and the family member's role card contain a goal (the goal is the same on both cards—for example, the goal could be "nurse must ask three questions and paraphrase two times"), but the nurse's role card does not contain the goal. The patient's card also contains a "truth," which is the content that the nurse is trying to get the speaker to reveal. As such, the nurse must continue to use the six steps of active listening until the goal has been met. Once the goal has been met (as determined by the directions for the patient and the family member role cards), the truth can be revealed to the nurse.

When distributing the role cards, be sure to emphasize that (a) the patient role may require a little "acting" and (b) the patient may have to stall the nurse until the nurse meets the goal listed on the role card. It takes approximately 15 minutes for members to complete the activity. To debrief the activity, solicit comments about the scenario and inquire whether the goal was met. For example, the instructor may ask: (1) how well each step of active listening was accomplished and (2) if the scenario were conducted again, how active listening could be improved. Ask students to indicate how the six steps of active listening could be incorporated into situations they encounter in palliative nursing.

REFERENCES AND SUGGESTED READINGS

Beebe, S. A., & Masterson, J. T. (2000). *Communicating in Small Groups: Principles and Practices* (6th ed.) New York: Longman.

Gibb, J. R. (1961). Defensive communication. *Journal of Communication, 11,* 141–148.

Scenario for Practicing Active Listening Exercise

Patient

Directions

1. Read the following scenario and be prepared to act it out.
2. DO NOT reveal the truth to the nurse until the nurse has met the goal. (This means you may have to stall and give excuses for not wanting to talk. Be creative.)

Scenario

You are talking with the nurse in between his/her patient care duties. The nurse says that you seem uncomfortable. You do not want to talk about your problem. It is still too upsetting to talk about, so you make up excuses until the nurse reaches the goal.

Goal

NURSE MUST ASK TWO QUESTIONS AND PARAPHRASE TWO TIMES.

When the nurse has reached the goal, you may now reveal the truth: During your cancer treatment, your significant other has been having an affair.

STOP LOOK LISTEN ASK QUESTIONS PARAPHRASE EMPATHIZE

Nurse

Directions

1. Read the following scenario and be prepared to act it out.
2. The truth of the situation will not be revealed to you until you have practiced the six steps of active listening as required by this exercise.

Scenario

A patient seems very preoccupied and is possibly upset about something. The patient has not been as outgoing as he/she has been on previous treatment visits, so ask what the matter is.

YOU MUST CONTINUE TO PRACTICE ACTIVE LISTENING, USING THE STEPS BELOW, UNTIL THE PATIENT REVEALS THE TRUTH TO YOU.

STOP LOOK LISTEN ASK QUESTIONS PARAPHRASE EMPATHIZE

FAMILY MEMBER

Directions

Read the scenario below. The NURSE will start by asking the PATIENT whether there is something wrong or if there is something the patient would like to talk about. The NURSE should practice active listening until the PATIENT reveals the truth.

Scenario

A nurse and patient are talking. The NURSE asks the PATIENT if there is something making him/her uncomfortable. The PATIENT is not prepared to talk at first, so the nurse must practice active listening.

Goal

NURSE MUST ASK TWO QUESTIONS AND PARAPHRASE TWO TIMES. You keep the pair communicating until the NURSE has met the goal and the PATIENT has revealed the truth.

DO NOT allow the NURSE to draw conclusions, express judgment, or give advice unless requested until after the required paraphrasing has been done.

STOP LOOK LISTEN ASK QUESTIONS PARAPHRASE AND EMPATHIZE

Adapted from Elaine J. Cichon, Florida International University, *Communication Teacher, Fall,* 2001, 11–14.

Exercise 2—Effective Listening Role Play

First review these principles for effective listening:

Effective Listening Guidelines
1. Focus on feeling words.
2. Note the general content of the message.
3. Observe the speaker's body language.
4. Do not fake understanding.
5. Do not tell the speaker how he/she feels.

Adapted from R. Bolton (1979). *People Skills.* Englewood, NJ: Prentice-Hall. In MacPhee, M. (1995). The family systems approach and pediatric nursing care. *Pediatric Nursing, 21,* 5, 417–437.

Working in nurse–patient dyads, the patient expresses a current problem (e.g., the patient is very concerned with how her oldest daughter is reacting to her poor prognosis). The nurse, with body posture that is relaxed but also alert and with good eye contact, encourages conversation about the problem by giving simple responses that let the patient know she is heard (e.g, "That sounds very difficult for you." "I'm so sorry you're having this problem.") The nurse should also use *open-ended questions/responses* that can serve as *prompts* (e.g., "What can I do to help you resolve this?" "Tell me how you see the problem being resolved."). The nurse might also use *silence* to allow time for the patient to express herself. *Paraphrasing* should be used to clarify the patient's concern and check it for accuracy: for example, "I'm hearing that you're very concerned about how your daughter is dealing with your prognosis." *Mirroring* back the patient's feelings can also be useful: "It seems that you're feeling sad and anxious about this."

After the role play, the patient should give the nurse feedback about whether she felt that the nurse heard her accurately and whether her nonverbal communication expressed concern and empathy. Then the two should exchange roles and repeat the exercise.

Adapted from MacPhee, M. (1995). The family systems approach and pediatric nursing care. *Pediatric Nursing, 21*(5), 418.

Exercise 3—Exercises for Empathy

Empathic Listening

The goal of this exercise is to enhance nurses' empathic listening skills and sensitize their perceptual differences. Pair students and have each student take a turn sharing a professional or personal joy or concern in his or her life. Provide students with a checklist for "attending behaviors" (Wolvin & Coakely, 1996):

1. maintaining an appropriate and comfortable gaze
2. open body posture
3. encouraging head nods
4. responsive facial expressions
5. vocalics expressed with a tone of care and involvement
6. beneficial silence

Dyads are given 10 minutes (5 minutes per person) to share their joys and concerns. Immediately after sharing, the speaker should write down responses to the following questions:

1. Did the person focus her or his attention?
2. What attending behaviors were present to show the person was listening empathically?
3. Did the listener offer any nonaccepting responses?

Using class time, or alternatively as a take-home assignment, have each student design a greeting card that expresses an understanding of what the other person is encountering. The essence of the card should paraphrase what the partner shared, in other words, the empathic listener's perception of the joy or concern. The card should be a combination of text and illustration. They should remember to feel and think with the other person in mind.

In addition to turning in cards as an assignment, instructors will have students give their card to their partner. As students read the original cards created just for them, they consider how well their partners paraphrased and perceived their feelings.

Note: An additional assignment can include grading their partner's card or allowing class time for partners to discuss and share the decision making behind card construction. This allows for further assessment and understanding of empathic listening skills and identification of what skills were exhibited or lacking.

Adapted from Burns, M. M. (2001). Exercises for empathy. *Communication Teacher, Summer,* 13.

REFERENCES

Wolvin, A., & Coakley, C. G. (1996). *Listening* (5th ed.). Dubuque, IA: Brown & Benchmark. (Provides summary of exercise created by Mari Miller Burns, Iowa Lakes Community College, Estherville, IA.)

Exercise 4—Meditation Practice to Foster Clinician Empathy

1. Take a moment and feel the rise and fall of your breath before meeting your next patient.
2. As you walk to the door, imagine that on the other side of the door another human being is waiting.
3. The human being is someone who is suffering, who has hopes and dreams, and who believes that you can help relieve his or her suffering.
4. Now open the door and say "hello."

Adapted from Morgan & Morgan (2005), as cited in Turner, K. (2009). Mindfulness: The present moment in clinical social work. *Clinical Social Work Journal, 37,* 95–108.

Exercise 5—Exercises for Mindful Presence

Preparation for and evaluation of an encounter to which you bring mindful presence requires reflection or what Johns (2008) refers to as the "beginner's mind" (p. 41). It is an openness to new ideas and new possibilities. Johns (2008) recommends this structured reflection exercise both to prepare for an encounter and to evaluate it.

Model for Structured Reflection

Bring the mind home.
Focus on an experience that seems significant in some way.
What particular issues seem significant to pay attention to?
How were others feeling and why did they feel that way?
How was I feeling and why did I feel that way?

What was I trying to achieve and did I respond effectively?

What were the consequences of my actions on the patient, family, and myself?

What factors influence the way I was/am feeling, thinking, and responding to this situation (personal, organizational, professional, cultural)?

What knowledge did or might have informed me?

To what extent did I act for the best and in tune with my values?

How does this situation connect with previous experiences?

Given the situation again, how might I respond differently?

What would be the consequences of responding in new ways for the patient, family, and myself?

What factors might constrain me from responding in new ways?

How do I *now* feel about this experience?

Am I able to support myself and others better as a consequence?

What insights have I gained?

Am I more able to realize my vision as a lived reality?

Figure 1, "Model for Structured Reflection"

Adapted from Johns (2008). Passing people by (why being a mindful practitioner matters). *Journal of Holistic Healthcare, 5*(2), 37–42.

Exercise 6—Mindfulness Meditation Exercises

Mindful Eating

Take one raisin from a box of raisins, just one. Look at it carefully, touch it, smell it, and then gingerly put it in your mouth. Bite into it and chew, then swallow.

Experience the burst of taste that you overlook when you eat raisins by the handful.

Adapted from O'Neal, J. S. (1997). Mindfulness: Treasuring the moments. *Creative Nursing, 3*(3), 8–9.

A variation on this exercise is to pretend you are aliens, just arriving on Earth and discovering this object (the raisin) for the first time. Pay attention to everything you can discover about the object so that you can report on it back home (Ott, 2002, p. 490).

Mindful Walking

One way to integrate awareness into your daily routine is through mindful walking.

Choose a short walk, such as the hallway outside your office, and begin walking, paying attention to the entire experience of walking. (You will not be walking in order to get anywhere but merely to attend to the act of walking itself.) Pay attention to all the physical details and sensations of walking. Be aware of both the self and the environment as you walk.

Adapted from Ott, M. J. (2002). Mindfulness meditation in pediatric clinical practice. *Pediatric Nursing, 28*(5), 490.

Body Scan Exercise

The body scan (described below) allows one to develop a focused awareness of the body. The body scan permits one to develop the ability "to be a compassionate witness to whatever is happening in the body at any particular moment in time, to be present without judgment, expectations, or demands and without a need to change anything" (Ott, 2002, p. 490).

Body Scan Instructions

When doing the body scan, it is important to be in a safe, comfortable place free from distractions and interruptions. It is also important to wear loose, comfortable clothing that will not restrict the body's breathing in any way. The body tends to cool when doing a body scan, so a light cover may be needed to keep the body comfortably warm. The body scan can be learned either lying down or in a seated position, although it is more easily learned lying down.

Begin by assuming a comfortable position lying on the floor or on a bed. (A pillow or rolled towel under the knees may be used to relieve pressure on the lower back.) Take a few slow, deep breaths focusing on the breath itself. Then gently allow your attention to move to the entire body as it is breathing.

Now, focus on the toes of the left foot so that the full attention is on the toes of the left foot. Then move the awareness to the left foot, ankle, on up the calf to the knee, the thigh, and on to the left hip. Breath is allowed to move in and out of each part of the body as it is scanned. Next, allow awareness to move across the pelvis and down to the toes of the right foot, then to the whole foot and up the calf to the knee, the thigh, and to the hip and pelvis. From here move awareness up through the lower abdomen and lower back, up to the chest, upper back, and shoulders.

Next focus awareness on the fingers of both hands, moving up the hands to the wrists and both arms and returning to the shoulders. From here move through the neck, throat, all parts of the face, the ears, and the top of the head.

When this is completed, breath is invited in through the toes, up through the entire body, and out an imaginary opening at the crown of the head, so that the breath is moving freely from one end of the body to the other. Finally, the breath is allowed to flow in through the top of the head, down through the whole body, and out the toes. End by feeling the entire body lying down breathing. When ready, gently deepen the breath bringing small movements to the fingers and toes, the arms, and legs. Roll over to one side, pause briefly, and then using the arms, slowly push up to a seated position, bringing the head up last. Pause in a seated position for a few breaths, noticing how the body feels before proceeding to the next activity.

Used with permission from: Ott, M. J. (2002). Mindfulness meditation in pediatric clinical practice. *Pediatric Nursing, 28*(5), 489.

Exercise 7

Table 4.4 Operational Steps in the STEDFAST Self-Aware Mindfulness Development Model

To develop self-aware mindfulness in the nurse–client relationship, progress through each step seeking help as needed. An answer of "no" at any step signals the need to mindfully focus on one's breath then non-judgmentally accept whatever thoughts and feelings arise on the way to returning to one's breath, finally emerging ready to practice self-aware mindfulness in the nurse–client relationship.

Self-Assess

- In this present moment, what is happening with me, can I first truly and non-judgmentally accept where I am right now and take on the therapeutic role? If no, mindfully breathe…accept…breathe…When ready (continue)

Therapeutic Role

- Am I springing fully alive into the nursing role, bringing competence and caring in the relationship? If no, mindfully breathe…When ready

Empathy

- As I interact, can I sense or imagine what it must feel like to live through what the client has experienced? If no, mindfully breathe…When ready
- Am I able to non-judgmentally accept where the client is at this present moment? If no, mindfully breathe…When ready

Detached Reflection

- Can I practice self-control to move part of myself away from the immediate client stimuli to think about my actions/reactions? If no, mindfully breathe…When ready
- Can I accept and deal with overly intense or disproportionate feelings enough to not spill beyond the boundaries of the nursing role? If no, mindfully breathe…When ready
- Am I using critical thinking and theory to help me monitor, analyze, and reevaluate the original experience? If no, mindfully breathe…When ready

Facilitated Debriefing

- Can I/have I access/accessed person(s) who can help me process feelings, thoughts, or actions? If no, mindfully breathe…When ready
- Can I accept my vulnerabilities signaled by changes in my behavior (ignoring or overreacting) and/or my disproportionate feelings (e.g., overly liking or even disliking the client)? If no, mindfully breathe…When ready
- Can I appropriately self-disclose at a level at which I feel safe? If no, mindfully breathe…When ready
- Can I use theory and feedback to help me identify blind spots, receive support, clinically problem solve, and reengage? If no, mindfully breathe…When ready

Alert Empathy

- Can I be alertly attentive and caringly connect with empathy yet also stay mindful about countertransference, my self-boundary, and needs as separate from the client's boundary and needs? If no, mindfully breathe…When ready

Table 4.4 (*continued*)

Self-Aware Mindfulness

- Have I learned anything new about me—about life? If no, mindfully breathe…When ready
- Do I more quickly enact self-control to accept and deal with intense feelings of changes in my behavior as signals of countertransference? If no, mindfully breathe…When ready

Therapeutic Use of Self

- Can I identify how, in the present moment, I distinctively use my unique fully alive self to facilitate the client? If no, mindfully breathe…When ready
- Can I, with boundaries intact, invest my nonjudgmental, aware, mindful self as the helping instrument? If no, mindfully breathe…When ready
- Am I ready to further develop self-aware mindfulness by reengaging the STEDFAST self-aware mindfulness model? If no, mindfully breathe…When ready return to Self-Assess

Used with permission from: Scheick, D. (2011). Developing self-aware mindfulness to manage countertransference in the nurse-client relationship: An evaluation and developmental study. *Journal of Professional Nursing, 27*(2), 114–123.

5

FAMILY

Harriet Grove was an 80-year-old woman living in a residential care facility. She was a retired nurse, and her 90-year-old husband was a resident of the adjoining dementia care unit. Harriet had three children, all in their late 50s, with one son residing 20 miles away and two daughters living out of state.

Six months ago Harriet was diagnosed with Stage IV ovarian cancer (OVCA). Harriet has moderate cognitive impairment with limited decision-making capacity and has relied on her son Bob for decision making for several years. At the time of the OVCA diagnosis, her three children (Bob, Jane, and Alice) met with the facility medical director and all agreed that chemotherapy or surgery would be too burdensome and that she should receive comfort care only. Harriet's three children are not close in relationships and communicate infrequently. The three children were in agreement about the treatment decision, although one of the daughters has since criticized her brother for not insuring that their mother "got better care" so her OVCA would have been diagnosed earlier. There have also been some financial conflicts, as Jane's husband has been very verbal in expressing his belief that Bob has wasted their inheritance by arranging for such an expensive facility for Harriet and her husband. Alice, who lives a thousand miles away, has been visiting monthly since the diagnosis and seems the closest to her mother.

Harriet has been seen by hospice in the residential care facility. They have been able to effectively treat her pain, constipation, and nausea. Harriet's three children have been very supportive of hospice and the goals of comfort care only. However, a few days ago Harriet developed severe intractable vomiting and increased abdominal pain. After 24 hours of uncontrolled symptoms, Bob requested that they move his mother to the hospital to see if more could be done for palliation of her symptoms.

On admission to the hospital, it is determined that Harriet's OVCA had further metastasized and she now has a bowel obstruction. The hospital intensivist recommends that they ask the palliative care team to consult and convene a family conference. Bob has not been on good terms with Jane but agrees to call her for the family conference. Alice arrives and becomes very emotional, panicked at the possibility that her mother will die. Alice asks the hospital staff to start tube feeding and to consider surgery as she just is not ready to let go. Bob becomes very upset at Alice's request and suggests that if she had visited more often, perhaps she wouldn't feel the need to prolong their mother's life.

The scene unfolding in the family conference concerning Harriet's care is all too common and represents a typical experience for a palliative nurse. Sometimes it's not the patient who requires the nurse's attention—it's the family! Families need help understanding a poor prognosis, interpreting physical and cognitive changes in the patient, and making decisions about treatment and care choices when there are no desirable options. Anger and frustration often result from family tensions, feelings about the disease, or fear and can be directed toward the nurse. Conflicts arise among family members, with family and staff, and between family and patient.

Unlike other clinicians who have structured interactions with families, the palliative care nurse has an intimate role with family members. Bedside care avails opportunities for the nurse to be "like family" for the patient and their loved ones. Attention to family advocacy (task communication) as well as the family's story (relational communication) facilitates the nurse's acceptability into the family unit. This chapter depicts the family as a system with predictable family communication patterns that can inform appropriate communication strategies to prevent as well as resolve conflicts concerning family. Although medical decision making is often left in the hands of individuals biologically or legally related to the patient, we also consider family members to include those with close, intimate relationships described as familial.

This chapter presents three tenets of family communication in palliative nursing. Family systems perspective will illustrate the importance of family members in the patient's clinical story, thus revealing their status as second-order patients. The next section will describe family communication patterns and present identifiable family caregiver types. By adjusting communication to a family's established communication pattern, nurses can collaborate with the family, which serves as a conduit to the patient. The final section of this chapter will focus on family meetings and how they can be tailored to meet the family members' needs. As the intricate layers of family communication are described in this chapter, we hope it will reveal the sensitive needs of the family and warrant the attention of palliative nurses.

TAKING CARE OF THE FAMILY

Communication with families is integral to hospice and palliative care as families and patients face decisions about aggressive care and the turn toward comfort only. Although families (and patients) assume that information will be given to them when asked, clinical staff typically provides updates and information to the family only when there is a clinical change (Gold, Philip, McIver, & Komesaroff, 2009). However, families report needing and wanting regular information updates (Gold et al., 2009; Rhodes, Mitchell, Miller, Connor, & Teno, 2008). In the absence of routine information, family communication efforts become focused on the nurse, who is left with the responsibility of filling in the communication gaps between clinical staff and family. The nurse provides a bridge between the front stage of bedside care with the patient and access to the backstage happenings of the medical system and other clinicians. Boxes 5.1 and 5.2 provide the perspective of family caregivers.

Box 5.1

"We would like to be asked if we want to be involved and how much we want to participate in her care. I know my Mom. It is very clear that the nurse and health care team believe they are responsible for the medical care, but as far as the emotional part, that is us. I had been her caregiver for three years, I felt like I needed to get in there and help and I couldn't. It is feeling that you are connected directly to what is happening and when they don't include you, you feel even more vulnerable." (Eggenberger & Nelms, 2007)

Box 5.2

"We had a great nurse ... He was willing to answer all our questions. If you asked him anything he was there ... just being personable. Telling us straight up what's going on is definitely helpful, but it is nice when they can bring it down to a level where we feel like they are explaining it to us. Having nurses and doctors be honest with us and keeping us informed helped us cope. No matter how bad it is, you would much rather hear the honest truth ... But somehow still maintaining some hope. They show us they care about us." (Eggenberger & Nelms, 2007)

Taking care of the family and providing family-centered care involves addressing family burden, advocating for the family, educating about disease and illness, providing emotional support, valuing family input, and enabling flexibility and easy access to the patient (Nelson et al., 2010). These efforts also involve helping the family work through their feelings and say good-bye (Kaasalainen, Brazil, Ploeg, & Martin, 2007). Not surprisingly, nurses are a central figure in the family's memories of the death—adequacy on the job, attitude, and empathy are remembered most, more than direct care, hospice, or patient preferences (Munn & Zimmerman, 2006). Good death experiences are derived from a singular nurse who is perceived to be in charge of care, actively providing accurate information and emotional support as needed (Rhodes et al., 2008).

Variations in family background and beliefs shape the nature and magnitude of family issues that can develop during hospice and palliative care. Family functioning and family beliefs and acceptability about prognosis vary. Families range from well functioning, characterized by a supportive environment and good conflict resolution skills, to dysfunctional families wherein family members have suppressed anger and hostility toward each other (Bartell & Kissane, 2005). Additionally, families have

Table 5.1 Common Problems with Family Communication

- Family doesn't understand what is being told to them.
  - o *"Generally, they act like they understand, and when the MD leaves the room they ask the nurse what he/she meant. The MD is usually in a hurry. The units are so busy that the staff doesn't have enough time to sit down and really talk and listen to the patient/family."*
- The concept of family is different for every patient and family.
  - o *"I suppose you could also look at the concept of family in that not everyone is directly affected by the change but may have a 'family' tie that is indirect to the central concept."*
- The family doesn't know the patient's wishes.
  - o *"It's hard to communicate to a family that their family member's health is progressively declining and then having to ask them about the patient's desires."*
  - o *"It's so hard when you don't know what the patient wants ... when you see the family members struggling, saying 'I don't know, I don't know. I know what I would want, but I don't know what he would want.'"*
- The family refuses help.
  - o *"On one occasion, I had a patient who was undergoing chemotherapy for breast cancer who needed extra support in her home. For example, she needed home health for physical therapy, etc. Her daughter felt that we were offering this type of service because we felt she was unable to care for her mother—and she became angry. I had great difficulty expressing to the daughter that I was trying to help her mother as well as her."*

a general belief about how end-of-life decision making is done within their family (Leichtentritt & Rettig, 2002) (Table 5.1).

These beliefs are grounded in family norms and the history of decision-making style within the family, how the family has previously negotiated disagreements, and their perceived obligation to the family as it pertains to care. Collectively, the patient and family have a shared past that sustains a communication dynamic best described as a *family system*—a system that warrants family as "second-order" patients.

FAMILY AS SECOND-ORDER PATIENTS

As nurses witness the patient's illness story, it becomes evident that it is embedded within a family system (see Chapter 2 for more on witnessing). A **family system** is comprised of bounded, interrelated individuals with identifiable communication behaviors. Family members are **interdependent**, as they have the ability to influence one another. The interdependent relationships among family members expose potential sources of conflict, reveal variations in health literacy within the family, and demonstrate positive or negative family coping. Family members are considered "second-order patients" in hospice and palliative care because they are part of a system of communication that influences the patient's adherence to care plans, treatment decisions, and hospice enrollment, and they share in the end-of-life care experience (Sherman, 1998).

With no beginning or end, family systems are constantly interacting with their **environments**, the people and information accessible to them, and respond by adapting to stress and change or through resistance. The family system has boundaries, which serve to protect family members. **Boundaries** define the system and communication between the system and other systems (Mehta, Cohen, & Chan, 2009). Boundaries can be permeated to allow information to come in and go out (Mehta et al., 2009). Nurses can gain insight on the permeability of family boundaries by paying attention to family member reactions to illness and communication between family members (including the patient).

Clinicians trigger boundaries within the family system by introducing new "plots" in the stories of patients and families (Sharf, Harter, Yamasaki, & Haidet, 2011). For example, families facing a crisis such as serious, chronic, or terminal illness make every effort to return the family to "normal" or pre-illness/diagnosis. Hospice and palliative care brings an imbalance to the family system and suggests an outcome that will ultimately result in a shift in the family system. Family roles and responsibilities are misplaced when a loved one is ill, and patients are often more concerned about the suffering of their family members than their own suffering (Sherman, 1998). By learning about family roles, nurses can shape their communication to protect or validate family member identity (Leon & Knapp, 2008).

Consistent exposure and interaction with the family also allows the nurse to recognize **predictable interactions**. Predictable interactions are repetitive interactions among family members within the system that depict informal guidelines which shape hierarchical roles and appropriate family communication. Patient care permits the nurse to enter the family system and learn the rules of the family (Elliott & Herndon, 1981) (Table 5.2).

Armed with this knowledge, the nurse can adapt his or her own communication and use family background to simultaneously provide task and relational communication in order to meet care goals. This involves understanding how illness has impacted family functioning and relationships, each member's emotional reaction and intensity, and variations in family-level involvement in care (Leon & Knapp, 2008).

Recognition of the family's predictable interactions tells us if the family is an open or closed system. In an **open system**, information is allowed in and out of the system. Family members disclose private information about the family and permit nurses to

Table 5.2 Family-Centered Approach

Family-Centered Approach
➤ Recognize that families have patient expertise and knowledge
➤ Recognize that relationships with families are reciprocal
➤ Recognize that no hierarchy can exist between nurse and family

Used with permission from: Leon, A. M., & Knapp, S. (2008). Involving family systems in critical care nursing: Challenges and opportunities. *Dimensions of Critical Care Nursing, 27*(6), 255–262. Doi: 10.1097/01.DCC.0000338866.47164.6d learn about **vertical stressors** that emerge from long-established family patterns and relationship history between family members (Leon & Knapp, 2008). On the other hand, in a **closed system** family members do not share background information or insight into family relationships. In these instances, nurses often face the challenge of working with families that haven't accepted or don't believe the terminal prognosis (Back & Arnold, 2005). Conflict is likely to occur as family members insist on aggressive care, even when nurses, physicians, and other clinical staff feel it is inappropriate (Fine, 2010; Luce, 2010). The nurse is left to provide patient care that may seem contradictory to the family or that the family may not approve of (Fine, 2010).

Working with patients requires attending to the communicative needs of the family. The goal is to match family needs with resources and empower them through education and support (MacPhee, 1995). Collaborating with the family requires ongoing, structured communication that is aligned with preexisting family communication patterns and is sensitive to the family structure (Leon & Knapp, 2008). The family is a conduit to the patient, and family competency is important to the overall care experience (MacPhee, 1995).

FAMILY AS A CONDUIT TO THE PATIENT

When faced with a difficult patient, a patient who refuses to take medication or cooperate with care instructions, the nurse can turn to the family for help and mediation. When patients are no longer able to communicate their wishes, the nurse focuses on family members who are responsible for serving as surrogate decision makers. Family members are important allies for the nurse. Establishing effective communication with family members enables the nurse to capture an accurate history, clarify goals of care for patient and family (which may be different), build relationships to develop trust, and reduce their stress (Bluestein & Latham Bach, 2007). Familiarity with the family teaches the nurse about established communication patterns that shape family coping and decision making. Learning to recognize these patterns will enable the nurse to understand and predict family communication behavior (Bluestein & Latham Bach, 2007).

Family communication patterns are the interpersonal scripts or rules for communication within a family (Fitzpatrick & Ritchie, 1994; McLeod & Chaffee, 1973; Ritchie & Fitzpatrick, 1990). Communication patterns represent learned behavior that has been shaped by a collective family history. These family rules are governed by two family beliefs about conversation and conformity. **Conversation beliefs** dictate appropriate topics for family discussion, the degree to which families spend time communicating, and whether or not the family engages in communal or individual decision making. **Conformity beliefs** inform the appropriate amount of time family members spend together, expected sharing of family resources, and obedience to parents.

Variations in family conversation and conformity beliefs are best summarized into four identifiable family communication patterns. Each distinguishing pattern gives the nurse direction on how to communicate with the family. **Consensual families** value parental decision making and explaining decisions to the children, and allow for the children to provide input. **Pluralistic families** have open discussions that involve all family members and value participatory decision making. Both of these family communication patterns illustrate open family systems that allow information to come into the family and be discussed. On the other hand, **protective families** and **laissez-faire families** represent closed family systems and rely on nursing intervention to facilitate family communication. Protective families rely heavily on obedience to parental authority, and family members engage in very little communication with each other. Similarly, laissez-faire families have little family interaction, and members are emotionally detached from each other. By distinguishing the patient and family's communication pattern, there is potential for family conflict to be identified. Nurses can then adapt their communication accordingly so that problem solving and solutions meet the family structure. One approach to working with families is to conduct a family meeting (also known as a family conference) to ensure that family members are involved in the patient's plan of care.

FAMILY MEETINGS

Family meetings facilitate decision making about the patient's care and include discussions about disease status, withdrawing or withholding artificial feeding, discharge options, and symptom distress (Hudson, Thomas, Quinn, & Aranda, 2009; Yennurajalingam et al., 2008). Pain and spiritual issues are more likely to be discussed and documented when a palliative care nurse or physician is present for the family meeting (Machare Delgado et al., 2009). Often a family meeting is prompted by the family's lack of understanding or information about the medical condition of the patient or following a critical incident (Radwany et al., 2009). Commonly, family meetings occur due to conflict between the patient and family and health care team (Yennurajalingam et al., 2008).

While the goal of these meetings is to enable collaboration between care staff and family members, they also benefit family decision making (Wittenberg-Lyles, Goldsmith, Ragan, & Sanchez-Reilly, 2010). First, communication in family meetings is meant to relieve the uncertainty that family members have about chronic care, dying, and death. Nurses educate families by translating medical knowledge (Dawson, 2008) (see Chapter 3 on health literacy). Second, nurses are there to support families and reassure them that they are making good decisions. Finally, family meetings are a place for nurses to help mediate family conflict.

Just as each family has its own unique communication pattern and style, each family member in a family meeting has varying needs in terms of literacy level, support, and family arbitration. The four family communication patterns mentioned previously inform a typology of family members that can be used to predict dominant areas of focus within the family meeting (Wittenberg-Lyles, Goldsmith, Demiris, Parker Oliver, & Stone, 2012). The **Manager Family Member** enjoys a privileged position in the family and is understood to be the head of the household. He or she is at the top of the family hierarchy. This family member is the self-appointed family spokesperson, limiting other family members in the decision-making process. Ultimately, this individual is positioned to make the majority of care-planning choices in accord with the patient. Palliative nurses must work to include other family members and make them feel part of the care process.

Providing support and reassurance becomes the nursing focus for family meetings with the **Carrier Family Member**. This individual surrenders to family authority, absorbing the greatest burden and sacrifices for patient care. Communication with other family members is limited and often the result of a long-established trend of hostility within the family. Acceptance of the patient's illness and treatment choices can be confounding because of limited talk, but the pressure to conform to the patient's wishes is given priority over his or her own needs. Caregivers welcome the opportunity to self-disclose to staff, as the family environment prohibits it. Information seeking and suppression are a common coping mechanism. Nursing intervention is immediately needed for the Carrier Family Member as this family member is dependent upon staff to facilitate patient requests.

Family meetings with the **Partner Family Member** emphasize education about the disease, placement options, and additional information that contributes to making an educated decision that meets the patient's need congrugent with family expectations for care. Typically this family member benefits from the patient's advance care planning and family-initiated internal meetings to facilitate decision making and support. As a result, nursing staff are there to provide further education and to support open family discussions and the sharing of care stress. Finally, the **Loner Family Member** is in greatest need of nursing intervention. This family member has little support for decision making and care provision. Limited communication and weak relationships with other family members results in high stress, burden, limited social support networks, and anger and resentment.

DEVELOPING CLINICAL PRACTICE SKILLS

This chapter summarizes family communication during hospice and palliative care. The diversity among families (and individual family members within the same family!) was highlighted through a discussion about family systems, family communication patterns, and family meetings. Specific communication tools are now provided to help accomplish family-centered clinical nursing practice.

Assessment

Understanding the family's system and the family role of the primary caregiver determines the overall communication approach of the nurse. Harriet's family from the opening case study reveals a closed family system as family members have low interdependence. The three children (Bob, Jane, and Alice) are not close, and while Alice

Table 5.3 The Survey of Family Fields

I. **Current Situation**
  A. Ask the patient and family about the onset of symptoms, include date
  B. Ask the patient and family about the early history of the problems, include date of prior symptoms

II. **Nuclear Family Emotional System**
  A. Courtship: where, when, how did couple meet; characteristics; major events during this period
  B. Marriage: when, where, who attended, attitude of families origin
  C. Major Events: year by year since marriage; make family diagram of nuclear family; include moves, illnesses, births, deaths, divorce, jobs, etc.

III. **Extended Family Emotional Systems**
  A. Major Events Between Leaving Home and the Marriage: include relationship with the extended family for both husband and wife; dating patterns; goal and career development; education
  B. Major Events in Both Families of Origin Prior to Home and Since Leaving Home: make a family diagram for the husband and the wife with dates and major changes; include sibling history and description of important triangles
  C. Parents' Relationship: meeting, marriage, history of major events in their lives; include family diagram for each parent

---

Used with permission from: Titelman, P. (Ed.). (1998). *Clinical Application of Bowen Family Systems Theory.* Binghamton, NY: Haworth Press, p. 55.

visits her mother monthly, she doesn't appear to be communicating with Bob. Thus, the three children have little influence on one another. As a result, the nurse cannot expect that any information given to one family member will be shared with another. However, families who enjoy an open family system are different, and information shared with one family member is likely relayed within the family.

To gain an understanding of the family system, use the outline of the "Survey of Family Fields" (Table 5.3). Begin by first identifying individuals who are in the nuclear family, and their gender, age, name, occupation, and educational background. Once this background information is obtained, invite the patient and individual family members to discuss the onset of the symptoms. This should be done with all members of the family collectively, as questions target major events within the family.

Delving deeper into the family history and individual relationships between family members (especially relationships with the patient) can provide direction on communication gaps within the family. Family communication gaps reveal points of tension for the family and indicate where conflict may occur. These gaps can include strained relationships that prohibit family members from speaking or show how families handle conflict, crisis, and stressful events. The following can be used to assess for family background (Box 5.3):

Box 5.3 Questions to be Posed by the Hospice Team to Derive a Care Plan

Horizontal Stressors

The family life cycle (to be considered by the hospice team member)

1.   In what stage of life is the family, and what are the related tasks?
2.   How might the terminal illness and death interfere with the accomplishment of these tasks?
3.   Will the death be out of the usual order of the life cycle events?

All of the following questions are to be posed to key family members:
Other family and environmental stressors

1.   What else is going on in your family's life?
2.   What has helped you in dealing with these stressors?
3.   What has not been helpful?

Vertical Stressors

Transgenerational coping styles

1.   Could you give an example of a difficulty your family has faced when you were growing up?
2.   What helped your family get through this?
3.   What was tried that did not help?

Family history of loss

1.   What other losses has your family experienced?
2.   What do you remember from those experiences?

Family rules, toxic issues, and secrets

1.   What values did you learn growing up that are still important to you now?
2.   What values did you learn growing up that don't work as well for you now?

Unresolved relationships

1.   Tell me about your family.
2.   Who is close to whom?

Spirituality and ethnic background
Information gathered indirectly through observation and the family's initiation of discussion.

Used with permission from: Knapp, E. R., & DelCampo, R. L. (1995). Developing family care plans: A systems perspective for helping hospice families. *American Journal of Hospice and Palliative Medicine, 12,* 39–47.

Table 5.4 Checklist to Assess Family Stressors

✓ *Coupling*—Are there any family members who are newly single or new couples?
✓ *Expansion*—Has the family recently increased in size due to addition of children or in-laws?
✓ *Contraction*—Has the family recently decreased in size due to adult children leaving, family members moving away, or death?

In addition to asking specific questions about prior family experiences, nurses should listen carefully (or witness patient/family stories; see Chapter 2) to capture information on family life cycles and communication patterns. There are three phases in family systems that represent varying family life cycles (Leon & Knapp, 2008). Use the following checklist to assess additional family stressors rooted in life cycle changes (Table 5.4).

Listen for indicators of the following communication as family members talk about communication with other family members (Box 5.4):

Box 5.4 Listening for Indicators of Communication Patterns

Open Communication
    Supportive statements
Blocked (direct communication)
    Hang up phone
    Refuse to answer
    Agree not to talk about illness
Blocked (indirect communication)
    Not responsive
    Appear uncomfortable
Self-censored speech
    Pro-active
    Fear of causing anxiety
Reactive
    Sensing someone does not want to talk and pulling back
Use of third parties
    Intermediaries
    Sounding boards

Used with permission from: Kenen, R., Ardern-Jones, A., & Eeles, R. (2004). We are talking, but are they listening? Communication patterns in families with a history of breast/ovarian cancer (HBOC). *Psycho-Oncology, 13*, 335–345.

Evidence of these types of communication characteristics among family members can help determine whether the family system is open or closed.

Plan

Knowledge about the family system can provide background and context for learning about the communication preferences of individual family members. For example, we see two very different types of family members from within Harriet's family. Bob has served as the designated proxy and family spokesperson and has had regular and routine communication with health care staff throughout Harriet's care. Comparatively, Alice and Jane have not played such an active role; however, Alice has maintained routine visits with her mother on a monthly basis. Given the low interdependence of these family members (even Bob is reluctant to call Jane when Harriet's condition changes), the nurse needs to treat these family members separately rather than as one unit that can be approached in the same way. After the family system has been assessed, the below chart can be used to determine specific family member types and identify family communication patterns (Table 5.5).

There is often a range of perspectives within one family, and conflict can arise between family members who think they know the patient best or because they are uncertain about patient preferences (Back & Arnold, 2005). For the nursing staff taking care of Harriet, differences among family member knowledge, communication with each other, and family role resulted in an intense family meeting caused by a lack of understanding of hospice (which led to Bob's request to transfer Harriet to the hospital), and filled with family conflict (between Bob and Alice) and denial (for Alice).

Table 5.5 Caregiver Types and Communication Patterns

Caregiver Type	Caregiver Burden (Identified with Family Communication Patterns)
Manager	• Caregiver's hierarchical family role overpowers open family communication. • Family input of differing viewpoints is limited.
Carrier	• Caregiver relies on clinicians to facilitate patient requests. • Caregiver follows directions from patient. • Caregiver isolation • Caregiver prioritizes family harmony/stasis over own feelings.
Partner	• Emotional—open, honest interactions with dying loved one • Potentially supportive environment • Potential for immediate family support • Potential for extended family support • Choices not made alone—decisions made as a family unit
Loner	• Little to no caregiver support or resources • Caregiver has limited choices, solo-provider. • Caregiver anger, resentment, abandonment, helplessness

Table 5.6 Themes Often Discussed in Family Meetings in the Palliative Care Setting

___ The nature of the illness and its symptoms.

___ Prognosis and future predictions about the course of the illness.

___ Caregiving roles about symptom management, medications, nursing care.

___ Liaison with medical team.

___ The emotional demands of the role.

___ Importance of self-care and respite from caregiving.

___ What to expect as death approaches.

___ How to talk with the patient about death and dying.

___ The process of saying good-bye.

___ How to manage a death in the home.

___ The positive aspects of the caregiver's role.

___ Teamwork and sharing the role of caregiver.

___ When to seek help and how.

___ Support from volunteers and other community resources.

Used with permission by Oxford University Press: Coyle, N., & Kissane, D. W. (2010). Conducting a family meeting. In D. W. Kissane, B. D. Bultz, P. M. Butow, and I. G. Finaly (Eds.), *Handbook of Communication in Oncology and Palliative Care*. New York: Oxford University Press, p. 168.

It is only when a change in Harriet's condition occurred that the family was brought together by a family meeting intervention. To plan for the family meeting, begin to prioritize communication and support needs using the information in Table 5.6.

First, checkmark appropriate information needs for the family. Then rank-order the checked topics to plan for what topics should be discussed first, second, third, and so on. Keep in mind that nurses serve important functions in the context of family meetings. The role of the nurse in the family meeting is summarized in Table 5.7.

Intervene

Hosting a family meeting involves providing information and creating a comfortable environment to allow family members the opportunity to share their feelings and

Table 5.7 Roles of the Nurse in Family Meetings

- Share the most current, up-to-date information about the patient's status
- Bridge established relationships built on trust between family members and newer, less known team members
- Capture the variance of messages (some conflicting) provided by multiple providers/team members
- Responsible for carrying out primary features of plan of care decisions
- Fulfill a professional role that includes carrying for the family

Adapted from: Nelson, J. E., Cortez, T. B., Curtis, J. R., Lustbader, D. R., Mosenthal, A. C., Mulkerin, C., et al. (2011). Integrating palliative care in the ICU: The nurse in a leading role. *Journal of Hospice & Palliative Nursing, 13*(2), 89–94.

thoughts (Hudson et al., 2009). There is no set standard for family meeting communication, and nursing intervention can either come from being a discussion leader or a contributing team member during the meeting (Hudson, Quinn, O'Hanlon, & Aranda, 2008). Regardless of role, the nurse should work to make sure the family meeting happens early in the patient's care (Hudson et al., 2008).

A typical conference format includes a premeeting to set goals (see planning phase above) and identify roles, followed by an initial inquiry to obtain the family's understanding and discuss relevant case issues (Machare Delgado et al., 2009). Table 5.8 provides a helpful tool when communicating with family members. Another way to engage family members is to ask questions. Table 5.9 shows how questions can be asked in different ways to elicit the response needed. For example, the opening case study does not indicate whether or not Harriet has advance care planning in place. To help her family think about her wishes and recall any advance care planning conversations, use these questions in Box 5.5.

Box 5.5 Eliciting Patient Goals

- Did [patient's name] ever tell you what he or she wanted for him/herself?
- Did [patient's name] ever talk about care of another family member and state whether they would have wanted the same type of treatment?

Used with permission from: Dahlin, C. (2010). Communication in palliative care: An essential competency in nurses. In B. Ferrell and N. Coyle (Eds.), *Oxford Textbook of Palliative Nursing* (pp. 107–133, Table 5–5). New York: Oxford University Press.

Finally, remember to listen and practice nonverbal immediacy when interacting with family members (see Chapter 2). Effective listening guidelines are summarized in Table 5.10.

Evaluate

While communication in family meetings is important—and family meetings can result in enhanced family learning and decision making—the nurse can extend care offered to families that goes beyond one or two family gatherings with the health care team. Nurses are easily available to families compared with other clinical team members and thus gain more knowledge about the family's coping process and early bereavement stages. Addressing family coping as part of the evaluation process can lead to increased or decreased nursing intervention and enable early bereavement care (Wittenberg-Lyles & Sanchez-Reilly, 2008). Move beyond documenting communication within the family meeting and evaluate the family's coping by asking key questions as suggested in Box 5.6. Early bereavement care can also begin by evaluating spiritual or religious needs of family members. Box 5.7 can be used as suggested prompts for a discussion about spiritual needs. Box 5.8 provides common responses of children to serious illness in the family.

Table 5.8 Strategies for Engaging Family Members in Communication

Strategy	Model Statement
Engaging Family Members/Companions in Interactions	
Personal Introduction.	"I'm [name] ... it is good to meet you. I am [patient]'s nurse; I'm glad you are here."
Identify others important but not present.	"Are there other family members or people close to you that you want to be included, either at the next visit or by phone call?"
Elicit concerns and expectations.	"Do you have particular questions or concerns that you would like us to discuss today?"
	"Some things that the family members of the other patients have expressed as concerns include ... Are these on your mind too?"
Check for accuracy.	"Am I correct that your question/concern about your wife's condition is ... ?"
Check for agreement.	"It seems that we agree that treatment X [or hospice] looks like it might be a good choice for us to consider ... Do you think so too?"
Validate convergence.	"It is helpful that together we understand and agree about the best treatment [care or placement] choices ... let's talk now about what to do and how to get started."
Reassure.	"It is good that you are here so we can talk openly about these things."
	"You have every reason to feel reassured that you are doing everything possible to help your husband."
	"It is okay if you and (the patient) want more time to think about your options. I'll continue to care for him/her and be here for you no matter what you decide."
Addressing Challenges to Convergence, Relationships and Alliances	
Control conversational dominance.	"I understand how you feel about this; now I'd like to hear it in his/her words."
Acknowledge family member/companion's response.	"It may be hard to understand the test results given that he doesn't seem to feel sick or have any symptoms."
Addressing anger at medical recommendation.	"These treatments don't always work the way we hope and expect they will. We are all understandably upset when this happens."

Used with permission by Oxford University Press: Albrecht, T. L., Eggly, S. S., & Ruckdeschel, J. C. (2010). Communicating with relatives/companions about cancer care. In D. W. Kissane, B. D. Bultz, P. M. Butow, and I. G. Finaly (Eds.), *Handbook of Communication in Oncology and Palliative Care* (pp. 157–164). New York: Oxford University Press. [Table 14.1]

Table 5.9 Communication Skills Used in Family Meetings

- *Circular question.* Ask each family member to comment in turn on aspects of others to promote curiosity and reflection by the group as a whole.
  For example, "How are your parents and sisters coping with Dad's illness? Who is most upset in your view?"
- *Reflexive questions.* Invite the family to reflect on possibilities, hypotheses and a range of outcomes to stimulate their internal efforts to improve family life.
  For example, "What benefits might come from caring for Dad at home? In what ways might this be hard for you or as a family group?"
- *Strategic questions.* Here a solution might be incorporated into the wording of the question to more directly guide the family toward an outcome that is considered preferable.
  For example, "What change in Dad's symptoms would need to occur for you to realize that admission to an inpatient hospice bed is necessary?"
- *Summary of family focused concerns.* The family's views are reflected back to highlight levels of tension or discordance in different member's opinions, while maintaining professional neutrality, yet inviting further problem solving by the family.
  For example, "As a family, you recognize your father's desire to die at home, your mother's commitment to meet his wishes, and yet your concern that his confusion is becoming unmanageable and a burden to your mother. There is no easy answer here, as whichever solution you adopt will appear to demand more of each of you for a time."

Used with permission by Oxford University Press: Coyle, N., & Kissane, D. W. (2010). Conducting a family meeting. In D. W. Kissane, B. D. Bultz, P. M. Butow, and I. G. Finaly (Eds.), *Handbook of Communication in Oncology and Palliative Care* (pp. 165–175). New York: Oxford University Press. [Box 15.2]

Table 5.10 Listening Guidelines

1. Focus on feeling words.
2. Note the general content of the message.
3. Observe the speaker's body language.
4. *Do not* fake understanding.
5. *Do not* tell the speaker how he/she feels.

Used with permission from: MacPhee, M. (1995). The family systems approach and pediatric nursing care. *Pediatric Nursing, 21*(5), 417–423, 437. Table 2. Reprinted from *Pediatric Nursing*, 1995, Volume 21, Number 5, pp. 417–423, 437. Reprinted with permission of the publisher.

Box 5.6 Questions to Address Patients' and Families' Coping

- Have you/your family been through something like this before? How did you/your family react/cope?
- Do you have a belief in a higher power that supports you?
- Is there anyone you'd like us to call?
- Can you anticipate any potential areas of concern for you and your family?
- Who could you call if you started to feel really sad?
- Did the patient ever tell you what they wanted for themselves?
- Is there anyone you think the patient would like to see?
- Who is supporting you now?
- Who can you call when things get more difficult?

Used with permission from: Dahlin, C. (2010). Communication in palliative care: An essential competency in nurses. In B. Ferrell and N. Coyle (Eds.), *Oxford Textbook of Palliative Nursing.* New York: Oxford University Press, p. 118.

Box 5.7 Assessing Spiritual Needs

- Does your particular tradition offer you helpful religious or spiritual counsel in this situation?
- Is there a particular person you turn to for spiritual help?
- Do you draw strength from any particular object or symbol, e.g., art, music, poetry, religious icons?
- Do you have a particular place where you find solace?
- Are there particular people or activities that lift your spirits?
- Do you feel your own spiritual or religious practices are being neglected and, if so, how may we assist you?

Used with permission by Oxford University Press: Hudson, R. (2009). Responding to family caregivers' spiritual needs. In P. Hudson and S. Payne (Eds.), *Family Caregivers in Palliative Care: A Guide for Health and Social Care Professionals* (p. 45). New York: Oxford University Press.

Box 5.8 Common Responses of Children to Illness

- Magical Thinking that results in feelings of guilt (e.g., "I once told Mommy I wished she were dead")
- Fears of abandonment, especially in younger children
- Fears of contracting the disease

(continued)

Box 5.8 (*continued*)

- Anger, withdrawal, being uncooperative, especially in adolescents
- Acting-out behavior with lack of usual attention
- Frustrations with an altered lifestyle because of decreased financial resources, less family fun activities because of the ill person's inability to participate, etc.
- Inability to concentrate and focus, especially regarding schoolwork

Used with permission from: Glass, E., Cluxton, D., & Rancour, P. (2010). Principles of patient and family assessment. In B. Ferrell and N. Coyle (Eds.), *Oxford Textbook of Palliative Nursing*. New York: Oxford University Press, pp. 87–106: Table 4–6.

CHAPTER SUMMARY

Families of hospice and palliative care patients need nursing care. They need someone to help them navigate the medical system, gain access to clinical staff and test results, and interpret unfamiliar medical terms. They turn to the nurse to meet these communication needs. Recognizing that the patient *and* family are impacted when a family member is seriously, chronically, or terminally ill can foster partnerships and bring supportive communication to the family's care experience. Inquiring about the family's history and background and the primary caregiver's family role, and actively seeking the coping needs of families are qualities of family-centered nursing care. Seeing patient and family as one can be a challenge in some settings; the next chapter provides instruction on how to manage various work settings and strive for quality improvement.

REFERENCES

Back, A. L., & Arnold, R. M. (2005). Dealing with conflict in caring for the seriously ill: "It was just out of the question." *JAMA, 293*(11), 1374–1381. Doi: 293/11/1374 [pii] 10.1001/jama.293.11.1374

Bartell, A. S., & Kissane, D. W. (2005). Issues in pediatric palliative care: Understanding families. *Journal of Palliative Care, 21*(3), 165–172.

Bluestein, D., & Latham Bach, P. (2007). Working with families in long-term care. *Journal of the American Medical Directors Association, 8*(4), 265–270. Doi: S1525-8610(06)00624-4 [pii] 10.1016/j.jamda.2006.12.022

Dahlin, C. (2010). Communication in palliative care: An essential competency in nurses. In B. Ferrell & N. Coyle (Eds.), *Oxford Textbook of Palliative Nursing* (pp. 107–133). New York: Oxford University Press.

Dawson, K. A. (2008). Palliative care for critically ill older adults: Dimensions of nursing advocacy. *Critical Care Nursing Quarterly, 31*(1), 19–23. Doi: 10.1097/01.CNQ.0000306392.02154.0700002727-200801000-00005 [pii]

Dias, L., Chabner, B. A., Lynch, Jr., T. J., & Penson, R. T. (2003). Breaking bad news: A patient's perspective. *The Oncologist, 8*, 587–596.

Eggenberger, S. K., & Nelms, T. P. (2007). Being family: The family experience when an adult member is hospitalized with a critical illness. *Journal of Clinical Nursing, 16*(9), 1618–1628.

Elliott, S., & Herndon, A. (1981). Teaching family systems theory to family practice residents. *Journal of Medical Education, 56*(2), 139–141.

Fine, R. L. (2010). Keeping the patient at the center of patient- and family-centered care. *Journal of Pain and Symptom Management, 40*(4), 621–625. Doi: S0885-3924(10)00573-7 [pii] 10.1016/j.jpainsymman.2010.06.008

Fitzpatrick, M. A., & Ritchie, L. (1994). Communication schemata within the family: Multiple perspectives on family interaction. *Human Communication Research, 20*, 275–301.

Gold, M., Philip, J., McIver, S., & Komesaroff, P. A. (2009). Between a rock and a hard place: Exploring the conflict between respecting the privacy of patients and informing their caregivers. *Internal Medicine Journal, 39*(9), 582–587. Doi: IMJ2020 [pii] 10.1111/j.1445-5994.2009.02020.x

Hudson, R. (2009). Responding to family caregivers' spiritual needs. In P. Hudson and S. Payne (Eds.), *Family Caregivers in Palliative Care: A Guide for Health and Social Care Professionals* (p. 45). New York: Oxford University Press.

Hudson, P., Quinn, K., O'Hanlon, B., & Aranda, S. (2008). Family meetings in palliative care: Multidisciplinary clinical practice guidelines. *BMC Palliative Care, 7*, 12. Doi: 1472-684X-7-12 [pii] 10.1186/1472-684X-7-12

Hudson, P., Thomas, T., Quinn, K., & Aranda, S. (2009). Family meetings in palliative care: Are they effective? *Palliative Medicine, 23*(2), 150–157. Doi: 0269216308099960 [pii]10.1177/0269216308099960

Kaasalainen, S., Brazil, K., Ploeg, J., & Martin, L. S. (2007). Nurses' perceptions around providing palliative care for long-term care residents with dementia. *Journal of Palliative Care, 23*(3), 173–180.

Leichtentritt, R. D., & Rettig, K. D. (2002). Family beliefs about end-of-life decisions: An interpersonal perspective. *Death Studies, 26*(7), 567–594.

Leon, A. M., & Knapp, S. (2008). Involving family systems in critical care nursing: Challenges and opportunities. *Dimensions of Critical Care Nursing, 27*(6), 255–262. Doi: 10.1097/01. DCC.0000338866.47164.6d00003465-200811000-00006 [pii]

Luce, J. M. (2010). A history of resolving conflicts over end-of-life care in intensive care units in the United States. *Critical Care Medicine, 38*(8), 1623–1629. Doi: 10.1097/CCM.0b013e3181e71530

Machare Delgado, E., Callahan, A., Paganelli, G., Reville, B., Parks, S. M., & Marik, P. E. (2009). Multidisciplinary family meetings in the ICU facilitate end-of-life decision making. *American Journal of Hospice and Palliative Care, 26*(4), 295–302. Doi: 1049909109333934 [pii] 10.1177/1049909109333934

MacPhee, M. (1995). The family systems approach and pediatric nursing care. *Pediatric Nursing, 21*(5), 417–423, 437.

McLeod, J., & Chaffee, S. (1973). Interpersonal approaches to communication research. *American Behavioral Scientist, 16*, 469–499.

Mehta, A., Cohen, S. R., & Chan, L. S. (2009). Palliative care: A need for a family systems approach. *Palliative & Supportive Care, 7*(2), 235–243. Doi: S1478951509000303 [pii] 10.1017/S1478951509000303

Munn, J. C., & Zimmerman, S. (2006). A good death for residents of long-term care: Family members speak. *Journal of Social Work in End-of-Life & Palliative Care, 2*(3), 45–59.

Nelson, J. E., Cortez, T. B., Curtis, J. R., Lustbader, D. R., Mosenthal, A. C., Mulkerin, C., et al. (2011). Integrating palliative care in the ICU: The nurse in a leading role. *Journal of Hospice & Palliative Nursing, 13*(2), 89–94.

Nelson, J. E., Puntillo, K. A., Pronovost, P. J., Walker, A. S., McAdam, J. L., Ilaoa, D., et al. (2010). In their own words: Patients and families define high-quality palliative care in the intensive care unit. *Critical Care Medicine, 38*(3), 808–818.

Radwany, S., Albanese, T., Clough, L., Sims, L., Mason, H., & Jahangiri, S. (2009). End-of-life decision making and emotional burden: Placing family meetings in context. *American Journal of Hospice and Palliative Care, 26*(5), 376–383. Doi: 1049909109338515 [pii] 10.1177/1049909109338515

Rhodes, R. L., Mitchell, S. L., Miller, S. C., Connor, S. R., & Teno, J. M. (2008). Bereaved family members' evaluation of hospice care: What factors influence overall satisfaction with services? *Journal of Pain and Symptom Management, 35*(4), 365–371. Doi: S0885-3924(08)00007-9 [pii] 10.1016/j.jpainsymman.2007.12.004

Ritchie, L., & Fitzpatrick, M. A. (1990). Family communication patterns: Measuring interpersonal perceptions of interpersonal relationships. *Communication Research, 17,* 523–544.

Sharf, B., Harter, L., Yamasaki, J., & Haidet, P. (2011). Narrative turns epic: Continuing developments in health narrative scholarship. In T. Thompson, R. Parrott, & J. F. Nussbaum (Eds.), *Routledge Handbook of Health Communication* (2nd ed., pp. 36–51). Mahwah, NJ: Routledge.

Sherman, D. W. (1998). Reciprocal suffering: The need to improve family caregivers' quality of life through palliative care. *Journal of Palliative Medicine, 1*(4), 357–366. Doi: 10.1089/jpm.1998.1.357

Titelman, P. (Ed.). (1998). *Clinical Application of Bowen Family Systems Theory.* Binghamton, NY: Haworth Press, p. 55.

Wittenberg-Lyles, E., Goldsmith, J., Ragan, S., & Sanchez-Reilly, S. (2010). *Dying With Comfort: Family Illness Narratives and Early Palliative Care.* Cresskill, NJ: Hampton Press.

Wittenberg-Lyles, E., & Sanchez-Reilly, S. (2008). Palliative care for elderly patients with advanced cancer: A long term intervention for end-of-life care. *Patient Education & Counseling, 71*(3), 351–355.

Yennurajalingam, S., Dev, R., Lockey, M., Pace, E., Zhang, T., Palmer, J. L., et al. (2008). Characteristics of family conferences in a palliative care unit at a comprehensive cancer center. *Journal of Palliative Medicine, 11*(9), 1208–1211. Doi: 10.1089/jpm.2008.0150

References and Additional Readings for Family Systems Theory

Bluestein, D., & Latham Bach, P. (2007). Working with families in long-term care. *Journal of the American Medical Directors Association, 8*(4), 265–270. Doi:S1525-8610(06)00624-4 [pii]

Bochner, A., & Eisenburg, E. (1987). Family process: System perspectives. In C. R. Berger & S. H. Chaffee (Eds.), *Handbook of Communication Science* (pp. 540–563). Beverly Hills, CA: Sage.

Broderick, C. B. (1993). *Understanding Family Process: Basics of Family Systems Theory.* Thousand Oaks, CA: Sage Publications.

Klein, J. M., & White, D. M. (2002). *Family Theories* (2nd ed.). Thousand Oaks, CA: Sage.

Knapp, E. R., & DelCampo, R. L. (1995). Developing family care plans: A systems perspective for helping hospice families. *The American Journal of Hospice and Palliative Care, 12,* 39–47.

Leon, A. M., & Knapp, S. (2008). Involving family systems in critical care nursing: Challenges and opportunities. *Dimensions of Critical Care Nursing, 27*(6), 255–262. Doi: 10.1097/01. DCC.0000338866.47164.6d

MacPhee, M. (1995). The family systems approach and pediatric nursing care. *Pediatric Nursing, 21*(5), 417–423, 437.

Mehta, A., Cohen, S. R., & Chan, L.S. (2009). Palliative care: A need for a family systems approach. *Palliative & Supportive Care, 7*(2), 235–243. Doi:S1478951509000303 [pii] 10.1017/S1478951509000303

Roberts, C. S., Baile, W. F., & Bassett, J. D. (1999). When the caregiver needs care. *Social Work in Health Care, 30*(2), 6–80.

Titelman, P. (1998). Family systems assessment based on Bowen theory. In P. Titelman (Ed.), *Clinical Applications of Bowen Family Systems Theory* (pp. 51–65). Binghamton, NY: Haworth Press.

Weinstein, R. K. (1981). Bowen's family systems theory as exemplified in Bergman's "Scenes from a Marriage." *Perspectives in Psychiatric Care, 19*(5–6), 156–163.

Wright, L. M., & Leahey, M. (1990). Trends in nursing of families. *Journal of Advanced Nursing, 15*(2), 148–154.

References and Additional Readings for Family Communication Patterns Theory

Carmon, A. F., Western, K. J., Miller, A. N., Pearson, J. C., & Fowler, M. R. (2010). Grieving those we've lost: An examination of family communication patterns and grief reactions. *Communication Research Reports, 27*(3), 253–262.

Fitzpatrick, M. (2004). Family communication patterns theory: Observations on its development and application. *Journal of Family Communication, 4* (3/4), 167–179.

Fitzpatrick, M., & Ritchie, L. (1994). Communication schemata within the family: Multiple perspectives on family interaction. *Human Communication Research, 20,* 275–301.

Hay, J., Shuk, E., Zapolska, J., Ostroff, J., Lischewski, J., Brady, M. S., et al. (2009). Family communication patterns after melanoma diagnosis. *Journal of Family Communication, 9,* 209–232.

Keaten, J., & Kelly, L. (2008). Emotional intelligence as a mediator of family communication patterns and reticence. *Communication Reports, 21*(2), 104–106.

Kenen, R., Ardern-Jones, A., & Eeles, R. (2004). We are talking, but are they listening? Communication patterns in families with a history of breast/ovarian cancer (HBOC). *Psycho-Oncology, 13,* 335–345.

Koerner, A. F., & Fitzpatrick, M. (2002). Toward a theory of family communication. *Communication Theory, 12*(1), 70.

Ledbetter, A. M., & Schrodt, P. (2008). Family communication patterns and cognitive processing: Conversation and conformity orientation as predictors of informal reception apprehension. *Communication Studies, 59*(4), 388–401.

McLeod, J., & Chaffee, S. (1973). Interpersonal approaches to communication research. *American Behavioral Scientist, 16,* 469–499.

Ritchie, L., & Fitzpatrick, M. (1990). Family communication patterns: Measuring interpersonal perceptions of interpersonal relationships. *Communication Research, 17,* 523–544.

Schrodt, P., Ledbetter, A. M., Jernberg, K. A., Larson, L., Brown, N., & Glonek, K. (2009). Family communication patterns as mediators of communication competence in the parent-child relationship. *Journal of Social and Personal Relationships, 26*(6–7), 853–874.

Schrodt, P., Witt, P. L., & Messersmith, A. S. (2008). A meta-analytical review of family communication patterns and their associations with information processing, behavioral, and psychosocial outcomes. *Communication Monographs, 75*(3), 248–269.

Wittenberg-Lyles, E., Goldsmith, J., Ragan, S., & Sanchez-Reilly, S. (2010). *Dying With Comfort: Family Illness Narratives and Early Palliative Care.* Cresskill, NJ: Hampton Press.

References and Additional Readings for Family Meetings

Albrecht, T. L., Eggly, S. S., & Ruckdeschel, J. C. (2010). Communicating with relatives/companions about cancer care. In D. W. Kissane, B. D. Bultz, P. M. Butow, and I. G. Finaly (Eds.), *Handbook of Communication in Oncology and Palliative Care* (p. 157–164). New York: Oxford University Press.

Coyle, N. & Kissane, D. W. (2010). Conducting a family meeting. In D. W. Kissane, B. D. Bultz, P. M. Butow, and I. G. Finaly (Eds.), *Handbook of Communication in Oncology and Palliative Care* (p. 165–175). New York: Oxford University Press.

Dahlin, C. (2010). Communication in palliative care: An essential competency in nurses. In B. Ferrell and N. Coyle (Eds.), *Oxford Textbook of Palliative Nursing* (pp. 107–133). New York: Oxford University Press.

Dawson, K. A. (2008). Palliative care for critically ill older adults: Dimensions of nursing advocacy. *Critical Care Nursing Quarterly, 31*(1), 19–23. Doi: 10.1097/01. CNQ.0000306392.02154.0700002727-200801000-00005 [pii]

Glass, E., Cluxton, D., & Rancour, P. (2010). Principles of patient and family assessment. In B. Ferrell and N. Coyle (Eds.), *Oxford Textbook of Palliative Nursing* (pp. 87–106). New York: Oxford University Press.

Gueguen, J. A., Bylund, C. L., Brown, R. F., Levin, T. T., & Kissane, D. W. (2009). Conducting family meetings in palliative care: Themes, techniques, and preliminary evaluation of a communication skills module. *Palliative & Supportive Care, 7*(2), 171–179. Doi: S1478951509000224 [pii]10.1017/S1478951509000224

Hudson, P., & Payne, S. (Eds.). (2009). *Family Caregivers in Palliative Care: A Guide for Health and Social Care Professionals.* New York: Oxford University Press.

Hudson, P., Quinn, K., O'Hanlon, B., & Aranda, S. (2008). Family meetings in palliative care: Multidisciplinary clinical practice guidelines. *BMC Palliative Care, 7,* 12. Doi: 1472-684X-7-12 [pii]10.1186/1472-684X-7-12

Hudson, P., Thomas, T., Quinn, K., & Aranda, S. (2009). Family meetings in palliative care: Are they effective? *Palliative Medicine, 23*(2), 150–157. Doi: 0269216308099960[pii]10.11 77/0269216308099960

Knapp, E. R., & DelCampo, R. L. (1995). Developing family care plans: A systems perspective for helping hospice families. *American Journal of Hospice and Palliative Medicine, 12,* 39–47.doi: 10.1177/104990919501200608

MacPhee, M. (1995). The family systems approach and pediatric nursing care. *Pediatric Nursing, 21*(5), 417–423, 437.

Machare Delgado, E., Callahan, A., Paganelli, G., Reville, B., Parks, S. M., & Marik, P. E. (2009). Multidisciplinary family meetings in the ICU facilitate end-of-life decision making. *American Journal of Hospice and Palliative Care, 26*(4), 295–302. Doi: 1049909109333934 [pii]10.1177/1049909109333934

Wittenberg-Lyles, E., Goldsmith, J., Demiris, G., Parker Oliver, D., & Stone, J. (2012). The impact of family communication patterns on hospice family caregivers: A new typology. *Journal of Hospice and Palliative Nursing, 14,* 25–33.

DISCUSSION QUESTIONS

1. What are the characteristics of a family system?
2. Why are family members considered "second-order" patients?
3. How do nurses come to understand family system boundaries?
4. What is a family-centered approach?
5. What challenges arise from closed family systems?
6. How is the nurse's role different between open and closed family systems?
7. In what ways are family communication patterns shaped?
8. How would you prepare for a family meeting with a Carrier Family Member?
9. From your (and your significant other's, if applicable) family background, what major events stand out as most influential in developing the family system? What family life cycles are currently present in your own family? What vertical stressors are present?
10. What family member type do you identify with? Explain.
11. What communication strategies would you use to engage Harriet's daughter Alice (from the chapter's opening case study)? Write out what you would say to her. What questions, if any, would you ask her?
12. What topics would you prioritize for a family meeting with Harriet's children? How would you rank-order the topics?

TEACHING RESOURCES AND MATERIALS

EXERCISE #1 - EXERCISES FOR FAMILY SYSTEMS THEORY

Patient: Let me take you back to the start. I was completely well. I was toodling along with two little kids and a husband. He is a physician. I was teaching school and one day I found a football-sized mass in my abdomen. It frightened me, but because it was so huge I felt it had to be benign. After all, something that big could not possibly be cancer and the word cancer never even entered my mind. I was too young, I thought. Anyway, I went into surgery not having a clue. The doctors really did not prepare me for it except to say I had a mass. I remember exactly what he said. I woke up from surgery to hear my surgeon say, "I have good news and bad news. I didn't have to remove any of your organs, but (pause) you do have cancer." It just blew me away.

During that year I had four surgeries and was in and out of the hospital. I had a lot of time to think about what I was going to do with the rest of my life, which was something you say when you have cancer. "Now what am I going to do? I don't know how long I am going to live." No one was sure of that prognosis, and I said to myself, "What I do know is that I don't like what I'm doing now. I do not want to teach school anymore. I want to do something health care related because I don't even know where any of my organs are and I need to know more about my body if I am going to work with my doctors intelligently."

While some people who interacted with me were really truly wonderful, others were horrendous, just horrendous. I thought I could make a difference. I stopped teaching and went into the medical field, which is actually one of the best things that could have happened to me.

Subsequently, I have had 13 abdominal surgeries, 4 months of chemotherapy, and 6 weeks of radiation therapy. I have a tumor right now. I have not been tumor-free in years. I have always had some tumor that is being watched. The tumor in my abdomen that they're watching now will have to be operated on, or I will get experimental therapy. I am having a computerized tomography (CT) scan next Tuesday, and so I am sort of on edge. I am very well aware of the size of the tumor because I feel it. So, I am very realistic about where I am at and about how things might go for me, and that's why I need to act.

Through my care, I have been in three different hospitals. I think my medical care has always been excellent. I left the two previous ones, not because I was unhappy with the medical care, but because I was unhappy with the communication with the doctors. After one complication, the surgeon did not speak to me for the whole admission. He would come into my room everyday to check the chart and examine me, but he never sat down to say, "This is what I found. This is what happened. This is what's going to happen. This is what we're going to do." I don't think he could deal with a bad result and I really was a bad result. So I left the hospital. Another doctor made me feel like things were just hopeless. Now I have found somebody who lifts my spirits and who is always going to tell me he's got something to pull out of his hat for me. I am realistic and I know that the hat is getting a little bit shallow, but the communication is there and I am part of a team, and that's very important. Patients really want to feel that they're part of a team.

I didn't have my cancer in isolation. I was married, was raising children, and I had two parents who were very distressed about my cancer. They were from an older generation where they couldn't talk about cancer. I took it upon myself to educate them. I remember one time we sat down in my living room and I said, "Okay now, on the count of five we are all going to say the word 'cancer'." They literally could not say it. They lived far away and tended to only see me during times when I was ill. Never when I was well. There were a lot of times when I was ill. And when I was ill, I was really ill. What they apparently were learning from my experience was not that you can survive cancer, but that it could be really horrible.

My father was 86 years old, a very healthy man, very robust, very active, didn't look a day over 70, never had a health problem, and was uncomfortable in a hospital setting. He was just scared for me, and would say, "I will never suffer like that. I think what you're going through is just torture," and at times, it really was. Some of those times were really horrible and there was no hiding it from him. He would say, "This isn't fair, people shouldn't suffer. Somehow you have the strength to do it, but I could never do that. If I had to suffer at the end of my life, I would be active."

My parents were becoming more frail and my mother suffered from depression. My father then had some rectal bleeding. He dismissed it for ages but finally he went to the doctor. The doctor sent him for a barium enema that showed an irregularity in his colon and suggested that he probably should have a colonoscopy. I said, "Irregularity is not a word that a radiologist uses. What does that mean? Call him back and ask for a copy of the report." He said, "Oh, the doctor doesn't sound alarmed. It doesn't sound like anything major. I am feeling fine. Just let me be. The colonoscopy is just a precaution." Meanwhile he had no contact with his doctor. All the contact he has with his internist was one telephone call to be told he had an irregularity. So I was thinking, maybe it's a polyp.

He finally went for the colonoscopy, and the gastroenterologist took one look at the barium enema and said to him, "I don't know why you are here. You clearly have a blockage. You should have gone to a surgeon 3 weeks ago." My father was understandably startled by that. That was the first time he had heard "blockage." He said, "You go home." It was Friday afternoon. "I will call your internist, and tell him you really need to be admitted because you need surgery." My father went home, called me immediately, related the story, and said, "Are they trying to tell me I have cancer?" This was the first time he had brought it up. I said, "Dad, let me get off the phone," and I had my husband call the gastroenterologist. So my husband called the gastroenterologist who said, "Your father-in-law certainly has colon cancer. He should have seen a surgeon weeks ago. He is almost completely obstructed. He really needs to have surgery tomorrow." I called my father back. He said, "Well, what did the doctor say?" I said, "Well, the doctor said you really need to go to the hospital and talk to a surgeon." He asked, "Is it cancer? Am

I going to need a colostomy?" I said, "Dad, first of all, it's not that low down. Number two, we don't know if it's cancer, but it's an obstruction, and an obstruction has to be removed. You can't just live like that." He said, "I can't do it. I don't want to do it." I could hear the distress in his voice. Evidently he got off the phone, didn't say a word to my mother, walked right by her, walked into another room where he had a gun, which nobody knew about, walked out of the house, and shot himself in the head.

His suicide has changed everybody's life. It's the most extraordinary experience. I had 16 years of cancer and my father couldn't deal with the possibility of it for an hour. I was upset that he couldn't turn to me and have me or his doctor say, "Let's talk about this. Ask me questions." My mother was also completely in the dark. My father hadn't verbalized any of his concern to her. But, 2 days before he committed suicide, he said to my mother, "Well, I am having the colonoscopy on Friday and then I will know if I have cancer or not." What he was saying to her was, "I will know if I am going to kill myself or not," because that same day he went to the bank, took out $5,000 and sent me a check for $5,000 that arrived in my mailbox the day after he killed himself with a little note that said, "Darling, here's a gift and mum's the word. Love, Dad."

After we buried my father, I made an appointment to see the internist, and I said, "Why didn't you pick up the phone and call me? You knew how concerned I was." And he said, "Because your father never told me to call you." I said, "But my father didn't know what he had. You didn't even give him the opportunity." I asked the internist, "How many times a month do you have a patient who has just been diagnosed with cancer?" He said, "Maybe once or twice a month." I was furious. "Did you ever think of how serious it is telling somebody that they have cancer? How much thought have you given it?" He said, "Maybe I never gave it a thought."

I am here today, because if only one person hears this story and understands just how traumatic giving a cancer diagnosis is, it will be worth it.

DISCUSSION QUESTIONS

1. Does the author describe an open or closed family system? Did she and her parents have high or low interdependence?
2. What evidence is there of system boundaries for this family?
3. What family communication pattern is characterized?
4. What family member type does this author represent?

Used with permission from: Dias, L., Chabner, B. A., Lynch, Jr., T. J., & Penson, R. T. (2003). Breaking bad news: A patient's perspective. *The Oncologist, 8*, 587–596.

REFERENCES AND SUGGESTED READINGS FOR THIS EXERCISE

Dixson, M. D. (1995.) Models and perspectives on parent-child communication. In T. Socha & G. H. Stamp (Eds.), *Parents, Children and Communication* (pp. 433–462). Mahwah, NJ: Erlbaum.

Framer, J. R. (1985). *Family Interfaces: Transgenerational Patterns.* New York: Brunner Mazel.

Galvin, K. M., & Brommel, B. J. (2000). *Family Communication: Cohesion and Change* (5th ed.). Boston: Allyn & Bacon.

Hoopes, M. (1987). Multigenerational systems: Basic assumptions. *American Journal of Family Therapy, 15,* 195–205.

McGoldrick, M., Gerson, R., & Shellenberger, S. (1999). *Genograms: Assessment and Intervention* (2nd ed.). New York: Norton.

EXERCISES FOR FAMILY COMMUNICATION PATTERNS THEORY

EXERCISE #1

See what kind of caregiver you are most likely to be!

Make copies of the following scale and administer to your students.

Use the scale below to answer the following questions about your family:

Strongly disagree				*Strongly agree*
1	2	3	4	5

___1. In our family we often talk about topics like politics and religion where some person disagrees with another.

___2. My parents often say something like "Every member of the family should have some say in family decisions."

___3. My parents often ask my opinion when the family is talking about something.

___4. My parents encourage me to challenge their ideas and beliefs.

___5. My parents often say something like "You should always look at both sides of an issue."

___6. I usually tell my parents when I am thinking about things.

___7. I can tell my parents almost anything.

___8. In our family we often talk about our feelings and emotions.

___9. My parents and I often have long, relaxed conversations about nothing in particular.

___10. I really enjoy talking with my parents, even when we disagree.

___11. My parents like to hear my opinions, even when they don't agree with me.

___12. My parents encourage me to express my feelings.

___13. My parents tend to be very open about their emotions.

___14. We often talk as a family about things we have done during the day.

___15. In our family we often talk about our plans and hopes for the future.

___TOTAL SCORE

___16. My parents often say something like "You'll know better when you grow up."

___17. My parents often say something like "My ideas are right and you should not question them."

____18. My parents often say something like "A child should not argue with adults."

____19. My parents often said something like "There are some things that just shouldn't be talked about."

____20. My parents often said something like "You should give in on arguments rather than risk making people mad."

____21. When anything really important is involved, my parents expect me to obey without question.

____22. In our home, my parents usually had the last word.

____23. My parents feel that it is important to be the boss.

____24. My parents sometimes become irritated with my views if they are different from theirs.

____25. If my parents don't approve of it, they don't want to know about it.

____26. When I am at home, I am expected to obey my parents' rules.

____TOTAL SCORE

Revised Family Communication Patterns Scale

Ritchie, L. D. (1991). Family communication patterns: An epistemic analysis and conceptual reinterpretation. *Communication Research, 18,* 548–565.

Ritchie, L. D., & Fitzpatrick, M. A. (1990). Family communication patterns: Measuring intrapersonal perceptions of interpersonal relationships. *Communication Research, 17,* 523–544.

Scoring Instructions

Have students add up their score for items #1–15 (conversation) and #16–26 (conformity). The range of scores for conversation is 15–75, with a score in between 15 and 45 as low conversation and 46–75 as high conversation. Similarly, the range of scores for conformity is 10–50, with a score in between 10 and 30 as low conformity and 31–50 as high conformity. After students have identified their high and low quality, they should use the family caregiver typology to determine their likelihood for a caregiver type.

EXERCISE #2

Use the following quotes from family members about their hospice and palliative care experiences to identify the family member type and/or family communication pattern. Additionally, describe what you would prioritize for a family meeting with this family/family member.

1. "I think it's hard for my sister. She is visiting from Florida and it's harder for her because she is the oldest in the family and there is a lot of pressure on her. I think she feels like she has to take care of everything and keep an eye on everyone and everything." (Eggenberger & Nelms, 2007)

2. A family of seven members, including a father, five children, and one grandchild, who had gathered from several states to be together at the bedside of their mother, said: "We are all here together and we are all doing this together. Our family has managed by everybody pitching in and being here ... being together is helping our family. It's just more comforting to know that you've got somebody ... It's been nice to know that I won't be the only one here, doing everything." (Eggenberger & Nelms, 2007)

3. Martin, primary caregiver for his mother who had Alzheimer's disease:

I didn't have a social support system. I think I had more support from friends and strangers than I did from family. Family just like totally abandoned us and like she (points to neighbor) would come over and baby-sit for me sometimes and then the lady across the street would baby-sit for me sometimes, but I never once had a sister-in-law or somebody ask "Can I come over and baby-sit your mama and you go to the movie?" or something like that. There was never once that anybody ever offered me any kind of relief.

I had my brother and his wife ... I let them stay with me for almost two years, and neither [of them] would just come into the room when I was changing her and ask "Can I help you turn her?" or something like that. Sometimes when I was just so tired and exhausted I would call my nephew and say, "Could you go ask your daddy if he can help me slide grandmother up a little bit. I want to turn her," and then he'd come in and assist. But it was never once where somebody just came in and volunteered and said "Can I help you do this?" or "Why don't you let me watch her tonight and you go do this and you go do that with your friends?" It wasn't that.... I didn't get mad about it.... I just said [to myself] you know you just do what God would have you to do and that's honor your mother and that's what I did. And I just honored her to the fullest by taking care of her.

EXERCISES FOR FAMILY MEETINGS

EXERCISE #1

A 94-year-old woman has three adult children, a son and two daughters. Her son and youngest daughter are present for the meeting. Up until 3 weeks ago, the patient was living on her own. She went to see her primary care physician and was diagnosed with a urinary tract infection. Shortly thereafter she fell at home and was taken to the emergency room at the local hospital. When she left the hospital, she went to her older daughter's home for 1 week where she fell again. The family decided it was better for the patient to return to her youngest daughter's home for care.

Within a week, the patient returned to the hospital and the family learned that she has cancer. The patient spent 5 days in the hospital. The youngest daughter explains, "It was a nightmare—every sound rattled her. She couldn't sleep, she didn't want to eat." The family requested a private room, and on the third day in the hospital she was moved to a private room. From the hospital, the patient was transferred to a rehab facility. During this time the daughter reports "she is in despair," and the patient's son explains "she's giving up."

Both children report that their mother has talked about dying and has specifically said what she wants, including specifications for what songs to play at her funeral, and a request "to be buried with daddy." Still, the youngest daughter reports numerous incidents of incoherence throughout the past 3 weeks. "At this point, it's not an option for her to go home so … "

Discussion

At this point, what would you say to this family? Here are some prompts to help you get started....

  * Attempt to explain the medical reasons for the patient's incoherence.
  * Explain the dying process.
  * Respond to the medical history of the patient ("This is all very normal.").
  * Focus on family dynamics ("Families like yourself that are close and communicate well are very lucky.").
  * Try to summarize their main concerns ("So you are concerned that she's not eating.").

FACULTY NOTE: This can be done as a classroom exercise or take-home assignment. You can divide students into triads or small groups and assign each of them one of these initial responses. Then have them share as a group or role-play.

The family meeting continues:

YOUNGEST DAUGHTER: "We haven't asked her if she's hungry; we just keep trying to feed her. I'm worried about her dehydration and suffering. If it wasn't the diarrhea, I would see it as a natural process … but I feel like it's me not taking care of her … [crying] I want to feel like I'm not bailing on her. I feel like I'm accelerating it."

SON-IN-LAW: "It's just so hard to believe that 3 weeks ago she was on her own."

SON: "How will she die?"

Discussion

At this point, what would you say to this family? Here are some ideas to help you get started …

* Introduce hospice and compare with hospital care/philosophy.
* Inquire if the family would be okay with the patient passing away at their home.
* Explain the dying process in patients with cancer.

The family meeting continues:

The youngest daughter cries. The patient's son suggests that the family should call their sister and ask her to come [she is about 8 hours away by car]. "Let's call her and have you talk to her," he says to the nurse. As his sister dials the number, he asks the nurse: "How long do you think it will be before my mother dies?" Before the nurse can answer, the two sisters are on the phone, the youngest daughter announcing: "It's looking like hospice." She can't say any more, begins quietly sobbing, and gives the phone to her brother. She leaves the room and her husband follows quickly behind her. The patient's son is able to provide a synopsis over the phone to his sister—she is concerned about the legal issue of choosing hospice on behalf of her mother. During this discussion, the youngest daughter returns to the meeting and announces that she simply cannot make a decision and that her siblings must decide.

Discussion

At this point, what would you say to this family? What type of family system are you working with (open or closed)? What family communication pattern does this family demonstrate? Do any dominant caregiver types emerge?

6

OPENINGS

Peter is an RN case manager in a major urban cardiac care hospital unit. He is currently caring for 56-year-old Felipe, an immigrant from Peru who has recently suffered an MI (myocardial infarction). Felipe and his family (wife Maria, sons Jose and Antonio, and daughter Carmen) speak little English and are overwhelmed by the CCU (cardiac care unit). Despite diabetes and COPD, Felipe has been the key family breadwinner for his own family, his elderly mother, and elderly mother-in-law.

Felipe owns an auto repair shop and his two sons work for him. He is extremely anxious about his MI and insistent that he must return to work soon. Felipe likes Peter very much as Peter speaks Spanish fluently, and Felipe feels Peter understands his responsibility as the head of the family. Unfortunately Felipe's hospital course has not gone well, and the damage from the MI was worse than first estimated. Felipe has limited mobility and becomes fatigued easily, and he and his wife are very emotional.

The diagnosis evaluation following the MI has also revealed that he has progressive renal disease associated with his diabetes, and while Peter is working to coordinate rehabilitation services, there is some doubt about Felipe's rehabilitation potential. Felipe and his family become easily confused and overwhelmed by the number of medical specialists who see him daily. They also feel that they get confusing messages from each service about his status.

Peter is now attempting to arrange a transfer from the CCU to a step-down cardiac unit. Felipe's wife becomes very joyful, expressing her thanks to God that this good news means her husband will be healed and back to normal. Peter feels that none of the physicians have discussed Felipe's actual status or prognosis.

Today, Felipe's daughter Carmen asks to speak with Peter and tells him that she really needs to know the truth about her father's status so she can know if Felipe will ever be able to return to work. The physical therapist has also paged Peter to clarify the goals of care for his transfer. Peter is now feeling overwhelmed as he faces a huge void in communication about Felipe's needs and prognosis.

Anxiety. Fear. Tension. These are feelings and emotions that indicate a nurse should promote effective communication and seek interdisciplinary collaboration rather than avoid finding a potential solution. Peter has observed the seriously complicated situation of Felipe and his family and has an accurate understanding of the complications that Felipe faces in the weeks ahead. But unlike the other clinicians working with this family, Peter is uniquely positioned to engage in communication during the most pivotal point of life for Felipe and his family. Peter can create an *opening* as he communicates with Felipe and his family and shares the "truth" that Carmen (the daughter) longs to hear, while moving beyond this bad news information to a productive conversation about transitions and goals of care.

The Oxford English Dictionary uses words like *connection, opportunity, possibility, launching,* and *start* to describe *opening*. This chapter examines the communication a nurse shares with patient and family at pivotal moments in illness; this communication can create openings for positive change. The junctures in illness explored in this portion of the book encourage a reframing of moments of tension. Rather than a nurse being repelled by fears of inadequacy in those junctures of transition, a nurse can champion a patient/family and use communication to engage some of the most challenging and rewarding clinical moments experienced in nursing practice. These are the moments when nurses can advocate for the best care by sharing in painful times of isolation and change for patients and families.

Some commonly experienced communication around junctures of care occurs at the time of initial diagnosis, around treatment decision making, at the point of recurrence or complication, as well as when coaching patients about how they can share their thoughts with family and how family can share thoughts with a patient. Nurses play a key role at the end of life as patients and families struggle to forgive one another, to say good-bye, and to locate spiritual support as they experience a loss of connection with the life they no longer know. These difficult moments present opportunities and possibilities for resilience, but resilience and coping are less possible if the patient/family as well as health care professionals participating in care do not attend to painful transitions, fears, and inevitable changes.

Now that the concept of *opening* has been introduced, this chapter will detail the complex patient/family communication that nurses can facilitate in transitions of care, describe a few communication concepts to refine thinking and provide support for improvements in clinical practice, and finally, provide practical applications to shape nursing care plans in palliative care.

PIVOTAL POINTS OF COMMUNICATION BETWEEN NURSE/PATIENT/FAMILY

The last two decades have seen a rise in scholarship about clinician communication and breaking bad news. Most of this information emphasizes the role of medicine and physician performance with little attention to the communication events encountered after the bad news has been shared/learned (Kruijver, Kerkstra, Bensing, & van de Wiel, 2000; McCabe & Storm, 2008; National Consensus Project for Quality Palliative Care, 2011; Neff, Lyckholm, & Smith, 2002). Communication and its importance are a bedrock need and skill for palliative care nursing. Research in nursing and other related health care specialties have established that communication is not a naturally acquired, naïve, artless, and gifted process. Instead, studied communication is central to all clinical practice decisions and processes and demands education, intensive practice, and reflection (Dahlin, 2010; Goldsmith, Wittenberg-Lyles, Rodriquez, & Sanchez-Reilly, 2010). This resource heralds the vital role communication plays and the increasing recognition of communication's importance by the field of nursing itself. Difficult conversations with patients and families coincide with transitions in care and truly require intimate and disclosive exchanges between patient/family and nurses.

Nurses perform the heavy lifting when it comes to stewarding patients and families to a sense of understanding throughout their disease process. As such, the pivotal points of communication that extend beyond the bad news exchange often mirror the disease process for a patient and family (Malloy, Virani, Kelly, & Munevar, 2010). But just as a disease does not travel the path of a script, neither does the unfolding/timing of conversations between a patient, family, and nurse. Nurse conversations with patients and family *after* the receipt of bad news have not been extensively studied, but scholars do know that this nursing communication task is rated as highly challenging and very common in occurrence (Malloy et al., 2010).

Discussing spiritual concerns with patient and family, talking about cultural needs and concerns at the end of life, processing suffering with patient and family, considering decisions about advanced directives, DNR orders, withholding or withdrawing support, and sharing in the news of recurrence or fear of recurrence with patients and/or family are some of the pivotal points that present themselves in intimate conversations with the nurse. Nearer a patient's death, a nurse might engage in conversations with a patient about saying good-bye to the family or with the family about saying good-bye to the patient. Talking about forgiveness can also be a profound need of patients and families at the end of life, and the nurse who has provided the intimate physical care and support will often be the likely interlocutor suited for these interactions.

The nurse is central to effective communication in these and other critical moments. Instead of approaching these transitions in care as a list to complete, which has historically been the medical model for communication protocols, the nurse's skill set provides opportunities for conversation in relationship with patient and family as they deal with serious illness. The nurse has special access and opportunity to respond to cues from the patient and family and accompany them through the most challenging conversations of serious and terminal illness. Research investigating communication about terminal illness prognosis indicates that adaptive communication is necessary and must be based on patient and family acceptability of information. Additionally, studies show that news of recurrence, prognostic estimations, or discussion about hospice placement must be diffused depending on how a patient/family receives the topic (Eggly et al., 2006; Wittenberg-Lyles, Goldsmith, Ragan, Sanchez-Reilly, 2008).

In other words, some may need to hear and discuss a particular feature of bad news many times and even then still might not understand or accept it. Further, some families may choose never to engage in a conversation about terminal prognosis but will still need to talk about transitions in care for the end of life. This chapter presents nuanced strategies for engaging these vitally important and intimate conversations essential for patients and families to experience the best quality of life at the end of life.

Physical Well-Being
- Self-care
- Treatment plan
- Place of care

Psychological Well-Being
- Distress
- Anxiety
- Fear
- Happiness
- Enjoyment

Nurse Communication: Intimate Openings Beyond Bad News

Social Well-Being
- Family dynamics
- Caregiver Burden
- Relationships external to family
- Identity

Spiritual Well-Being
- Connectedness
- Meaning of illness
- Meaning of suffering

FIGURE 6.1 **Quality-of-life model and communication**
Adapted from Ferrell, B. R., Dow, K. H., & Grant, M. (1995). Measurement of the quality of life in cancer survivors. *Quality of Life Research, 4,* 523–531.

Intimate conversations that facilitate openings for patient and family can profoundly and positively impact the quality-of-life domains as depicted in Figure 6.1.

Talking with a patient and his or her family, or demonstrating presence without verbally communicating, can and does affect clinical outcomes and costs not only for the patient and family, but also for all stakeholders (Matsayuma, Reddy, & Smith, 2006; Zhang et al., 2009). As the quality-of life-domains are applied to concepts of communication, two particular communication constructs, or theories, will support the challenge of engaging patients and families in their intimate moments of illness transition: Communication privacy management theory, and social penetration theory. Both theories wrestle with the problematic of disclosure and boundaries. Also, each theory actively represents the relational connection human beings share—a concept understood and valued by nurse clinicians.

COMMUNICATION PRIVACY MANAGEMENT

The intimacy of nursing creates an environment for frequent and unsolicited patient and family self-disclosure. Ironically, some of this information is just plain "too much information"; however, nurses must make decisions about *how, when,* and *if* this information should be communicated to other family members as well as team members.

Communication privacy management (CPM) outlines how individuals become owners of private information and how this ownership gives them control of private disclosures (Helft & Petronio, 2007).

Nurses are often in the position of receiving and delivering private information and thus have **private information ownership.** For example, a nurse in oncology may be asked to share lab results, which will indicate a patient's worsened status. Family members often stand in shock as physicians inform them of the terminal status of a patient. When the physician leaves, it is the nurse who is left to explain the information, answer questions, and help families face the meaning of the information. As such, nurses address the actual *process* of telling and revealing the *content* of private information (task communication), as well as facilitating the impact on the individual to whom the private information is connected and other people associated with that individual (relational communication) (Petronio, 2002). In palliative care, private information becomes one or more of the following pieces of information: (a) the terminal prognosis, (b) hospice and palliative care services, and/or (c) patient/caregiver feeling of burden (Wittenberg-Lyles, Goldsmith, Ragan, & Sanchez-Reilly, 2010).

Control of Private Information and Coordinating Boundaries

The way that people manage the flow and exchange of private information is a major tenet of this theory. Boundaries can become linked as people form alliances with information and include additional parties as recipients of certain pieces of news. But boundaries can be restructured and revisioned as a result of time and information, and especially as a result of relational change. Some boundaries are known as *thick* and difficult to permeate, while others might be *thin* and more accessible.

Commonly, families request that patients not be told about their diagnosis and hospice enrollment (Gentry, 2008). Some families have a relational history of avoiding difficult topics or speaking indirectly about serious topics; still, limited disclosure about hospice care can facilitate protection of family emotions and sustain denial (Gentry, 2008).

The decision to reveal private information, such as the nurse's knowledge about the disease, disease trajectory, and/or prognosis, can create a **privacy dilemma** (Petronio & Lewis, 2011). When a privacy dilemma occurs, nurses are positioned to communicate either vaguely or directly.

The emotionally charged nature of palliative care means that families are not as transparent about private matters. Nurses are often inclined to soften the news, evoke hope, and remain ambiguous. If a patient or family member asks a nurse if their loved one is going to die—what does this mean according to CPM? Contrary to the physician's role, nurses don't feel like they have ownership of the information. But they do! They are in a privacy triangle! When patients or family members share private information about their health choices or family situations, they are inviting the nurse into their family and their disclosure comes with communicative responsibilities.

In the instance that patient disclosures or actions diverge from what has been disclosed, there is a privacy dilemma for nurses. When the information is given to a nurse, the nurse carries the task of maintaining confidentiality. The nurse must interpret the message, carry the burden or responsibility of knowing the information, and face the challenge of delivering the message to others (Petronio & Lewis, 2011). In essence, nurses take on the role of privacy advocate.

TURBULENCE: PRIVACY DILEMMA

Turbulence is the upset of privacy boundaries and the communication fallout that follows. A dilemma in privacy may be handled by not talking about private information, or an impromptu and informal boundary condition that can emerge from disclosure of the terminal prognosis.

Turbulence also can emerge as family members try to protect the patient from his/ her own private information. Especially when physicians do not adequately disclose terminal prognosis, family members attempt to create their own private information. In some instances hospice and palliative care services can be deemed private information owned by the family (Clayton, Butow, Arnold, & Tattersall, 2005). It is not unusual for families to request that the use of hospice services be withheld from the patient (Gentry, 2008). Additionally, the desire to keep the patient from knowing that they are dying is sometimes articulated by the family. Families instruct health care providers not to mention hospice, not to tell the patient that he or she is terminal, and not to talk about death and dying in front of the patient (Planalp & Trost, 2008).

Feelings and emotions associated with the caregiver role can also create turbulence in the disclosure of private information. While disclosure is typically used to make sense of unexpected events and as a way of seeking support (Helft & Petronio, 2007), turbulence is created for caregivers who do not want to disclose these feelings to their terminally ill loved one.

The drive for search and cure can reconfigure or underscore previously established relationship privacy rules or communication that regulates the flow of private information between family members. Violation of privacy rules becomes necessary to keep the hope for cure alive. For example, providing Joe with hope became a new privacy rule that his wife Kay used to sustain their family in illness. Turbulence is created in the family, especially when terminal news disclosures are not clearly articulated. The traumatic event in this instance is the terminal prognosis triggering dialectical tension, or pull between two alternatives: privacy and disclosure.

The negotiation of privacy, rather than open communication, creates multiple boundaries as families struggle to protect the patient as well as others by not talking about the prognosis. The hospice perspective, which includes open sharing and discussion about the prognosis, collides with the family's desire for privacy around the issue.

Boundary turbulence occurs when the coordination of a boundary is unclear, or when privacy expectations clash. For instance, if Mary is in the late stages of cancer and is in intractable pain concealed from her husband, Bob, this would be Mary's private information. Mary disclosing this information to a nurse to mediate the pain would shift that boundary from a private one to a collective boundary. Mary's desire to keep Bob from knowing about her pain reveals the boundary type between spouses. The nurse's desire to let Bob know and help Mary with this pain could cause boundary turbulence.

Once private information is self-disclosed to another individual, that individual assumes co-ownership of the information. Boundaries are then managed through rule management processes that are negotiated between individuals (Petronio, 2002). Personal boundaries between dyadic partners can be expanded to become collective boundaries between multiple persons, each with different boundary conditions. Thus, individuals manage personal, dyadic, and group boundaries of private information through privacy rules, which dictate boundary conditions. When a family member is chronically or terminally ill, each family member itemizes different things that become private in the midst of knowing that someone is changing/dying. Terminally ill patients and their family members must ultimately manage collective boundaries in the uncertainty of illness.

Personal boundaries between nurses, patients, and family members expand to become collective boundaries such that each has a different set of boundary conditions. **Boundary coordination** is based on the complexity of co-owning or sharing private information that belongs to people collectively (Petronio, 2002).

SOCIAL PENETRATION THEORY

Another concept from communication that helps explain ways in which disclosure impacts relationships is social penetration theory (SPT). The essence of SPT describes all relationships as being in development, or progress, and that self-disclosure is at the nexus of relational development. In this theory, *social penetration* refers to the process of bonding that moves a superficial relationship to a more intimate one (Altman & Taylor, 1973). The idea of penetration is endowed with two capacities: *breadth* and *depth*. *Breadth* refers to the number of topics discussed in a relationship while *depth* refers to the level of intimacy guiding a discussion topic.

Another idea central to SPT is reciprocity, or the return of openness from one person to another. An individual's willingness often leads to the other individual's willingness, and as such reciprocity has been shown to be a significant component that advances relationships. Both SPT and the previously described CPM can be used to support and further strategize what is known in nursing research literature about the most productive interpersonal choices a nurse can make when caring for patients.

Think of the talk that people exchange with strangers on an airplane. Specifically, reflect on any instances in which a total stranger disclosed heavily to another stranger with whom he or she shared a row. These two people might not ever know the other's name, but still the depth of information shared can be impressive. There are also instances in which one traveler in a row of seats discloses heavily to a seatmate, but the seatmate does not reciprocate this level of disclosure in breadth or depth. The demonstrated behavior in these airplane scenarios gets at the heart of social penetration theory. Translating this theory to the end-of-life context enlightens some of the communication complexities that nurses and other health professionals encounter with family, teams, and patients.

INTIMATE OPENINGS DURING ILLNESS

Until the 1960s, nursing literature and research promoted a distancing nursing practice that featured "control" communication and management of events with patients
(and rarely families). Closed questions, rapid succession of leading questions, and direct
statements were identified as techniques to focus on and facilitate task completion
(Clark, 1982; Meleis, 2012). But these established ideas about detachment crumbled as
the nursing process was introduced, as well as the later development of primary nursing
(Dowling, 2008). These changes in nursing heralded individualized care and a focus
on personal relationships necessitating a reframing of the nurse–patient relationship
to include commitment, closeness, and involvement as opposed to distance, control,
and detachment (Dowling, 2008). The ideas of private information disclosure and
self-disclosure are pertinent in this new modeling of nursing practice. As part of this
new conceptualization, the idea of intimacy takes on a central role and is characterized
by "closeness at physical, psychological, and spiritual levels" (Muetzel, 1988, p. 98).

Despite this paradigm shift in the nurse–patient relationship, there are still inaccura-
cies and false assumptions about sharing difficult conversations/communications with
a patient and/or family. Avoidance of situations and challenges that cannot be "fixed"
by the nurse are a common cause for avoiding intimate conversations (Gauthier, 2008).
Table 6.1 is a simple compilation of common myths about terminal illness communication shared between nurses, patients, and families.

Table 6.1 Common Myths Associated with Communication about Dying

Common Myths: Communication with Patients and Families about Dying	Communication Realities
Avoid silence in difficult moments. Silence only creates more awkwardness.	Silence allows for patient and family disclosure and communicates interest and presence.
Dying patients and family members only want to talk about positive things.	Patients and family have existential concerns and fears to process.
Patients and family members don't want to ask a clinician questions about dying and loss.	Patients and family want to share a relationship with clinicians and process their questions about dying and loss.
When a patient is dying, there is little health care professionals have to offer.	Health care professionals can provide comfort measures and assistance to a family transitioning their place and goals of care when a patient is dying.

Adaptations from Gauthier, D. (2008). Challenges and opportunities: Communication near the
end of life. *MESURG Nursing, 17*(5), 291–196. Knauft, E., Nielson, E. L., Engelberg, R. A., Patrick,
D., & Curtis, J. (2005). Barriers and facilitators to end-of-life care communication for patients
with COPD. *Chest, 127,* 2188–2196. Kristjanson, L. (2001). Establishing goals: Communication
traps and treatment lane changes. In B. R. Ferrell & N. Coyle (Eds.), *Textbook of Palliative Nursing*
(pp. 331–338). New York: Oxford University Press.

Of course, one person alone cannot experience intimacy. Intimacy is engaged via self-disclosure, confiding, and sharing—within a trusting relationship established on the premise that the best solutions will be identified and enacted. The roles that both the patient and nurse play (or the family and nurse) are significant. The dynamic communication they share will make this intimacy possible (Reis & Shaver, 1988).

Knowing a patient allows a nurse to truly care for that patient (Zomorodi & Foley, 2009). The core of intimacy stems from disclosure of personal information with the expectation that there will be understanding and acceptance. Although planning and problem solving can occur without self-disclosure, problem solving is elongated and protracted for the person who does not self-disclose (O'Connell, 2008). In nursing, disclosure affirms and recognizes the interdependence of the patient and nurse, or family and nurse.

Nurses often develop a level of health care intimacy with patients and families in the course of caring for them (Dowling, 2008). This leads back to the idea of social penetration theory (SPT) and nursing. If a nurse develops a relationship of psychosocial care and disclosure with a patient and family, what does that mean for the nurse in terms of communication? The following elements from social penetration theory will guide a nurse in strategizing communication behavior to maximize opening opportunities.

Complementary behaviors demonstrate interest in a speaker (patient/family) as they disclose information. These behaviors maintain the focus on the patient or family, for instance, and do not "one-up" the story, need, or concern of the individual with the primary concern. So, for example, if a colleague complains of a cold and the long hours he or she is working, complementary behavior would include receptive communications rather than communications that would pull focus toward the recipient, and his or her health and exhaustion. Complementary behaviors are more important and beneficial to the creation of patient/family/nurse intimacy than *reciprocal behaviors* and communication (Prager, 1995).

Reciprocal communication equals and even surpasses the other's conversational content in terms of breadth and depth of disclosure. An example might be a patient who is in her final stages of advanced cancer. A palliative care clinician comes by this patient's room and overshares about her own children and Thanksgiving plans in response to the patient's polite inquiry. A focus on the patient, her family, her children, and her atypical Thanksgiving experience needs to be processed instead. In other words, for the patient/family, it is more important that the clinician engage in communication behaviors that express investment, care, and attention rather than a reciprocated disclosure. In fact, a reciprocal disclosure has the potential to diminish and even dismiss the difficulty experienced and imparted by the patient or family. Another way to describe this is to say that intimacy in the clinical setting is to position the nurse in the meaning-making process *with* the patient or family, rather than separate out a nurse's meaningful experiences *from* the patient/family. Examine the two versions of the same interaction in Box 6.1.

In the first version, an opening for the nurse's self-disclosure occurs with a family member in the course of interaction. The nurse makes good use of this self-disclosure to establish commonality and trust but, most importantly, keeps the focus *on* the

---

Box 6.1 Communication Scenarios

Version #1

NURSE: I can see the sadness on your face.

MRS. HOLBROOK: Yes. The idea of not talking to my Mom makes me so sad. But more terrified really. My entire world during the last 6 months has been taking care of her, first at home, then at the long- term care facility. A look or a soft touch from her made every day better. I knew that I was a good daughter. Overnight she doesn't even know me. And I don't know me. I can't explain it.

NURSE: It is horribly scary, terrifying. I went through something very much like this with my Mom 3 years ago. It was awful.

MRS. HOLBROOK: So you know. You get it.

NURSE: Well, I understand what it was like for me. I want to understand what it is like for you.

Version #2

NURSE: I can see the sadness on your face.

MRS. HOLBROOK: Yes. The idea of not talking to my Mom makes me so sad. But more terrified really. My entire world during the last 6 months has been taking care of her, first at home, then at the long- term care facility. A look or a soft touch from her made every day better. I knew that I was a good daughter. Overnight she doesn't even know me. And I don't know me. I can't explain it.

NURSE: I've been there. My Mom died 3 years ago after 6 years with Alzheimer's. It was awful. Each day she forgot something else that just tore at my heart.

MRS. HOLBROOK: Oh no. How did you deal with it?

NURSE: Well, I …

---

patient/family member—continuing the interaction. Note that the impulse for disclosure of private information operates as concern for the family member and her experience and seeks to find ways that Mrs. Holbrook can find meaning in her current struggle. In the second version, the nurse also shows concern and orientation in the direction of this family member's angst. However, the nurse, presented with an identical opportunity for disclosure, shifts the meaning-making intent away from Mrs. Holbrook and onto the nurse's personal trial of caregiving. While there is not a sense that the nurse is removing a caring presence from this family member, there is a readjustment of self-disclosure that moves into *reciprocal* rather than the *complementary* behavior/communication. It is exactly at this moment of tension and privacy disclosure that the nurse can facilitate the patient or family member in making meaning and processing inevitable transition choices in his or her path. Maintaining focus on patient or family disclosure will continue to communicate trust and an expression of interest and concern.

Table 6.2 Team Meeting

TEAM MEETING AND OBSERVATIONAL NOTES:

*Mr. Turner is an 81-year-old man with liver metastasis and pneumonia. He is now
unresponsive. The medical fellow reports to the team that he is dying. The DNP explains that
Mr. Turner just found out 3 weeks ago that he had liver cancer. He has a female friend that he
has been involved with for 5 years—and the two of them are very active and dance regularly.
Mr. Turner has children who are out of state, and they are making arrangements to come
to the hospital. The DNP reports that Mr. Turner's girlfriend, KT, is at his bedside, crying.
Mr. Turner is breathing five breaths per minute. He's comfortable, his eyes are open, but he's
actively dying. The team physician asks if the children will get to the hospital in time—and
the DNP responds that this is unlikely.*

*Upon reaching Mr. Turner's hospital room, the team finds KT very distraught. The DNP begins to
talk to her while she is standing next to his bed holding his hand. KT tells the DNP that she does not
want to talk in front of him. They step outside of the hospital room into a family meeting room. KT
begins telling the DNP about the events of the last 3 weeks and how they found out he had cancer.*

DNP: The cancer has spread. He's very, very sick. I think you know this … because of all of the changes in him these last many days. GIRLFRIEND (KT): But he's very active. We have horses, and he rode in a parade 3 weeks ago. You can't go by his age. He's a young 81. He is in great shape really.	**Tension** indicated, as KT reveals her hope that he is in good health, and possible denial of his active dying process. **Intimate opening** opportunity.
DNP (explains that he is actively dying): This must be so difficult to experience. As the nurse on his team, I really think he is living out his final hours, maybe days. This is the time for his children to be with him.	**Collective boundary**—the private information of impending death is disclosed for ownership by KT as well as health team.
KT (doesn't acknowledge the actively dying language. Instead, she describes his children's travel plans) DNP: Did you tell him they [his children] are coming? [pause]. KT (does not speak but looks at DNP, eyes welling with tears) DNP: Right now our main concern is to keep him pain free. KT: Yes, that's so important. You all have done a wonderful job. DNP: We really want to make him comfortable and keep his eyes moist as well as his mouth. And those are things you can help him with, too. (KT nods, tears running. Long pause.) I also wanted to talk to you about the reality that he's not hungry, and we will not be feeding him. The IVs will actually lead to more pain	**Intimate opening** to discuss the goals of care. **Collective boundary**—disclosure describing withdraw of fluids.

(continued)

Table 6.2. (*continued*)

and swelling. Discomfort him. (Long pause). So we want to keep him comfortable, and right now that means keeping his mouth moist. So we are going to concentrate on that.	
KT (Continues crying, talks about how much she loves him and how she lost her own husband to lung cancer. She cries heavily.) (Silence)	**Self-disclosure-depth** (social penetration theory)
KT and DNP grab hands. DNP: How can we help you?	**Tension** and **intimate opening opportunity**
KT: I need an aspirin. I have my own health problems, and car problems, and everything is happening at once.	**Self-disclosure-depth** (social penetration theory)
DNP: We can get you the aspirin. As many as you need. I always think these hard times come to me in groups, too. What is the hardest thing right now?	**Complementary disclosure/behavior** as opposed to reciprocal.
KT: He needs me. When he had surgery, I would sit in the chair next to him and hold hands [with him]. I would get in the bed and cuddle with him. DNP: Well, he has a private room so you can do that. You can get in bed with him. KT: I can? Oh great. DNP: Will you stay here tonight? KT: (nods yes) DNP: There are five things that I think help to know in times like this—things that people might want to say to each other—I love you, I forgive you, please forgive me, I'm sorry, good-bye. Would you like me to write this down?	**Intimate opening opportunity**
KT: Yes. I don't have anything to forgive except him dying. (crying again) DNP (writes it down and gives it to her) KT: I hate to tell him good-bye. I'll just tell him I love him and I don't want to be without him and I'll always love him.	Family member demonstrates a level of understanding facilitated by nurse disclosure and intimate openings.

As the meeting ends, KT asks DNP about his ability to see. DNP explains that it is not likely and to focus on his hearing. DNP reminds her to bring in music for him. KT hugged DNP and went back to patient's room. Two days later Mr. Turner died.

To demarcate movement through an actual interaction of intimate openings, the following observation from a veteran's facility will be marked with some of the elements described in this section about intimate openings (Table 6.2). Note the information in the superimposed boxes next to the conversational turns shared between a Doctor of Nursing Practice (DNP) on the palliative care team and Mr. Turner's girlfriend, KT. Some background observations to the events leading up to this interchange via the team meeting are included.

This single conversation between the DNP and the family member (KT) of a terminally ill patient provides an opportunity to look very closely at the communication events that contribute to intimate openings, self-disclosure, and ultimately facilitating transitions for a patient and family in this challenging time. Though this example of Mr. Turner's girlfriend, KT, closely examines the conflicted need to face active dying and saying good-bye, there are other transformative communication opportunities that can be facilitated by a nurse.

The extended case study in Figure 6.2 includes identifiers that note intimate openings the nurse will communicate during the course of Mr. Romero's illness, not only to Mr. Romero, but also to the many stakeholders in this family's experience of complicated terminal illness. Central to the work of nursing is soliciting information from patients and families, but also receiving information that might not have been requested (Petronio, 2011). As nurses have noted in previous research, the more challenging disclosure events present predicaments that influence communication with the patient and the family, create moral distress for the nurse, and can potentially mediate the delivery of appropriate care (Schulter, Winch, Holzhauser, & Henderson, 2008). Some research identifies a unique challenge in the nurse–patient or nurse–family dynamic that can include *information dumping*, in which high rates of disclosure are revealed to the reluctant nurse confidant (Helft & Petronio, 2007). Communication coping and adaptability to manage this sticky situation will be further explored in Chapter 7.

Mr. Romero is a 70-year-old retired bus driver who had a history of hypertension, diabetes, and COPD. He was diagnosed with congestive heart failure six months ago and has been seen frequently by a cardiologist in the clinic setting. He has been managed with several cardiac medications but over the last few weeks has had several acute episodes of dyspnea. Today, the cardiology clinic nurse, Eva, asks Mr. Romero if there is something "going on" in his life, as she is concerned about his increased shortness of breath and anxiety. Mr. Romero admits that his wife was diagnosed with breast cancer and he has been devastated. He said with a great sadness- "Just when I thought nothing could be worse than this heart failure, my wife is struck down with breast cancer. She is my life. How can this be? Is there no God? My wife, she never did a thing wrong. And now- Cancer."

Time Out for Intimate Opening
- Tension (patient anxiety = opportunity)
- Self-disclosure
- Psychological well-being

FIGURE 6.2 Case study

The nurse, Eva, offers her support and assures Mr. Romero that the clinic is "there for him". Eva listens quietly as Mr. Romero goes over again what it was like to hear the news of his wife's cancer.

Time Out for Intimate Opening
- Tension (shared silence = opportunity)
- Self-disclosure
- Psychological well-being

Eva assists Mr. Romero into the exam room and then she confers with Dr. Evans before he sees Mr. Romero to share the information about Mr. Romero's wife.

Three weeks later Mr. Romero returns to the clinic accompanied by his son. Eva is struck by the rapid decline in Mr. Romero's status. His cardiac evaluation reveals decreased cardiac function, worsened dyspnea, edema and also weight loss. Accompanied by his son John, Eva takes the opportunity to ask John how things are going at their house. John shares that both of his parents are doing very poorly and how after 51 years of marriage they seem to be both slipping away, each suffering in the awareness of the other's illness. John also tells Eva that his mother is now on hospice care as she declined chemotherapy and has insisted on having her remaining months of life devoted to caring for her husband. Eva gives John her card and suggests he have the hospice nurse contact him so that they can talk about how to best coordinate care for his parents.

Time Out for Intimate Opening
- Tension (caregiver burden = opportunity)
- Self-disclosure
- Physical well-being

One week later Mr. Romero is again seen in the clinic. His cardiac status continues to decline and he is now dependent on oxygen and constant assistance. John tells Eva that he and his siblings are now rotating weeks to stay with their parents as both decline. Eva asks John if his father has completed an Advance Directive. She notes that she had given Mr. Romero an Advanced Directive form to complete but it was never returned. John becomes almowst hostile, insisting that his father will not complete such a form as it is "against their beliefs." Eva asks John to describe their beliefs and how Mr. Romero would want to live at the end of his life in regard to those beliefs.

Time Out for Intimate Opening
- Tension (goals of care at end of life)
- Self-disclosure about family processing and family roles
- Trust built and knowledge exchanged between nurse/family/patient
- Spiritual well-being

FIGURE 6.2 (*conitnued*)

John also shares that his sister Martina is "furious" with everyone who has given up on her parents and she wants both to change doctors and get some "real" care. Eva offers to speak with Martina and John expresses his thanks. He says "my crazy sister" always shows up to claim I can't do anything right for them.

Two weeks later Eva receives a call in the clinic from John to say Mr. Romero was admitted to the hospital with acute chest pain. He is in the CCU. Eva conveys the message to Dr. Evans who will be making rounds later in the morning. Eva also calls the hospital social work department and talks with the Cardiology Social Worker to convey information about Mr. Romero. Later in the day Dr. Evans returns to the clinic and is sad to report that Mr. Romero has had a MI, is on a ventilator, and is unlikely to survive. Dr. Evans is very distressed, telling Eva that he has known this family for over three years and is very fond of them. Eva listens to Dr. Evans distress, assures him of how much his care has meant to the family. Eva also suggests that Dr. Evans consult the palliative care service, suggesting that the family would benefit from the services of chaplaincy and the palliative care team as they face decisions about life support.

Time Out for Intimate Opening
- Tension (goals of care at end of life)

- Self-disclosure about family

- Trust built and knowledge exchanged between nurse/physician

- Spiritual well-being

Dr. Evans expresses hesitancy that he doesn't want to "abandon" his patient, Eva assures him that involving palliative care would be a great sign of his concern for Mr. Romero and his family. Eva also offers to call the palliative care service to convey the information for the referral.

Later in the week, Mr. Romero's family participates in a family conference lead jointly by Dr. Evans and the palliative care team. With the support of the hospice, Mrs. Romero was able to come to the hospital although very ill herself, to say goodbye to her husband. The chaplain arranged for the anointing of Mr. Romero and served communion to the family. The family also agreed to a DNR order and two days later Mr. Romero died.

Three weeks following MR. Romero's death, Eva received a call from John to say that his mother had died peacefully at home with hospice. Eva thanked John for calling and expressed gratitude for having had the opportunity to support this family during this time. She was able to hear about the positive as well as challenging final days John experienced with his family.

Time Out for Intimate Opening
- Tension (goals of care at end of life)

- Self-disclosure about family

- Interpersonal nurse/family trust

- Social and spiritual well-being in bereavement

- Spiritual support in the works for the Romero family

FIGURE 6.2 (*conitnued*)

Table 6.3 Communication Tension or Avoidance

Communication Tension or Avoidance Triggers in Illness	Quality-of-Life Domain(s) Heavily Impacted			
	Physical	Psychological	Social	Spiritual
Time of initial diagnosis	✓	✓		✓
Communication around treatment decisions	✓	✓		
Talking with patients about talking with family		✓	✓	
Communication around recurrence		✓		✓
Talking with family about talking with patient		✓	✓	
Communicating about saying good-bye			✓	✓

Narrative nursing invites the patient/family story and does not expect a certain ending or outcome. Rather, narrative nursing, in conjunction with many of the ideas in this "O" chapter, advocates for the individual experience of a patient/family, and finding ways to help them navigate and process that experience. Facilitating access to private health information, creating intimate openings to process transitions in life and care, and understanding the impact of self-disclosure on patient/family relationships all play an important role in practicing COMFORT.

DEVELOPING CLINICAL PRACTICE SKILLS

This element of the COMFORT model offers unique tools to assist the nurse in traversing the challenging yet profoundly rewarding moments of transition that require the clinical practice of intimate communication with patient and family. The second portion of this chapter will offer practical applications that are reflective of the nursing care plan design. The case study that introduces this chapter situates Peter, an RN, in an untenable situation not only with his patient and family, but also with many other health professionals. All of the dynamics were there to facilitate an intimate opening between Peter and Felipe, his patient. But this opening never occurred. The deterioration of a patient can precipitate and force conversations and decisions that would have been better experienced as an illness was unfolding. Examining the needs of a patient and family is the first step in helping them make sense of their challenging experience.

Table 6.4 Factors Indicating Poor Prognosis

Congestive Heart Failure	Chronic Obstructive Pulmonary Disease
• New York Heart Association class IV (symptoms at rest) • Serum sodium levels <134 mmol/L or creatinine level >2.0 mg/dL attributable to poor cardiac output	• Cor pulmonale • Intensive care unit admission for exacerbation • New dependence in 2 ADLs (activities of daily living) • Chronic hypercapnia
Dementia	Cancer
• Dependence in all ADLs, language limited to several words, and inability to ambulate • Acute hospitalization (especially for pneumonia or hip fracture)	• Karnofsky score <50 • Eastern Cooperative Oncology Group Score >2 • Liver metastatic tumors • Multiple tumor sites • Malignant bowel obstruction • Malignant pericardial effusion • Carcinomatous meningitis

Used with permission from Casarett, D. J., & Quill, T. (2007). "I'm not ready for hospice": Strategies for timely and effective hospice discussions. *Annals of Internal Medicine, 146*, 443–449.

Assessment

Nursing the whole patient includes assessing the *needs* of the whole patient, including his or her life outside of the hospital or outpatient facility. The factors of social, spiritual, and psychological well-being become crucial in terminal illness care planning for nurses as physical cure fades from the picture. Patients' comfort and happiness, but most particularly their social situations, are quintessential concerns as transitions and goals of care are assessed. As an example, nurses identify their concern about family coping as more intense than their concern for patient coping at the end of life (Peterson et al., 2010). Despite nurse awareness of the profound impact of family and home on patient care and location, nurses feel that a consideration of these issues is still mightily underemployed in end-of-life nursing communication skills (Reinke et al., 2010). Peter, the RN case manager, is surrounded by information about Felipe's social life but still does not identify a way to engage either Felipe or his family in an intimate opening about the difficult reality of Felipe's prognosis and care needs.

The quality-of-life domains are a most useful construct to employ in assessing the transitional needs of a patient. Examining this initial checklist will provide a starting point for thinking about sharing in transitional communication with patient or family. Table 6.3 is a list of potential tension or avoidance triggers and QoL domain impact areas (Ferrell, 1996). As noted in previous sections of this chapter, the desire to disengage from these areas of tension will produce and reproduce more tension the longer it is avoided.

Keeping in mind all of the sensitivities of cultural difference, health literacy levels, and the individual patient, the tensions of end-of-life care remain somewhat consistent across patient populations as decisions about place and goals of care are inevitable.

The literature on palliative and end-of-life nursing and medicine provides very specific information about the physical indications of a declining body. Identifying the physical needs of a patient who is struggling with serious illness is one source of assessment information that can indicate to a nurse that a conversation about transition is of primary import. Table 6.4 includes some factors that are associated with a limited prognosis and can provide basic triggers for communication addressing palliative or hospice care.

Observing patient or family communication will provide a great deal of information about the needs of a patient facing life-limiting or terminal illness. In the context of life-limiting and terminal illness, patient expression to hasten death is an outstanding invitation for discussion about his/her suffering. Often the need for relief is closely related to transition in place of care, goals of care, or accepting the reality of imminent dying and death. Patient communication can occur in the spoken word, through silence, in writing, or by action. Here are some examples of communication about the hastening of death that indicate an intimate nurse–patient opening:

- In written form on health care forms or personal material
- In verbal form shared with spouse or caregiver
- In verbal form shared with physician, nurse, or health care professional
- In a form of action by accepting transfer of care that the patient indicated would hasten death
- In verbal form with the physician or nurse; discussing administration of medication
- In verbal form triggering more frequent contact from staff
- In verbal form asking clinicians how to perform self-administered overdose
- In the form of action by declining any treatment or care that might prolong life and improve quality of life

It is likely that Felipe knew he was very sick but may not have talked about this with anyone, least of all his health care team. His clinicians, despite their expert professionalism, did not successfully address the triggers in Felipe's case. Felipe's and his family's need to know about his life-limiting illness was not part of their decision-making process in his care plan.

Plan

Felipe's wife believed that Felipe was improving. At the same time, Peter knows that there is a heavy suspicion of doubt among the children of Felipe as the daughter, Carmen, asked to hear the truth about Felipe's prognosis. With this information, Peter could have planned for conversations with Felipe and his family about the reality of his prognosis and all of the ramifications this will have on their goals and place of care.

Table 6.5 Tensions, Boundaries, and Depth of Disclosure

• *Tension Identified*	• *Boundary Understanding*	• *Depth of Disclosure*
- What is being avoided between clinicians and patient?	- Does the patient possess this private information about his or her situation?	- Has the nurse gathered patient perspective on this tension?
- What is being avoided between patient and family?	- Can the patient possess this private information about his or her situation?	- Has nurse gathered family perspective on this tension?
- What is being avoided between family and patient?	- Does the family posses this private information about their situation?	- Has the nurse presented prompts to collect patient/family disclosure?
- What is being avoided between patient/family and health care team?	- Can the family possess this private information about their situation?	- Identify prompts that would accomplish patient/family disclosure.
- What is being avoided between health care team and patient/family?	- Describe the boundaries around this family. o Thick o Thin o Permeable	- Recognize that nurse self-disclosure is useful in reaching intimacy with patient/family.
	- Describe the boundaries around this patient. o Thick o Thin o Permeable	- Employ self-disclosure within the realm of complementary disclosure as opposed to reciprocal.
	- What kind of boundary turbulence is predictable based on knowledge of family/patient?	- Supply communication that will facilitate meaning making and understanding among patient and family.

Once the point of tension and temptation to avoid communication have been identified, a plan for engaging a patient and/or family about a challenging time or transition in illness can be designed. The two theories that support the ideas in this COMFORT component are central to preparing for this kind of conversation. First, communication privacy management theory helps explain how private information is shared and protected. Second, social penetration theory theory provides an understanding about the ways in which self-disclosure (amount and detail) advances personal relationships and decision making.

Determining the amount of private information that has or has not been shared with a patient and family, as well as identifying the kind of boundaries that are upheld in a family, is important as a nurse plans for an intimate conversation about illness.

Table 6.6 Tensions in Patient and Family Communication

Tension Identified—Openings	Boundary Understanding/ Communication Strategies	Depth of Disclosure/ Communication Strategies	Patient and Family Communication Indicating Tension
•Initial diagnosis •Treatment choices •Family disagreement •Recurrence •Place of care •Patient/family onflict at end of life •Spiritual distress	Gentle questions - How are things going for you? - What have your doctors told you? - How do you see things going? - What do you see for the future? - Is your family in open communication about this illness? - Have you had this conversation before?	Gentle questions - How are you feeling about this news? - What can we do for you? - What is important right now? - What have you relied on during other challenging times? - Can you tell me more?	"I want to die now." "I am scared. What is happening to me?" "Am I dying?" "I feel like I am losing everything." "No one has told us this before. Why didn't you all do something sooner? We asked for that scan weeks ago." "Is she dying? Is that what is going on here?"
	Rephrasing - You describe your family as working hard to keep your parents from having to know the challenging and hard things.	Rephrasing - So, it sounds like anger toward your Dad is about his choice to decline dialysis.	
	Statements - Every family is unique. My family is unique. With its own set of challenges. - Sometimes great opportunities emerge for families to connect in the most challenging times.	Statements - Tell me what is important to you right now. - I have also had very hard times that seemed impossible.	

For example, perhaps the family is protecting the patient from knowing the prognosis. Inviting the patient/family to share their experience with difficult information or changes in care is essential to palliative care. The patient and family must make meaning out of the experience, and nurse self-disclosure should only serve this end; thus, complementary disclosure is the most clinically sound practice in providing the best care for patient and family. Essential elements in planning intimate opening communication are identified in Table 6.5. The chart does not demand a sequential application to accomplish planning, but rather, an awareness of the components impacting planning. Depending on the particular situation, some of these categories may be more knowable to the nurse than others.

The nurse might be in possession of a wealth of information concerning patient and family awareness but has avoided assessing and planning for these challenging moments of communication. However, through intervention a patient and his or her family can be propelled into a much-improved quality of life.

Intervene

Locating the language or the verbal communication to use in challenging transitional moments with patients and families can produce anxiety in clinicians and has, in fact, been a motivating factor behind the recent movement to provide clinicians with communication protocols. Backing away from the idea that anxiety and tension must be removed and avoided, and thinking instead that these sensations herald a very positive opportunity for nurse, patient, and family, is an approach that honors the patient experience and unleashes his or her stories and needs to help all other stakeholders in the illness process provide the best care for patient and family (Gunaratnam & Oliviere, 2009). There are no sequences of talk *prescribed* in the COMFORT framework, but instead, principles and components guide a holistic communication experience in an effort to care for the entire patient. Nonetheless, it can be extremely helpful to gain a sense of particular language or communication behavior that could be potentially employed or borrowed to assist in a particular instance. Intervention involves

Table 6.7 Language to Address Tensions

Tension Identified	Potentially Useful Language
Clarify goals/values.	- What do you hope for most in the next month?
Readjust goals.	- In case you cannot make it to the wedding in person, could you think of another way to be there? A letter we could help you write, or a special videophone visit the day before the wedding?
Identify needs.	- Do you think you might need support at home?
	- What kinds of help might you need?
	- Would it be helpful if we could arrange _____?
Connect goals with care needs.	- It sounds like you want to be at home, enjoy your pets, and see your husband as much as possible. A service called hospice would support all of those hopes by…

(continued)

Table 6.7 (*continued*)

Tension Identified	Potentially Useful Language
Introduce hospice.	- The best way we know to give you the help you need and assure that you can be at home is through a care service called hospice.
	- A team of professionals will care specifically for you and enable you to stay at your house. This team is specifically trained and experienced in caring for very ill people at their homes.
	- You seem upset. Does talking about hospice make you sad?
	- Are you surprised to learn about how sick you are?
	- I can imagine this must be very hard for your family, to know how sick your sister is; you obviously are a very close and loving family.
	- As long as I have been in health care, when it came to deciding on hospice for my family member it was still very emotional.
Explore distress/ anxiety.	- Tell me about your sadness.
	- What is upsetting you the most?
Reassure.	- Hospice helps people live as well as they can for as long as they can.
	- Hospice has the goal of giving you the best quality of life possible—and that means being at your house with your family.
	- You can make the most of your time.
	- Whatever you decide, I will be your nurse. I will continue to care for you.
	- How about we all think this over? You know I will be here to talk with you about this, to process this decision.
	- I would be glad to talk with you more about this, and we can even invite a hospice nurse to join us to get more perspective on things.
	- Let's talk about this tomorrow. You are upset. Be with your wife now.

Adapted from Casarett, D., & Quill, T. (2007). "I'm not ready for hospice": Strategies for timely and effective hospice discussions. *Annals of Internal Medicine, 146,* 443–449.

communicating in these challenging transition times. So many of these opportunities were missed in the case of Felipe. For instance, once it was clear that Felipe was experiencing major loss of mobility and extreme fatigue as a result of the MI, a trigger opportunity presented itself. It was passed by, and Peter as well as the entire care team moved on to address the next curative-only intervention without an intimate and open communication with Felipe and his family.

Basic principles to observe in employing an intimate opening intervention include being (a) honest and truthful, (b) always connecting to the patient's goals and values, (c) encouraging patient/family questions, (d) considering what would cause the nurse anxiety if this issue were occurring in his or her own life, and (e) reserving time to be present and listen during communication events (Gauthier, 2008). In Table 6.6, elements in the planning grid in Table 6.5 are related to interventions. Here, connections are made between patient and family communication needs in transition and potentially useful strategies.

Late-stage hospice intervention is still the trend in the United States. For clinicians and health care professionals, talking about the hospice intervention can be the most difficult discussion to share with a patient and family. In many cases, this occurs because little open communication about prognosis or disease progression has been shared between clinicians and patient/family, or patient/family acceptability is so low that information processing is unsuccessful (Wittenberg-Lyles, Goldsmith, Ragan, & Sanchez-Reilly, 2010). A crisis often precipitates the conversation about hospice care benefits, further compromising the communication abilities of all parties involved. Language suggestions might be of some service in intervening in a patient's course of care with the concept of transitioning to hospice care (see Table 6.7).

Evaluate

Once navigated, an essential step to evaluate any nursing plan and practice is to evaluate the action taken and its outcome(s). Chapter 5 describes some components of reflection and its fruitful impact not only on patient and family care, but also on increased resilience for nurses as they face a grueling schedule of interactions and conflicts. The evaluative suggestions for this COMFORT component are presented in three parts: self, peer, and patient/family reflection.

Following an intimate opening interaction that was initiated in response to tension in the care of a patient/family, consider the following points of reflection:

• What was the transitional interaction addressing?
• What was the tension, or work to avoid a crisis, keeping the patient/family from addressing?
• What communication strategies/language were used in this interaction?
• Were they successful? How?
• What was unsuccessful?
• What would constitute a productive change in communication in this situation?

Understanding a patient's needs or family need first begins with considering the nurse's needs, qualities, and uniqueness. Reflecting on challenging interactions enables the clinicians to become more self-aware of how they engage certain situations and also what effect they can have in complex illness, and ways in which others' lives can be improved (McGuigan, 2009).

A second element of reflection is moving beyond self-reflexivity and widening the learning lens to include a collaborative experience (Atkinson & Claxton, 2000). The support offered through a small group discussion or dyadic interaction introduces additional perspectives for a nurse. Evaluate intimate opening experiences with a colleague using these guidelines:

• A nurse can ask a colleague to her/his reflective evaluation of a communication experience.

- The nurse provides a description of the challenging communication event.
- The nurse describes how that event made him/her feel.
- The nurse will ask the colleague/colleagues to share their views on how the event was approached and any suggestions about the communication that was exchanged.

A third dimension of evaluating communication in difficult transition periods involves reconnecting with a patient or family. The family and patient can be surprised when asked for their opinions and advice on care. It is helpful to explain that clinicians learn best about communication if there is an awareness about how patient/family achieved an outcome (Price, 2004). One or two prompts can provide the most salient evaluation of communication effectiveness. Below are suggested prompts that can be adjusted for a particular context and engage patient/family in the learning process.

o You seem like you are feeling better about things today. I am interested to know what helped you.
o Was my explanation too complicated during our previous meeting?
o What would have helped you in our discussion last week that you did not receive?

With a three-tiered effort (self/colleague/patient and family), reflective evaluation can expand strategies in narrative understanding, listening, being present, and communicating during the most vital points of transition for a patient and family.

CHAPTER SUMMARY

This chapter offers specific tools to assist the nurse in traversing the challenging yet profoundly rewarding moments of transition that require the clinical practice of intimate communication with patient and family. Revisioning tension and avoidance as a sign that communication is needed rather than a sign that encourages evasion is essential in helping a patient/family make meaning out of their loss. Observations of tension might be clear indications of a needed transition in place or goals of care. Complex interactions with patients and families coincide with transitions in care and require intimate and disclosive exchanges between patient/family and nurses.

Communication privacy management theory considers what is private information and how that information is private depending on the relationship people share. Social penetration theory assumes that all relationships are in development, or progress, and that self-disclosure is at the nexus of relationship development. Together, both of these theories support communication strategies that nurses can employ to achieve positive outcomes in these intimate opening conversations. Intimacy in the clinical setting places the nurse in the meaning-making process *with* the patient or family, rather than separating out a nurse's meaningful experiences from the patient/family. Self-disclosure that is complementary rather than reciprocal will enable the patient and family to experience a helpful closeness with the nurse.

Facilitating appropriate access to private health information, creating intimate openings to process transitions in life and care, and understanding the impact of self-disclosure on patient/family relationships all play an important role in practicing COMFORT.

REFERENCES

Altman, I., & Taylor, D. (1973). *Social Penetration: The Development of Interpersonal Relationships*. New York: Holt, Rinehart, & Winston.

Atkinson, T., & Claxton, G. (Eds.). (2000). *The Intuitive Practitioner: On the Value of Not Always Knowing What One Is Doing*. Maidenhead, UK: Open University Press, Milton Keynes.

Casarett, D., & Quill, T. (2007). "I'm not ready for hospice": Strategies for timely and effective hospice discussions. *Annals of Internal Medicine, 146*, 443–449.

Clark, J. (1982). Development of models and theories on the concept of nursing. *Journal of Advanced Nursing, 7*(2), 129–134.

Clayton, J. M., Butow, P. N., Arnold, R. M., & Tattersall, M. H. (2005). Discussing end-of-life issues with terminally ill cancer patients and their carers: A qualitative study. *Support Care and Cancer, 13*(8), 589–599.

Dahlin, C. (2010). Communication in palliative care: An essential competency for nurses. In B. R. Ferrell & N. Coyle (Eds.), *Oxford Textbook of Palliative Nursing* (pp. 107–133). New York: Oxford University Press.

Dowling, M. (2008). The meaning of nurse-patient intimacy in oncology care settings: From the nurse and patient perspective. *European Journal of Oncology Nursing, 12*, 319–328.

Edson, M. (1993). *W;t*. New York: Faber and Faber, Inc.

Eggly, S., Penner, L., Alrecht, T., Cline, R., Foster, T., Naughton, M., et al. (2006). Discussing bad news in the outpatient oncology clinic: Rethinking current communication guidelines. *Journal of Clinical Oncology, 24*, 716–719. doi: 10.1200/JCO.2005.03.0577

Ferrell, B. (1996). The quality of lives: 1525 voices in cancer. *Oncology Nursing Forum, 23*, 909–916.

Ferrell, B. R., Dow, K. H., & Grant, M. (1995). Measurement of the quality of life in cancer survivors. *Quality of Life Research, 4*, 523–531.

Gauthier, D. (2008). Challenges and opportunities: Communication near the end of life. *MESURG Nursing, 17*(5), 291–196.

Gentry, J. (2008). "Don't tell her she's on hospice": Ethics and pastoral care for families who withhold medical information. *Journal of Pastoral Care Counseling, 62*(5 Suppl.), 421–426.

Goldsmith, J., Wittenberg-Lyles, E., Rodriguez, D., & Sanchez-Reilly, S. (2010). Interdisciplinary geriatric and palliative care team narratives: Collaboration practices and barriers. *Qualitative Health Research, 20*(1), 94–104. doi: 10.1177/1049732309355287.

Gunaratnam, Y., & Oliviere, D. (Eds.). (2009). *Narrative and Stories in Health Care: Illness, Dying, and Bereavement*. New York: Oxford University Press.

Helft, P., & Petronio, S. (2007). Communication pitfalls with cancer patients: "Hit and run": Deliveries of bad news. *Journal of American College of Surgeons, 205*, 807–811.

Knauft, E., Nielson, E. L., Engelberg, R. A., Patrick, D., & Curtis, J. (2005). Barriers and facilitators to end-of-life care communication for patients with COPD. *Chest, 127*, 2188–2196.

Kristjanson, L. (2001). Establishing goals: Communication traps and treatment lane changes. In B. R. Ferrell & N. Coyle (Eds.), *Textbook of Palliative Nursing* (pp. 331–338). New York: Oxford University Press.

Kruijver, I., Kerkstra, A., Bensing, J. M., & van de Wiel, H. (2000). Nurse-patient communication in cancer care: A review of the literature. *Cancer Nursing, 23,* 20–31.

Malloy, P., Virani, R., Kelly, K., & Munevar, C. (2010). Beyond bad news: Communication skills of nurses in palliative care. *Journal of Hospice and Palliative Nursing, 12,* 166–174.

Matsayuma, R., Reddy, S., & Smith, T. (2006). Why do patients choose chemotheraphy near the end of life? A review of the perspective of those facing death from cancer. *Journal of Clinical Onoclogy, 24,* 3490–3496.

McCabe, M. S., & Storm, C. (2008). When doctors and patients disagree about medical futility. *Journal of Oncology Practice, 4,* 207–209. doi: 10.1200/JOP.0848503

McGuigan, D. (2009). Communicating bad news to patients: A reflective approach. *Nursing Standard, 23,* 51–57.

Meleis, A. I. (2012). *Theoretical Nursing: Development and Progress.* New York: Wolters, Kluiwer Health; Lippincott, Williams, & Wilkins.

Muetzel, P. (1988). Therapeutic nursing. In A. Pearson (Ed.), *Primary Nursing: Nursing in the Burford and Oxford Nursing Development Units* (pp. 89–116). London: Chapman & Hall.

National Consensus Project for Quality Palliative Care. (2011). www.nationalconsensusproject.org. Accessed April 16, 2011.

Neff, P., Lyckholm, L., & Smith, T. (2002) Truth or consequences: What to do when the patient doesn't want to know. *Journal of Clinical Oncology, 20,* 3035–3037.

O'Connell, E. (2008). Therapeutic relationships in critical care nursing: A reflection on practice. *Nursing in Critical Care, 13,* 138–143. doi: 10:111/j1478–5153.2008.00273.x.

Peterson, J., Johnson, M., Halvorsen, B., Apmann, L., Chang, P. C., Kershek, S., et al. (2010). What is so stressful about caring for a dying patient? A qualitative study of nurses' experiences. *International Journal of Palliative Nursing, 16*(4), 181–187.

Petronio, S. (2002). *Boundaries of Privacy: Dialectics of Disclosure.* Albany: State University of New York Press.

Petronio, S. (2011). Disclosure predicaments arising during the course of patient care: Nurses' privacy management. *Health Communication, 26,* 255–256. doi: 10.1080/10410236.2010.549812

Petronio, S., & Lewis, S. S. (2011). Medical disclosure in oncology among families, patients, and providers: A communication privacy management perspective. In M. Miller-Day (Ed.), *Family Communication, Connections, and Health Transitions* (pp. 269–298). New York: Peter Lang Publishing, Inc.

Planalp, S., & Trost, MR. (2008). Communication issues at the end of life: Reports from hospice volunteers. *Health Communication, 23*(3), 222–233.

Prager, K. (1995). *The Psychology of Intimacy.* New York: Guilford Press.

Price, B. (2004). Demonstrating respect for patient dignity. *Nursing Standard, 19,* 45–52.

Reinke, L., Shannon, S., Engelberg, R., Dotolo, D., Silverstri, G., & Curtis, R. (2010). Nurses' identification of important yet under-utilized end-of-life skills for patients with life-limiting or terminal illness. *Journal of Palliative Medicine, 13*(6), 753–759. doi: 10.1089/jpm.2009.0423

Reis, H., & Shaver, P. (1988). Intimacy as interpersonal relations. In S. Duck (Ed.), *Handbook of Personal Relationships: Theory, Research, and Interventions* (pp. 367–389). New York: Wiley & Sons.

Saunders, J. (2004). Handling unexpected distress on the telephone: The development of interdisciplinary training. *International Journal of Palliative Care Nursing, 10,* 454–459.

Schulter, J., Winch, S., Holzhauser, K., & Henderson, A. (2008). Nurses' moral sensitivity and hospital ethical climate: A literature review. *Nursing Ethics, 15,* 304–321.

Tuffrey-Wijne, I., & McEnghill, L. (2008). Communication difficulties and intellectual disability in end-of-life care. *International Journal of Palliative Nursing, 14,* 189–194.

West, R., & Turner, L. (2007). *Introducing Communication Theory: Analysis and Application* (4th ed.). New York: McGraw-Hill.

Wittenberg-Lyles, E., Goldsmith, J., Ragan, S., & Sanchez-Reilly, S. (2008). Communicating a terminal prognosis in a palliative care setting: Deficiencies in current communication training protocols. *Social Science and Medicine, 66*(11), 2356–2365.

Wittenberg-Lyles, E., Goldsmith, J., Ragan, S., & Sanchez-Reilly, S. (2010). *Dying With Comfort: Family Narrative and Early Palliative Care.* Creskill, NJ: Hampton.

Zhang, B., Wright, A., Huskamp, H., Milsson, M., Maciejewski, M., Earle, C., et al. (2009). Health care costs in the last week of life: Associations with end-of-life conversations. *Archives of Internal Medicine, 169,* 480–488.

Zomorodi, M., & Foley, B. J. (2009). The nature of advocacy vs. paternalism in nursing: Clarifying the "thin line." *Journal of Advanced Nursing, 65,* 1746–1752.

ADDITIONAL RESOURCES

International Listening Association (ILA): www.listening.org

This site contains comprehensive information and convention and resource material about the process of receiving, constructing meaning from, and responding to spoken and/or nonverbal messages.

Play Therapy International: www.playtherapy.org

This site is intended to provide an international information resource for therapeutic play, play therapy, filial play, and creative arts therapies. It is designed for anyone interested in helping children with emotional literacy.

Schaefer, C. E., & Kadson, H. (Eds). (2006). *Contemporary Play Therapy: Theories, Research and Practice.* New York: Gilford Press.

ADDITIONAL REFERENCES FOR PRIVACY MANAGEMENT THEORY

Baider, L. (2010). Cancer and the family: The myth of words and silence. *Journal of Pediatric Hematology Oncology, 32*(1), 54–57.

Cleary, M., Hunt, G. E., Escott, P., & Walter, G. (2010). Receiving difficult news: Views of patients in an inpatient setting. *Journal of Psychosocial Nursing and Mental Health Services, 48*(6), 40–48.

Petronio, S. (2000). The ramifications of the reluctant confidant. In A. C. Richards & T. Schumrum (Eds.), *Invitations to Dialogue: The Legacy of Sidney M. Jourard* (pp. 113–150). Dubuque, IA: Kendall/Hunt Publishers.

Petronio, S. (2010). Communication privacy management theory: What do we know about family privacy regulation? *Journal of Family Theory and Review, 2,* 175–196.

Petronio, S., Ellemers, N., Giles, H., & Gallois, C. (1998). (Mis)communicating across boundaries—Interpersonal and intergroup considerations. *Communication Research, 25*(6), 571–595.

Petronio, S., & Lewis, S. S. (2011). Medical disclosures in oncology among families, patients, and providers: A communication privacy management perspective. In M. Miller-Day (Eds.), *Family Communication, Connections, and Health Transitions* (pp. 269–298). New York: Peter Lang.

ADDITIONAL REFERENCES FOR SOCIAL PENETRATION THEORY

Altman, I., Vinsel, A., & Brown, B. (1981). Dialectic conceptions in social psychology: An application to social penetration and privacy regulation. *Advances in Experimental Social Psychology, 14,* 107–160.

Taylor, D., & Altman, I. (1975). Self-disclosure as a function of reward-cost outcomes. *Sociometry, 38,* 18–31.

Werner, C., Altman, I., & Brown, B. B. (1992). A transactional approach to interpersonal relations: Physical environment, social context and temporal qualities. *Journal of Social and Personal Relationships, 9,* 297–323.

DISCUSSION QUESTIONS

1. What are some challenges that might occur in navigating the private boundary of a patient when you have news that they do not yet know?
2. At what point does a private boundary become a collective boundary? Identify an example from clinical practice that clearly demonstrates this change.
3. Describe how a nurse might deal with the boundary turbulence produced when one adult child (a long-distance caregiver) arrives at her father's bedside and disagrees with other adult child's care choice to withhold IV fluids. The local child had not shared these care decisions with the sibling for fear there would be dissent.
4. How can a nurse recognize the importance of self-disclosure and its impact on the patient–nurse relationship, but also monitor the importance of using a complementary rather than reciprocal kind of self-disclosure?
5. Apply CPM to Peter's case. What private information is Peter already in possession of, and what boundary turbulence might be predicted?
6. Peter had a great deal of breadth knowledge about Felipe's case. What specific communication strategies could have been used to gain depth and potentially move into an intimate opening with this patient/family?
7. Think back on an instance of patient/family tension. How was it handled? Name some specific communication strategies that could have produced a better outcome.
8. What are some ways to initiate an intimate opening for a delirious or unconscious patient who has received curative-only care?

TEACHING RESOURCES AND MATERIALS

Exercise #1: Moving Theory to Practice with Communication Privacy Management

In this teaching exercise, the instructor will introduce basic ideas from communication privacy management theory. Boundary coordination describes the ways in which people manage information that is co-owned. In order for co-ownership to occur, private information has to become collectively owned.

The objective of this activity is to illustrate one aspect of communication privacy management theory, allowing nurses or students to clarify the concepts of personal and collective boundaries. Nursing students will separate out into dyads. Each dyad will be assigned a specific relationship (mother–son, friend–friend, romantic couple, long-term married couple, and so forth). In dyads, they are to (1) develop a role play illustrating a conversation between the two people in their assigned relationship, and (2) center the context and topic on palliative care. The role play should contain both text (what is spoken) and subtext (what is meant). The text should represent what the partners actually say to each other. The subtext describes what the partners are thinking but not sharing aloud. For example, in an exchange between a nurse and patient, the text could look like this:

PALLIATIVE CARE CONSULT NURSE: Your brain tumor will not go away.

END-STAGE CANCER PATIENT: You will have to talk to my oncologist about our plan.

PALLIATIVE CARE CONSULT NURSE: We can make you more comfortable and relieve the pressure, but we cannot take the tumor away.

END-STAGE CANCER PATIENT: She (oncologist) told me the radiation was our next plan. I will be home soon. I just want to get my arm back moving.

The subtext of this exchange will look quite different:

PALLIATIVE CARE CONSULT NURSE: Your brain tumor will not go away.

(SUBTEXT: You will not survive this tumor's growth and spread.)

END-STAGE CANCER PATIENT: You will have to talk to my oncologist about our plan.

(SUBTEXT: I am working with my oncologist, not you. We are working toward my restoration.)

PALLIATIVE CARE CONSULT NURSE: We can make you more comfortable and relieve the pressure, but we cannot take the tumor away.

(SUBTEXT: We want to work with you, too, and give you support and comfort. You will not survive this tumor.)

END-STAGE CANCER PATIENT: She (oncologist) told me the radiation was our next plan. I will be home soon. I just want to get my arm back moving. (SUBTEXT: I want a cure and am seeking one. I will be home just like before I got sick.)

In pairs, students will perform their "scripts" with text and then again including subtext. Following their scripts, they should share a discussion addressing how the shared information forms a *collective* boundary while the withheld information creates a *personal* boundary. Nursing students should be encouraged to think about how the ratio of the collective boundary to the personal boundary affects the relationship and vice versa.

Exercise adapted from West, R., & Turner, L. (2007). *Introducing Communication Theory: Analysis and Application* (4th ed.). New York: McGraw-Hill.

Exercise #2: Caring for Dorothy and Bob

Nurses often face patients with little information about their lives or relationships yet are required to provide care that is responsive to their needs. A particular set of challenges occurs when the patient and the caregiver are both intellectually impaired, and the patient's case is so complicated that a major change in care and coping must occur:

Bob and his slightly younger sister, Dorothy, arrive at the clinic. Both siblings are single and in their early 70s. Bob is Dorothy's caretaker. The two of them live alone in their childhood home. Dorothy is wheelchair bound from her end-stage cardiac disease and also has COPD and dementia. She is on oxygen. Bob is attentive, but overwhelmed and unprepared by the increasing demands of Dorothy's care. In addition to her breathing challenges, Dorothy is barefoot, feet swollen and unkempt. Bob shows kindness and calm as he deals with his sister, but also limited ability to understand her disease or communicate with others. As Bob checks in at the front desk, Dorothy begins to scoot her wheelchair across the lobby floor at a snail's pace. She is purposeful in her effort, her lungs fighting for air with each movement. As Bob finishes his interaction with the office staff, he notices Dorothy has positioned herself at the door to the lobby restroom, but cannot muster the strength to move forward over the ½" grouted crevasses in the tile floor. "Dorothy, I can't get you in there. I can't. You can't get yourself in there," says Bob. Dorothy stares down the half-open door and black void that is the restroom. She cannot go further. Bob cannot take her further. "Unlock your chair and let me push you back over here." Dorothy mutters in a slurred sound, "I don't know how to unlock the chair." Bob releases the locks on her chair, and it is easy to imagine his deep weariness. Moments later, Dorothy's name is called by a young office assistant. Bob sinks blankly into his chair, knowing that for these 15 minutes he can rest. Someone else will have oversight of Dorothy. Dorothy, struggling for air, frustrated and hurt by her brother's response, goes down the hall to meet the nurse practitioner: someone unaware of Dorothy's life, relationships, or circumstances.

After sharing this story with a class, encourage students to meet in groups and discuss how to proceed with this patient from a communication transition standpoint. Here are some questions that will facilitate a discussion about moving Dorothy toward transition.

- Would it be obvious to a nurse practitioner that this patient needs further support and care in addition to the care provided by her brother?
- Would the nurse practitioner try to find out about the home caregiver, even if this person were not in attendance at the appointment?
- What would the nurse do upon realizing Dorothy's dementia?
- Without a previously existing relationship with Dorothy and her family, how does the nurse proceed moving this family toward a better care situation?

Exercise #3: The M&M/Skittles Game—Sharing Information

In this course project, students will demonstrate the level of willingness or unwillingness associated with sharing various types of information.

Necessary supplies include a large bag of M&Ms or Skittles, enough so that members of the class can all have several, as well as a chart of "colors of candies" and the disclosure associated with each color. Create a category for each color of candy. The disclosures associated with each color should range from impersonal to more personal.

    Examples: Red = Favorite movie
                Brown = Ideal vacation, destination
                Yellow = Pet peeve
                Green = Thing that would ultimately make me happiest
                Blue = Thing I fear most

How to proceed:

1. Before revealing the color chart or the instructions for disclosure, pass around the bag(s) of M&Ms or Skittles. Instruct students to take as many as they want from the bag, but be sure to tell them that they *must* take at least one.
2. After all students have taken at least one piece of candy, then display the chart that lists the type of disclosure associated with each color of candy used.
3. In groups or as a class, instruct students to answer the question for *each* candy that they chose from the bag. If students chose several candies, they must answer

several questions. Students may find that they will be answering the same question multiple times, but using different answers, if they chose several of the same color of candy.
4. Lead a class discussion that focuses on these questions:

• How would you apply the concepts of *breadth* and *depth* of disclosure to the information that you just shared during this exercise?
• Which types of information were easier to share with the group/class? Why? Which were most difficult? Why?

Exercise adapted from West, R., & Turner, L. (2007). *Introducing Communication Theory: Analysis and Application* (4th ed.). New York: McGraw-Hill.

COMPREHENSIVE EXERCISES FOR CHAPTER MATERIAL

SUSIE AND THE POPSICLES: IDENTIFYING SOCIAL PENETRATION THEORY AND COMMUNICATION PRIVACY MANAGEMENT THEORY

The Pulitzer Prize–winning play *Wit* is a powerful tool for all clinicians training to deal with terminally ill patients. Near the end of the play, Vivian Bearing, the protagonist, is succumbing to death from OVCA. She has been engaged in aggressive research trials for several months and is very sick. The play depicts Vivian's own journey of stripping away personal identifiers, such as professional status, treatment of others, family connections/disconnection, and personal successes. As she is actively dying, Vivian finds her humanity and embraces what she believes matters most in life. In one of the final scenes, Susie, her nurse throughout most of the play, shares a long scene with her in which a DNR decision is finally discussed. Susie displays a great deal of skill in her clinical communication practice with Vivian. This learning session with require access to the HBO version of the script, and a basic understanding/summary of the movie. What follows are the steps and questions to incorporate as part of the *Susie and the Popsicles* exercise.

• Show video segment. Share a brief discussion about this segment and the characters of Vivian and Susie.
• Revisit the scene and search for moments of social penetration theory demonstrated by Susie. Note examples of depth.
• Revisit the scene and search for moments of social penetration theory demonstrated by Vivian. Note examples of depth. Note examples of breadth. How many of each?

- Is reciprocal or complementary communication at work between Susie and Vivian in their self-disclosure?
- Revisit the scene and search for moments of private information disclosure from Susie to Vivian. What strategies does Susie use?
- How can the boundary between Susie and Vivian be described?
- What does their shared boundary quality say about their relationship?

Source used in this exercise: Edson, M. (1993). W;t. New York: Faber and Faber, Inc.

MOVING TOWARD THE TENSION: BRIEF COMMUNICATION ROLE PLAY SCENARIOS

Four brief role play scenarios are included here and should be explored in very small groups (three to four). Reverse/change roles after you have worked with the situation for 5 minutes. After completing two versions of the role play, the participants should discuss:

1. What verbal/language strategies were most helpful?
2. What verbal/language strategies were least helpful?
3. What nonverbal communication strategies were most helpful?
4. What nonverbal communication strategies were least helpful?

Role Play #1

Ms. Smith is a 42-year-old single mother with moderate COPD. She has been in and out of the emergency room many times. However, this time, she is terrified as she is more short of breath. She asks you, "People don't die from this do they?"
How do you respond?

Role Play #2

Dr. Martha Rollin is a neurologist caring for Molly, a 21-year-old who has Huntington's chorea. Molly has had more difficulty speaking and moving. It has become apparent to you and all other nursing and medical team members that Molly is declining, and yet Dr. Rollin has been reluctant to inform Molly, her fiancé, or her parents of her prognosis. One of the other nurses shared in report that Dr. Rollin once mentioned that Molly reminded her of her own granddaughter, and the resident mentioned that Dr. Rollin told him that Molly was one of her longest-term patients. The nursing staff has become increasingly frustrated as they feel Molly, her fiancée, and her parents need to be informed of her status. Late this evening, Dr. Rollin returns to the hospital for a new admission, and you decide this is a good time to discuss Molly's care with her.

How do you initiate the discussion?

Role Play #3

Valnezio Quartera is a 76-year-old man with heart failure, severe coronary artery disease, and aortic stenosis. He is currently back in the hospital for dyspnea and chest pain. His wife died one year ago from a myocardial infarction. As you, the critical care nurse, enter the room to hang an IV diuretic, Mr. Quartera asks you, "Susie, you don't think I'm going to die do you?"

How do you respond?

Role Play #4

Paulo Rodriquez is a 49-year-old with a recurrent brain tumor currently hospitalized after experiencing seizures. Paulo was diagnosed at age 44 and has had extensive surgery, chemotherapy, and radiation therapy. Three months ago, the brain tumor team advised Paulo and his family that there were no further treatment options, at which time his family took him to Mexico where he has had numerous herbal therapies and traditional folk remedies. He has experienced weight loss, increasingly severe headaches, nausea, and now seizures. Following a severe seizure last week, his girlfriend brought him back to the emergency room for care. As you wait with Paulo for a scan, he tells you he is so tired of treatment and being taken far away and just wishes his girlfriend and children would "give up and just let me be at home so I can play with my dog and be with my friends."

How do you respond?

Exercise Source

ELNEC Critical Care Training Program. (2010). *Communication Module Six: Supplemental Teaching Materials, Figure 5. Communication Role Play Scenarios.* COH & AACN. The End-of-Life Nursing Education Consortium (ELNEC) Project is a national end-of-life educational program administered by City of Hope Medical Center (COH) and the American Association of Colleges of Nursing (AACN), designed to enhance palliative care in nursing. The ELNEC Project was originally funded by a grant from the Robert Wood Johnson Foundation with additional support form funding organizations (the National Cancer Institute, Aetna Foundation, Archstone Foundation, and California Foundation).

ADDITIONAL SUPPLEMENTAL MATERIALS

Table 6.8 Suggestions for Communicating with Patients or Family Members with Limited Understanding

- Double the consultation time if possible or schedule at a time in the day most likely to provide the most time.
- Communicate directly with the challenged individual and then to a support person or interpreter. Maintain nonverbals that are directed at the primary person in the interaction.
- Rearrange a question if the previous attempt garnered inconclusive or unproductive results.
- Preview the contents of the consultation before it begins.
- Utilize additional aids (i.e., pictures, writing, symbols, etc.) and supports to increase the health literacy level for the patient/family.
- Practicing a teachback approach might be helpful, in which the patient/family explains back to the clinician what has been discussed or decided.
- Use language that is accessible to this person.
- Use events and places in conversation that the person will likely relate to and understand.
- The person in the consultation might have little understanding of a cause–effect dynamic when it comes to his or her illness (e.g., continued smoking will make COPD worse).

Adapted from Tuffrey-Wijne, I., & McEnghill, L. (2008). Communication difficulties and intellectual disability in end-of-life care. *International Journal of Palliative Nursing, 14,* 189–194.

Table 6.9 Potentially Helpful Things to Say During the Distressed Phone Call

Situation	Communication
To understand emotion better	"You sound pretty low."
	"I can hear the frustration in your voice."
Identifying the issue	"Earlier in the call you asked … "
	"So, what I think you are saying is that …"
Periods of crying/silence	"Take your time."
	"I'm here when you want to speak."
	"Remain silent."
Rudeness/abusive behavior	"I want to help you but will not continue this call if you are shouting."
	"I really want to help you, but if you continue I will have to hang up."

Adapted from Saunders, J. (2004). Handling unexpected distress on the telephone: The development of interdisciplinary training. *International Journal of Palliative Care Nursing, 10,* 454–459.

7

RELATING

Billy Green was a 4-year-old African American diagnosed with a brain tumor. Over the next 3 years, he went through surgery, chemotherapy, and radiation, and twice he experienced remissions of 10–12 months, during which time there was hope for his long-term survival. Billy's mother and maternal grandmother were devout Baptists who believed in miracles, and despite each recurrence they persisted in their faith for his recovery. Billy's father voiced concern as he now experienced yet another recurrence, this time the tumor causing seizures and extensive neurological deficits.

Billy's parents have been asked to meet with the pediatric oncology team to make treatment decisions. His oncologist acknowledges that there are no further traditional treatments available but does offer a new clinical trial. Mrs. Green questions the physician about potential side effects, and the oncologist describes possible side effects, which could include worsened seizures, hypertension, and hemorrhage. Mr. Green then becomes very angry and emotional, announcing, "I think it's time you leave my boy alone. Enough!" Mrs. Green sobs but clutches her Bible and begins to pray and chant. Billy's grandmother comforts her daughter and son-in-law and assures both that Billy will pull through, saying, "God isn't going to take our boy."

Billy's grandmother cannot accept any outcome other than cure, at least at this moment. Billy's father wants to withdraw his son from curative medical interventions and pain-inducing procedures, at least at this moment. Billy's mother is able to consider the impact of a clinical trial on his fragile quality of life. Each of these three caregivers has a radically different way to engage the news delivered to the family. What they all face is the decision of care for Billy; what each needs is more conversation and communication that takes into account who they are as people and as a family. This can happen if the relationship between the clinician and the family/patient is prioritized.

This chapter presents relating as a strategy to advance patient and family understanding. The surface of the spoken word is peeled back to consider what the action or force of language might include. A complex architecture of goals is always at play, no matter who is doing the speaking. Because the true motives and goals of a speaker are rarely fully understood or realized, the recommendation in this chapter is to attend to the relationship goal (sharing meaning) always, in order to facilitate the instrumental goals (providing specific health care) of nursing. Throughout this portion of the book, there is the opportunity to examine more closely the phenomenon of patient/family non/acceptance of an illness status, as well as understanding patient/family perspectives on adjusting to new information unfolding throughout a serious or terminal illness.

A set of theory-driven ideas from communication is brought together with nursing research to ground this element of the COMFORT model. All of the concepts presented here create a mosaic of knowledge that demystifies misunderstandings, conflict, and disconnection experienced between clinicians and patients/families during a time in the illness trajectory when all of these parties feel the greatest need for support and communication connection.

ADAPTING TO THE PATIENT/FAMILY

Clinicians might assume what information will be easily processed or understood by patients and families and what information will be difficult to engage. In fact, this latter assumption—what will be "bad news," or difficult news—is often presumed by clinicians. Such presuppositions are questioned in this chapter and fall into the sender-based perspective on communication that discounts the unique circumstances of each patient case and person.

Consider the case of Bob, whose wife is just coming out of an exploratory laparoscopy. This procedure was at last pursued to finally locate the source of her troublesome appetite and weight loss, as well as bouts of great nausea and cramping. Bob is ushered down to a private meeting room, and upon entry he sees a chaplain, the surgeon, and the nurse. Bob is very anxious simply by the efforts made to seclude him in this room and by the conspicuous presence of the hospital chaplain. His pulse races with concern. He sweats. He notes the tension in the room and the anxiety projected by the chaplain and two clinicians. The surgeon tells Bob that she has the "worst possible news" for him. In the surgical procedure, one large cancerous mass was found in his wife's upper bowel, and two lymph nodes excised were also positive. The discovery made in surgery was a devastating one.

But, for Bob and his wife, this news carries with it relief. For 14 months her diagnosis had been elusive, and three physicians had dismissed her symptoms as being related only to anxiety or suggested she had only a minor inflammatory bowel dysfunction. In the past year, her quality of life had been reduced so radically that she was no longer able to travel with her job or to see family. Weakness and abdominal pain had tortured and worried both of them these many months. Learning a firm diagnosis that explained all of her pain and loss felt more like a relief than staring down the worst news of Bob's life. The couple had already known this was a devastating health situation. Without taking into account some of the experiences of the patient and family, the clinician has nothing to adapt to and communicates using his or her own experience as a measure for how to deliver information.

Talking and communicating in a way that is **radically adaptive** assumes that the clinician cannot know the reaction or perspective of the patient/family without first receiving it. Removing the clinician's own response and opinion from the expected communication outcome puts the "other" first. The idea of narrative nursing is underscored again here, and one of its central tenets is to accept that the end of the story is not known, and that the outcome of the interaction is just as dependent on the patient and family as it is on the clinician.

Observations of patient and family interaction with clinicians reveal that repetition, redundancy, rejection, and selection are very present in the communication process of absorbing illness status (Eggly et al., 2006; Wittenberg-Lyles, Goldsmith, Sanchez-Reilly, Ragan, 2008). Additionally, there is a flawed conception among clinicians that information central to decisions about care in illness will be clear to the patient and family if it is presented as one focal piece of information. In fact, many patients/families change the subject of a conversation topic during "bad news" discussions in order to process concerns that *they* have, that are difficult for them, that are blocking them from moving forward in their care. A singularity of topic is rarely experienced in actual interactions, though that is commonly the preparation clinicians receive in their curriculum.

Diversified approaches and responses to a subject can be referred to as the **diffusion of topic**. For instance, consider Ben, a nurse from a palliative care team sent to discuss plans of care with Maggie. The report Ben received from the attending physician was that Maggie was impossible to talk to and seemed to be on another planet in terms of facing her care decisions. When Ben visited with Maggie about care options as she faced the end of her life, Maggie was resistant and indicated many times that she needed to get to a place "where her legs would work again." After Ben realized he was going down the same road as the attending physician, he stopped pressing Maggie to do the care planning and listened to her. The investment in Maggie paid off quickly. Ben learned that Maggie was responsible for the care of her adult autistic son and his three dogs. She viewed these dogs as central to her son's health and functioning. Though Ben originally arrived at Maggie's room with the intent to "make a plan" for her, this central topic had to be diffused to address Maggie's deep concern—which was for her son, not herself.

A term that is infinitely useful in explaining patient or family acknowledgment of changing health status is **acceptability**. To accept news or change is to acknowledge that it is real and assent to that information in planning, behavior, and communication. Acceptability is arrived at with more ease if the patient/family is adapted to first and foremost in terms of their experiences and needs. Patients and families bring lifetimes of patterns and "baggage" into one of the most difficult chapters in life—end of life.

Revisiting the opening pediatric case study, the grandmother could be a major factor in delaying acceptability, as Billy's case becomes palliative and hospice appropriate. Adjusting for these challenges can be so rewarding, especially when clinicians lay down their own personal goals and checklists and invest in individual(s) with limited acceptability. Acceptability coincides with a shift in patient/family narrative from one that is chaotic, or tightly grips the promise of restoration, to a narrative that looks ahead to the possibilities presented through illness.

QUEST NARRATIVE

As palliative care is initiated, patients and families have a high degree of uncertainty about the care-planning process. Many families report that they "have never done this before" and are unsure about working with patients to provide care at home. This ambiguity leaves them searching for an alternative way of living with illness (Frank, 1995). Since cure is no longer a viable outcome for their illness story, patients and families look for other sources of meaning as a way of managing their uncertainty. The discovery of something useful from the experience of illness is called a **quest narrative** (Frank, 1995). These are stories that illustrate patient/family acceptability and often include acknowledgment of significant changes (both vocational and personal) following an illness (Frank, 1995). Though Frank's naming and observation of the quest narrative is not empirically based, the authors suggest that this kind of narrative can be a useful goal for nurses caring for patients and families facing serious and terminal illness.

As the illness story is told, the goal is to support patients and families as they work toward rewriting a no-longer-useful story of cure. Three distinct phases comprise the quest narrative and point to specific junctures in a patient/family member's story identifying the quest. In the first part of an illness story, symptoms are disregarded and refused, only to give way to acknowledgment of the disease/illness. This acknowledgment signifies a threshold that indicates a move toward acceptability (Frank, 1995). Next, there is a major turning point in the illness story that is typically described (through metaphor) as a crisis or unsuccessful treatment (e.g., surgery, chemotherapy, radiation). Following this critical turning point (treatments have not been effective, a critical health/safety condition arises, or no other treatment options exist), the patient/family gains awareness and realizes where they are in the illness journey. Discovery is gained from the event or critical turning point and brings a sense of identity related to the illness. Finally, changes as a result of the illness are brought to the forefront of the patient/family's character, and the lessons learned reveal perseverance and the richness gained through suffering. Box 7.1 provides an example of a patient's perspective that is consonant with the quest narrative. The point of this chapter, though, is to emphasize the role the nurse plays in making a narrative like the quest narrative more likely and attainable. The quest narrative becomes more possible if the nurse uses communication to intervene.

Box 7.1

"I have learned how much I love life and how precious it is … I have learned that no matter what, the journey doesn't have to be all about dark and dreariness and the end."
—*ALS patient*

The nurse's task is to enact communication skills that reduce uncertainty and reauthor the illness journey toward a quest narrative. By encouraging patients and family members to reflect on the illness and its impact, the nurse can identify patient/family sense making (why they believe this is happening, how they are interpreting changes), allow them to assert control over their story, point out prior decisions and results, establish a sense of community with the patient/family, and distinguish new identities (Sharf & Vanderford, 2003). Nurses need to assess acceptability and adapt communication accordingly.

Patients and families are often inclined to share their story as a way of acclimating to new staff. It is during this first storytelling that nurses can begin to decipher acceptability. Take, for example, the first-time meeting between a hospice nurse and the mother of a 29-year-old woman who has been referred to hospice. The referral sheet shows that this young patient had a kidney transplant at age 7. The kidney failed approximately 14 years later. For the last 8 years, the patient has been on dialysis and has had three strokes, and she has been bedbound with a feeding tube for over a year. Her mother recalls the events leading up to this initial hospice visit as illustrated in Figure 7.1a.

"We are down to our last location for dialysis. Two weeks ago she came down with a rare form of e-coli and had a temperature of 103 for three days. And because she's hypotensive, they had to put her on IVs and antibiotics and several heart medicines. Her hands and feet turned black. Now she's off and her hands are pink... She has been at home with us and has been able to walk and move. She has limited vision and now her vision is totally gone. She has incredible joint pain. It's not going to get any better. We can take her some place, like long term care, but I don't know what good it will do. She's very susceptible to infection. It's time... "

Nurse: This started a year ago?

> Critical Turning Point – Acknowledges that no other options exist following this health crisis

"Yes, Karen had an infection in her catheter. She's been on dialysis for 8 years. She was born with this. She knows. Last year she had an ulcer in her esophagus, it eroded and she had a stroke. She was in the hospital from July through January ... My head has already made the decision, but my heart is just breaking. You (hospice) have been recommended from folks who have used you – they (hospital) would like her gone today."

> Acknowledges disease and its progression.

Nurse begins to discuss hospice philosophy, focusing on time frame to death once dialysis is stopped.

"I think she's there, but she doesn't want to die."

Nurse: "Of course, she doesn't want to die and no mother ever wants to have a daughter die. In hospice we have cared for many families whose circumstances are very much like yours. We find that even in these very difficult circumstances, patients and families do best when they can openly talk about what is happening now at the end of life, say goodbye and to let each other know how much you love each other. You said a few minutes ago that "It's time ...". It seems like you really are aware that your daughter has only a few weeks of life remaining. Can we talk about how we can best support you and Karen in the days ahead?"

> Nurse attempts to identify meaningfulness in the illness story, shifting this toward a quest narrative.

FIGURE 7.1ᶜ ! Illustration

In this case, a family meeting is held to determine plans and place of care for a 58-year old male. The wife is under suspicion of attempted murder of the patient, her husband. He has been shot from the rear twice within two months. As a result of this second shooting, the patient has been wounded in the back and lung. He is unconscious, and will not recover.

If the wife goes to jail, she loses all rights to make decisions therefore decision-making would transfer to the patient's five children, of which only one son has kept in regular contact with the patient.

The wife of the patient and her brother are present for the family meeting. Health professionals present include a nurse, social worker, resident (R), and attending physician (AP).

Brother: What is his condition? It's changing drastically.
[Team introduces themselves.]
Brother: He's had a dope habit, very bad.*

Direct Act	Indirect Act	Multiple Goals
-Informing team	-Deflecting blame	TASK: protect sister
	-Identifying factors contributing to shooting	RELATIONAL: reveal self as in control of family knowledge

[Brother says to wife:] Tell them the truth, nothing but the truth, or they can't help him. *

Direct Act	Indirect Act	Multiple Goals
-Advising sister	-Demonstrating innocence	TASK: present family roles to team
	-Assuring team of sister's innocuous role in the demise of patient	RELATIONAL: demonstrate care of sister to the team

Wife: He's aggressive.*

Direct Act	Indirect Act	Multiple Goals
-Announcing character of her spouse	-Denying fault	TASK: explain her innocence
	-Attributing shooting to his bad behavior	RELATIONAL: present herself as victim to the team

Brother: They have lost everything, there are lots of problems.*

Direct Act	Indirect Act	Multiple Goals
-Disclosing loss	-Positioning husband at fault	TASK: convey a vast amount of difficulty and complication to team
	-Positioning wife as victim	RELATIONAL: manage caregiver for her sister

RN: Is there any other family?
Wife: Yes, he has five kids that live in Nebraska. His father is dead and his mother lives in an Alzheimer's facility.
RN: How long have you been with him?
Wife: 16 years.
RN: Do you have any kids?
Wife: Not any more.
Brother: She lost her only son to suicide. We have lost lots of family to suicide.

FIGURE 7.1A! Family interaction (no patient present)

Wife: You should know my husband is an ex-felon. [she discusses past experiences of gunshots produced by dying husband].*

Direct Act	Indirect Act	Multiple Goals
-identifying husband as criminal	-exonerating herself of blame	TASK: clarify her innocence
	-deflecting guilt	RELATIONAL: evoke sympathy from team
	-gaining protection	

→   AP: [talks about the patient's care and where the patient has been and what the healthcare team has been doing]. He's barely responding to any stimuli. He's not communicating.
Wife: Why are there so many changes in his condition?
Resident: [explains gunshot wound impacts many physical systems which means the patient is at risk for many complications—though the man is stable currently.]
Brother: Well, the other doctors have said to look into long-term care.
AP: Let's talk about that. First, he's not a candidate for rehabilitation because he cannot communicate. The next choice is long term care and that's probably what will happen. He needs constant 24-hour supervision for care.
RN: Has he ever talked about what he would want if he was in a condition like this?
Brother: We'll yes he said put me in my favorite car and drive me off a cliff.
RN: Well yes that comment is helpful. Did you share any other talks?
Wife: [explains that the patient has changed his mind many times about end-of-life extension– and she gives examples]
Brother: He's been addicted to many different drugs, pain medication, and stuff.
Wife: [talks about life troubles and being thankful for her brother]
Brother: Is he conscious?
RN: [explains that he doesn't have consciousness]. He doesn't have the capacity to make decisions.*

Direct Act	Indirect Act	Multiple Goals
-disclosing that husband is unconscious and unable to direct his own care	-suggesting that decisions of care must be made by someone in family	TASK: clarify husband's status
	-impressing upon family that decisions are needed	RELATIONAL: remind wife of her role as spouse

Resident: I agree.
RN: It's about following the patient's wishes. What do you think he wanted?
Wife: [breaks down crying] I don't know.
Brother: [holding sister's hand] [says to healthcare team] I'm sorry, but she can't handle this. She's never been able to [talks about patient]
[RN explains code status is about resuscitating him if his heart stops.]
The wife and her brother do not make a decision about code status and meeting is concluded.

FIGURE 7.1b (*continued*)

PROBLEMATIC INTEGRATION

Changing probabilities about the disease and changing values about acceptable quality of life create uncertainty for the patient and family; nurse communication is necessary to facilitate discussions about uncertainty and shift toward a quest narrative. With multiple parties involved in a patient's plan of care, including nurses, numerous physicians and specialists, and a range of family members and family involvement as well as other health care providers, there are large variances of communication ranging from open, to limited, to none.

As a result, a **collective dilemma** exists when communication becomes nonexistent or limited, and life-prolonging treatment continues as a means to managing uncertainty about a prognosis (Hines, Babrow, Badzek, & Moss, 2001). Finding the courage and resources to start a conversation with patients and families about how to manage new information, make sense of ambiguous communication about prognosis, and initiate information seeking depends on how uncertainty is managed (Step & Ray, 2011). **Problematic integration theory** explains how patients/families attempt to manage uncertainty (Babrow, 1992; Babrow & Mattson, 2003). It includes two components used in producing and coping with uncertainty: **probability**, the likeliness of the event/issue occurring, and **evaluation**, an assessment of the goodness of the outcome. Uncertainty results from the problematic integration of the way a person feels about something (positive or negative emotional value) and their perceived probability that something will occur.

When probability and evaluation do not complement one another, then communication and decision making become difficult. Nurses must be careful to assess the patient/family's acceptability and recognize that the same information needed to make informed decisions will also facilitate their coping (Hines et al., 2001). One of four things can happen when there is no consistency between what we value and what we think will occur. Table 7.1 provides an overview.

Ultimately, communication is often the source of problematic integration as well as a resource for coping. Communication and decision making are easier when probability and evaluation judgments merge. But the uncertainty of illness leaves patients/families asking difficult questions that clinicians, many times, cannot answer to the satisfaction of the patient or family. Nurses are often asked:

➤ Why is this happening to me? Why is this happening now?
➤ How long do I have to live?
➤ Do you think I am dying?

The following examples illustrate uncertainty in various forms (the four types of problematic integration) and include attention arrows (→) to signal cues or prompts produced by nurses to help patients/families navigate uncertainty.

Example #1: Divergence

NURSE: Anything I can do for you?
PATIENT: I just want it like it was before.
→NURSE: What do you mean, "like before"?
PATIENT: Everybody was nice. Now they want me to leave.
→NURSE: Are you ready to go home?
PATIENT: I'm not ready to go home but they told me to go home. I don't have nobody [*sic*] to call to take me home.

Table 7.1 The Four Forms of Problematic Integration

Communication Behavior When What We Value and What Might Occur Clash	Example
Divergence Discrepancy between what we want (evaluative) and what is likely (probabilistic)	"After these treatments I will be right back at work and running my kids around."—Patient
Ambiguity Probability of the event is unknown or uncertain.	"I don't feel like a woman anymore and the word 'freak' is always there. Plus I was told it may spread to the other breast which is like walking about with a bomb waiting to go off"—Breast cancer patient
Ambivalence When two equal evaluations are present or an event produces two contradictory responses	"He (patient) knows he's going to die. He realizes that. About a week ago he was having a hard time and he said, 'I really need to go, but I really don't want to go.'"—Caregiver
Impossibility When an individual feels absolutely certain that an event will not happen. This is problematic for seriously ill individuals who maintain hope that they will get better and live longer	"This is such a shock because we thought we beat everything and we've been saying 'you're going to die at an old age.' Just last week he said to me, 'You know it's ironic that both my parents died in their 90s and it looks like I'm going to die the same way.'"—Caregiver

NURSE: You were too sleepy yesterday to go home. I know it is scary to go home, but we will be sending the nurses to your home to check on you there. And I bet you will be glad to be in your own house again. Who will be at home to help care for you?

PATIENT: My daughter.

NURSE: Well, I know she came up here last night and your daughter wanted to take you, but they couldn't get you awake. Do you remember that?

PATIENT: Oh, yeah.

NURSE: They will be back today.

For this patient, there is a discrepancy between what he wants (to stay at the hospice inpatient facility) and what is likely (he will go home with his daughter). The nurse focuses the patient's communication on upcoming interactions that will clarify what the patient wants, in order to move the patient to acceptability.

Example #2: Ambiguity

SISTER OF PATIENT: She looks so good. She's improved so much in the last 24 hours. Her color is good and she even ate breakfast this morning.

NURSE: I'm glad she's perked up, too. We need to be cautious, though, in thinking about her getting better. Sometimes people "rally"—meaning they are very sick but then they perk up. I wanted to let you know that we are also very pleased since she is really enjoying today and especially your visit.

SISTER OF PATIENT: Yesterday we thought she was leaving, but today I don't.

→NURSE: Overall, while this is a good day for her; unfortunately, we know that her body is getting much worse. Her kidneys are failing and her heart is also much weaker. It's very hard for loving families to have this "roller coaster" of ups and downs. We want to really seize days like today to enjoy while also preparing for what is to come.

In this instance, the sister of a patient focuses on aspects of health care that involve a move toward recovery or cure. The nurse uses ambiguity here to remind this woman that her sister's rally is joyful, but she also communicates that the patient is moving closer to death rather than farther from it. By using the dissonance in the sister's statements, the nurse is able to reiterate that her sister is still dying despite changes in her affect and interaction. It would have been the less complicated path to simply allow this family member to remain in a state of hope about a revival, but this nurse has the wisdom to move the sister toward a clearer understanding of her loved one's illness trajectory.

Example #3: Ambivalence

HUSBAND [OF PATIENT]: He [referring to oncologist] just came in here and told us we could either try for a clinical trial or do nothing and that either one would get us the same amount of time with her.

→NURSE: Oh. [silence] Okay. Did the doc give you some specific information about the trial?

HUSBAND: No. Honestly, I don't want to know about either option right now. I can't really imagine either outcome, and they both seem to be the same thing. A nightmare in the end.

→NURSE: Have you talked to her about it (referring to spouse)?
[silence]

NURSE: Maybe you can just be with her now. How about I come by in a couple of hours and talk about the options with you guys?

Although this husband is ambivalent about this wife's condition in that he is presented with two equally difficult choices, the nurse quickly identifies that more communication and family interaction would be a helpful first step in determining what really matters for this family. By providing some specific directions and a timeline (2 hours), this nurse is able to prioritize the husband's planning and provide direction for moving forward.

Example #4: Impossibility

PATIENT [31-YEAR-OLD WOMAN WITH STAGE IV CERVICAL CANCER, BRAIN METS, LEFT LEG AND RIGHT ARM PARALYSIS FROM SPINAL METASTASIS]: I just need to get back to a place where I can get around with the walker. Then I can get home. My daughter needs me. I just need to get home where I can really focus on getting better. I am on a LISTSERV for people with this cancer, and some say they have lived with it for 25 years. I will be one of those people.

NURSE: Is there anyone at home to take care of you?

PATIENT: Taking care of my daughter *is* me taking care of me. That is how I have beaten this thing.

→NURSE: Your daughter is the most important thing to you, it sounds like. [silence]
And it sounds like you are a tremendous mother. And facing all you have faced the way you have done it, you love her so much.

PATIENT: She is my life.

→NURSE: I would like to come back in a little while with Ben, the social worker. We would like to help you think about what kind of help you need once you go home to take care of yourself and your daughter.

Readily seeing the difficulty this patient faces in understanding a shift toward active dying, the nurse begins with a small step/plan that she shares with the patient to a focus on her priority concern of her daughter. Sharing an understanding with the patient about her concern and offering a next step in addressing the primary concern is an effective way to move patients/families who seem stuck in their thinking or action about care planning.

Problematic integration invites clinicians to recognize indicators of low acceptability from patients and families as they grapple with their end-of-life challenges. Each of the arrows noted in the above exemplars correlates with relational concerns/content for these patients/family members. These interactions demonstrate the forces present in conversations and recognize a patient or family member's relationships and the role relationships play in decision making. Relationship is core to the patient/family and can serve to connect nurses with always-salient issues at end of life. Searching for additional cues from talk can be achieved by applying an idea called *speech act theory*. This concept enlightens the work of identifying acceptability by also considering what is actually being said (and done) when words are spoken.

SPEECH ACT THEORY

The core of Speech Act Theory claims that words act, or perform action. In other words, even though words (utterances, phrases, talk) encode information from one speaker to another, people are clearly doing more things with words than just conveying information. And when people convey information, oftentimes they communicate much more than their words encode. It is this series of complications that is addressed in speech act theory, and the intention here is to connect the knowledge of these ideas to the practice of palliative care nursing.

Speech act theory clarifies that words are often received in a way *not* intended by the sender; this is true for a patient, family member, or clinician in the context of life-limiting illness. Despite assessing, planning, and intervening with communication, the patient and family bring elements to the experience of care that no clinician or team can guess or control.

J. L. Austin (1962) claims that producing an utterance is also the performance of an action. Searle (1969) further extrapolated on Austin's foundation by arguing that context shapes acts of speech. Austin establishes three very distinct classes of action that are happening when we talk. Put simply, he identifies the act *of saying* something, what a person is *doing in saying it*, and the *effects of the saying*.

Austin names these three levels with their own unique terms. The meaning of an utterance itself is referred to as the *locutionary* act (the act *of saying* something). The *illocutionary* speech act (what a person is *doing in saying* it) performs its deed at the moment of utterance. This level of action in speech demonstrates a contextual function. A speech act produces a force and in action does something simply by being stated (e.g., describing, answering, identifying). *Perlocutionary* acts (the *effects of the saying*) cause a secondary effect on the listener following the illocutionary act that often cannot be predicted (Austin, 1962). Rules and requirements necessary for certain acts of speech and their illocutionary and perlocutionary properties are the essence of speech act theory. Perlocutionary acts are infinite and unpredictable, and are fully subjective depending on the speaker, listener, relationship, and context (Butler, 1997). Refer here to the third category in Table 7.2 in which the news of the test result will have effects.

Table 7.2 Speech Acts

Utterance:		
Your test result was positive.		
Locutionary act: the meaning of a statement itself	**Illocutionary act:** contextual function of the act	**Perlocutionary act:** effects on listener (predicable and not predictable)
The act of saying something	**What someone does in saying something**	**The effects of saying something**
- To tell someone that a test result had a positive outcome	- To deliver bad news of a biopsy test	- In sharing news of this now known bad news, the effects on this listener could range from acceptance and understanding to denial and misunderstanding.

Adapted from Austin, J. L. (1962). *How to Do Things With Words*. Oxford, UK: Oxford University Press.

Speech act theorists showcase the sequence of interaction and have exhaustively established rubrics and flowcharts to demonstrate the connection between one speech act and the next (Table 7.2).

Butler (1997) thinks of speech acts as interpolations of the very same utterances that came before and will come after. She places force and rich meaning in the historicity of utterances and their previous uses and contexts. This is a powerful concept in nursing, as many subjects for patients and families are reified by the nurse after having been initially but too minimally addressed by a physician or other health professional.

Following a terminal diagnosis delivered by a physician, curative treatment therapies are often the primary point of discussion and decision making for patients and families (The, 2004). If a diagnosis of Stage IV pancreatic cancer is shared, followed by a discussion of chemotherapeutic choices while prognosis talk is evaded, the physician and the patient/family bypass the larger matter of goals of care in the life remaining. Butler (1997) calls this phenomenon *constraint*. "The effort of constraining a term or phrase culminates in its very proliferation—an unintended rhetorical effect" (p. 131). In not discussing something, or using language that is threatening; the thing itself *is* discussed, remade, proliferated, and enlarged. The nurse is often the partner with whom constrained topics can be engaged.

DIRECT AND INDIRECT SPEECH ACTS

Sometimes an utterance *that does something* (illocutionary, e.g., "How is your pain?") is actually doing something else by way of performing another act. In the example question about pain, the nurse is also (depending on the context and previous conversation) making a statement that she is concerned that the patient is not experiencing good pain control. In essence, a direct speech act presents one action but in actuality is acting on two or possibly more matters of action with that one utterance. In examining these, it is quite plausible to see how any one utterance can accomplish multiple actions. The direct speech act unpacks the content of *what someone does in saying something*, while the indirect speech act category presents plausible additional actions exerted through the spoken word (Clark, 1979).

Understanding the way in which speech acts actually work means that they have to be considered in light of several factors. In conversations, speakers will say something with total confidence—assuming that other participants will fully comprehend their indirect meaning. Consider the following scenario. If travel partner Jo asks travel partner Bill, "Are you sure this is the right gate for us?" as they await an outbound flight, there are indirect meanings at work. Jo might be meaning that he and Bill are waiting at the wrong gate. Jo might mean that he is doubting the trust he placed in Bill's navigation. However, if Bill misses these indirect meanings, he might simply assure Jo without addressing these indirects. Sometimes a very different indirect meaning or action is interpreted instead of the one intended by the speaker.

In an effort to classify direct speech acts, it would be simplest to consider the idea of illocutionary acts in which the speaker utters something and means exactly and literally what he or she said. But quite frequently, when a speaker says something, the force, or action of his or her speech can carry more than one meaning. For example, "Have we fed the dog today?" not only has the illocutionary force of finding out whether or not the dog has been fed this day, but also whether or not the receiver of the question could/would feed the dog.

The chart below (Table 7.3) describes the four major categories of illocutionary acts (what *someone does in saying* something) (Back & Harish, 1979). Examine the direct speech act assigned to each of these four categories, and the possible indirect speech acts that could be produced. This should begin to help in identifying multiple actions that are carried out within most human speech communications.

MULTIPLE GOALS THEORY

The action that is produced in speech and the multiple goals that are accomplished in an interaction share common objectives. In fact, multiple goals theory is derived in part from speech act theory. In earlier parts of this volume, the ideas of task and relationship are addressed as processes undertaken in any communication exchange. These ideas have particular salience in nursing communication. Within the course of an interaction, people have more than one purpose; this is the basic premise of goal multiplicity. This idea of goal multiplicity accepts that goals and conversation are tightly intertwined, and that people almost always want more than one thing when they engage in interaction together (Tracy & Coupland, 1990). Because communicators pursue multiple and often competing goals, problems and dilemmas can be common in interaction. Add to this the context of end of life, and differing perspectives are quickly compounded.

Every person accomplishes, or attempts to accomplish, multiple goals in interactions. Sometimes these goals are emergent, and sometimes people enter an interaction knowing very clearly what they need/want to achieve. The strategies that people use to manage and accomplish these goals remain ambiguous and of special interest to communication researchers, especially in the context of health. Two communicator goals are considered present in every communication. The first is an instrumental goal, or what is seen as the basic purpose of the interaction. This instrumental goal has received the label of "task" in previous aspects of this volume—so these terms can be thought of interchangeably. But in addition to the "task" at hand, most people are concerned with how they present themselves and the impact of the interaction and goal pursuit on their relationship with the person(s) in the interaction (Tracy & Coupland, 1990). These identity/relationship concerns become their own cluster of goal multiplicity in an interaction. So, what takes priority? And how do interactions go wrong or right? Communication scholars deduce that sometimes people might cue one goal orientation more heavily than the other—leading to unpredictable outcomes in the interaction. New goals will also emerge as each speaker/partner makes certain conversational moves in the interaction. It is possible to see the very clear impact of communication on this experience of relating. The authors suggest that in the COMFORT model, prioritizing the goal conditions of the relationship will facilitate the task goals that are undoubtedly weighty.

Table 7.3 Speech Act Categories

Speech Act Categories	Utterance	Direct Acts	Indirect Acts
Constatives: Affirming, alleging, announcing, answering, attributing, claiming, classifying, concurring, confirming, conjecturing, denying, disagreeing, disclosing, identifying, informing, insisting, predicting, ranking, reporting, stating, stipulating	*You have low blood counts.*	Informing a patient/ family that lab results are not in the normal range.	• Expressing that the patient is facing an additional medical problem • Preparing the patient and family for planning care in light of results
Directives: Advising, alleging, asking, begging, dismissing, excusing, forbidding, instructing, ordering, permitting, requesting, requiring, suggesting, urging, warning	*You need to cut fast food out of your diet in order to control your blood pressure and weight.*	Instructing a patient/family to eat foods lower in calorie and containing higher nutritional value.	• Warning that a patient is in danger of further comorbidities • Asking a patient to change his or her life
Commissives: Agreeing, guaranteeing, inviting, offering, promising, committing, pledging	*You will feel better before you know it.* (Given as a false assurance to someone who is terminally ill)	Guaranteeing improvement and restoration.	• Avoiding the complicated reality of a declining health situation • Promising a state of improved health in order to distract
Acknowledgments: Apologizing, condoling, congratulating, greeting, thanking, accepting	*Hey, your creatinine levels are in the normal range. You did a great job with increasing your liquids like we asked you to do.*	Congratulating patient on regulated kidney function.	• Accepting that recovery and improvement are in sight • Acknowledging the patient/family effort in solving organ problems that can be affected

Speech act categories adapted from Austin, J. L. (1962). *How to Do Things With Words.* Oxford, UK: Oxford University Press.

NURSING AND RELATING

In order to unpack the theories briefly described so far in this chapter, each will be identified in the following two interactions. Both conversations analyzed here were observed in a clinical setting at inpatient hospice units or in a VA (Veterans Administration) palliative care consultation setting.

In the first exemplar, a collective dilemma unfolds in a family meeting. The circumstances of the patient case are unique. The wife (present at the family meeting) is under heavy suspicion of shooting her husband, the patient, and permanently disabling him. The meeting described here is an attempt to deal with the patient's needs and circumstances in the midst of this acute family drama. The utterances analyzed for speech act function and goals are noted as central in shaping the outcome of this interaction. Following the dialogue, a further analysis of problematic integration issues will highlight other communication pathways that could have resulted in increased productivity and support on behalf of this patient (see Figure 7.1b).

The boxed analyses inserted near selected utterances reveal that this family cannot, at this time, address the matters prompting the meeting. The brother of the wife consistently holds a position of defensiveness for his sister, and this is all they can manage. The intent to arrange a DNR and a place of care is never explored in a way that reaches an active decision. The brother, in particular, has campaigned to have their side of the story heard. This must happen first before the husband's care can ever really be addressed.

The physician explicitly states, "He's not communicating." After this declaration, some false starts are made at moving this wife/brother duo to engage end-of-life planning, and specifically DNR orders. These attempts (i.e., he doesn't have the capacity to make decisions; it is important to talk about code status) lead to an inconclusive end for the time being.

Examining this interaction using the ideas from problematic integration theory helps demonstrate why some families find it impossible to engage the quest narrative. Rewriting the dying story so that it can include opportunity requires some acknowledgment of symptoms and the reality of a prognosis. In this interaction, the brother and wife are tightly tied to the narrative of refutation, focusing instead on the patient's life choices (i.e., he's had a dope habit, very bad; there are a lots of problems; we've lost lots of family to suicide; he's aggressive; you should know my husband is an ex-felon; he's been addicted). Team members attempt multiple times to guide the narrative toward end-of-life decisions for this family, but this family demonstrates divergence. Their expectation was that this patient would not still be living (Why are there so many changes in his condition?), and now they are faced with the probable outcome that he indeed will live in an unconscious state for some time and require extensive care planning.

The next interaction (Figure 7.2) features an 84-year-old man with late-stage prostate cancer. This patient is alone and terminally ill in an inpatient hospice. He is also experiencing dementia and was observed having repeated memory loss about his wife's death. This is a fairly common challenge for nurses. The exchange highlights the relationship between the clinician and patient above all else.

This exchange took place between a registered nurse and an in-patient hospice patient.

RN: Mr. X, you okay? You sleepy today?
Pt: Yes. Have you seen [wife's name]?
RN: No, [wife's name] passed away in April. You were here.
        She died peacefully. *

Direct Act	Indirect Act	Multiple Goals
-clarifying that wife is deceased	-comforting -supporting	TASK: orienting patient to reality RELATIONAL: condoling

Pt: Yes (pause).
[RN pats the patient on the back.]
RN: Do you need anything? Are you in any pain?
Pt: No.
RN: Okay, I need to take your blood pressure.
[Pt starts crying, sobbing.]
RN: I know you miss her a lot. It's not been a good year. Hang in there (he continues to rub and pat the patient's back).
Pt: 46 years we were married.
RN: Yes, I know. How many grandchildren do you have?
[Patient is now crying, stoically.]
RN puts blood pressure cuff on the patient, continuing to rub his back.
RN: Alright my friend, 174/84.
[Pt looks away.]

Direct Act	Indirect Act	Multiple Goals
-asking patient status from patient	-recognizing emotional distress -empathizing in pain of loss	TASK: pursuing response RELATIONAL: caring for and acknowledging loss

RN: Are you okay?
RN [grabs his hand]: I lost my wife too.
[The two men hold hands. Silence.]
Pt: I need a tissue.
RN brings tissue and returns to nursing other patients.

FIGURE 7.2 Patient interaction (no family present)

The RN described how the patient's dementia caused him to relive the realization of his spouse's death three to four times a day. He would call his daughters at home and ask for his wife. A large sign was eventually placed on the wall of his room that said "[patient wife's name] died on [month, day]." When this RN was asked how he handled this over and over again, he said: "You let him know that she has passed away and then try to refocus his attention. The chaplain and I actually take turns handling it because it drains you to do that 3–4 times a day … I can't imagine what it does to him." This passage of talk displays the importance of the patient/clinician relationship goals, while task goals such as checking for pain control and blood pressure are also pursued.

The type of problematic integration this demented patient communicates is *ambivalence*—in which two contradictory realities are constantly at odds (his wife is alive/his wife is dead). His dementia moves him several times a day between two realities; one in which his wife is there but out of reach, and one in which he learns his wife is dead. These two places of awareness are the primary trauma and concern for this patient. In the interaction above, the RN has a keen understanding of this patient issue and readily orients to the very point of ambivalence for this man.

DEVELOPING CLINICAL PRACTICE SKILLS

What is unknown in Billy's case, our opening case study, is what nursing or interdisciplinary care plans, if any, were designed to address the family's low acceptability of his terminal illness. What is known is that this family is now in crisis and has not considered other pathways of life other than that of cure. The father is deeply fatigued and at odds with his wife and mother-in-law. This fissure will become explosive at the stage of illness they face as a family. A great deal of work is needed to steward them through the likely death of their precious boy in the weeks ahead. Relating using communication interventions is the most effective tool left for nurses to use with this family.

ASSESS

What Billy and his family were actually revealing about their ability to process updates about disease progression could have been identified in their communication with family and clinicians. From the case study, it is possible to ascertain that Billy's mother and grandmother are steadfast in thinking that dying is an impossibility if they rely on their faith. Billy's father, of course, wants his son to live and recover but has indicated concern over the aggressive treatments on more than one occasion. Within this one family, at least two types of problematic integration are observable (divergence: father, impossibility: mother/grandmother).

The four pillars of problematic integration (divergence, ambiguity, ambivalence, and impossibility) are identifiable in patient and family communication. Simply being aware of types of problematic integration can move the nurse clinician in the direction of improved communication. Patients and families attempt to manage uncertainty when what they want (restoration/cure) is not likely to happen, and they perceive a declining status. For some, engaging in communication strategies that suppress, sustain, or even increase uncertainty indicates that very important matters at this point in life are not being addressed (Sharf, Stelljes, & Gordon, 2005).

As described in this chapter, direct and indirect speech acts provide clinicians with a greater understanding of what actions are being expressed in communicative behaviors, and as a result offer potential ways in which clinicians can connect relationally with patients/families. Assess for red-flag rationalizations in patient/family decision making that signify a need for more clinician connection in order to move through the illness process and better care for those suffering. Table 7.4 identifies rationalizations and definitions, example statements that might serve as vehicles for these rationalizations and their definitions, and the four areas of problematic integration—one of which will resonate most strongly with a particular rationalization.

Table 7.4 Rationalizations in Decision Making

Rationale	Definition	Example/Circumstance of This Rationalization	Problematic-Integration Type Indicated
Self-efficacy	Emphasizes patients'/families' own internal controls, abilities to influence their own health outcomes	*I am really focusing on my strong cells and sending them the best energy I can. This can change the whole prognosis for me.*	• Impossibility: When an individual feels absolutely certain of an event or outcome
Minimizing threat	Statements minimizing risk factors, possibility of prognosis, severity of illness	*We can get through this, no problem. Cancer is not a death sentence anymore; you just get it fixed.*	• Ambiguity: When the probability of an event is unknown or uncertain
Fatalism and faith	Emphasizes the importance of powers that outweigh self-control, i.e., fate or God	*The outcome here is already written. We just have to trust in all the technology and try everything. God gave us this technology.*	• Divergence: Discrepancy between what we would like and what is likely
Distrust	Suspicion of health information, medical procedures, motives of staff	*They are after the money with these treatments. How can I even know if I need these if everyone is motivated by how much they can make off of me?*	• Impossibility: When an individual feels absolutely certain of an event or outcome
Desire for information	Requests for information or complains about not having enough	*I would feel better if we could get a third opinion on this. Neither clinic has been very forthcoming about the side effects I read about.*	• Divergence: Discrepancy between what we would like and what is likely
Living with uncertainty	The capacity, or even desire, to live without knowing one's diagnosis	*I am not interested in finding out what is going on. I have lived with this for 3 years and so far so good.*	• Divergence: Discrepancy between what we would like and what is likely
Futility	Denies or questions utility of treatment or procedure	*They can't do anything for me. I have tried a specialist already; I know how to take care of this on my own.*	• Impossibility: When an individual feels absolutely certain of an event or outcome
Postponing	Puts off having treatment without refusing, delays medical treatment after self-recognition of symptoms	*I guess I am not interested in moving forward with these diagnostics. We know things are not good, and I think I need to think about this a while.*	• Divergence: Discrepancy between what we would like and what is likely

(continued)

Table 7.4 (continued)

Rationale	Definition	Example/Circumstance of This Rationalization	Problematic-Integration Type Indicated
Physical discomfort	Concern for pain or discomfort caused by medical procedures, anticipated, experienced	*I can't go through the PET scan. I just can't face that again. I completely panicked about it the entire day before but I know I have to do this.*	• Ambivalence: When two differing evaluations are present
Will to live	Emphasizes the power of self-determination to survive	*I am not giving up. My kids need me, and I am determined this will not put me down. I know that my test results are declining, but my team tells me to stay determined.*	• Ambivalence: When two differing evaluations are present

Adapted from Sharf, B., Stelljes, L., & Gordon, H. (2005). "A little bitty spot and I'm a big man": Patients' perspectives on refusing diagnosis or treatment for lung cancer. *Psycho-Oncology, 14,* 636–646.

Just as rationalizations can be posited as speech acts, so can turning points in dealing with serious and terminal illness. Shifts in thought, understanding, emotion, connectedness, and more can produce patient as well as family turning points. Turning points for a patient or family sometimes are identified in the way that they are communicated. For example, John has been diagnosed with end-stage small-cell lung cancer. He has withdrawn from his job and has told his friends and family that he is ready for hospice. His plan and place of care are clear. As John is spending his last night as an inpatient before heading home, he asks his bedside nurse, "What will it feel like to die?" John needs this conversation. He has made all of the recognizable and somewhat public gestures of adjusting to his status as a terminal patient. But he makes the private turn to that reality after the formal planning is over. Nurse-identified themes indicating turning points for serious and terminally ill patients are included in Table 7.5. The emergence of these themes in conversation can be used to assess what a patient/family needs.

PLAN

Does Billy have a voice in his own illness and its progression/treatment? This is unknown without more conversation to gain an understanding of this family's quality of life across all domains. In designing a plan of care to increase acceptability and understanding, the quality-of-life domains provide grounding in the aspects of life that need attention (Ferrell, Dow, & Grant, 1995). Creating a plan of care using these domains is also facilitated by an awareness of the narrative told by patient/family.

Frank's (1995) three illness narratives serve to create a goal trajectory when planning to intervene with patients/families. The **restitution narrative** includes the story of returning to the state of previous health. This narrative type can coincide with overuse of curative therapies. The **chaos narrative** includes the story that no one involved has control and every aspect of life is held hostage by contingencies. The **quest narrative** has been described previously in this chapter, and stories illness (sometimes a new diagnosis and sometimes a new realization of a previous diagnosis) as a new opportunity to live differently/better. The quest narrative does

Table 7.5 Potential Turning Point

- A patient wants to talk about life, dying, and/ or death.
- A patient shows signs of protecting privacy.
- A patient's anxiety shifts from treatment to existential matters.

Adapted from Brataas, H. V., & Thorsnes, S. L. (2009). Cancer nurses narrating after conversations with cancer outpatients: How do nurses' roles and patients' perspectives appear in the nurses' narratives? *Scandinavian Journal of Caring Sciences, 23,* 767–774. doi:10.1111/j.1471–6712.2008.00679.x not include physical restoration as the focus but, rather, meaningful ways to connect to others and what exists as important for that patient and family. Designing a communication intervention for increased family acceptability will inherently include a movement from either the restoration or chaos narrative toward the quest narrative.

Bringing together the quality-of-life domains and Frank's illness narrative allows a nurse to get at the very domain(s) in need of conversation/communication. Figure 7.3 portrays patient/family movement to the quest narrative. This combination of ideas also can showcase the very dissonant understandings that patients/families can maintain as identities shift, family roles are strained, and losses multiply. In serious and terminal illness, nothing will be the same. The restoration narrative stories the return to a predisease body, the same relationships, same activities, and same capabilities. But patient and family resistance to engaging a reality that adjusts for the physical, psychological, spiritual, and social costs of terminal illness is an indicator that communication intervention is needed. Similarly, inability to move forward with any planning out of fear and confusion (chaos narrative) can be present whether it occurs in the domain of physical health decisions, psychological care, spiritual concerns, or social well-being.

INTERVENE

The language and conversation needed to move patients and families to increased understanding and acceptance are explicated throughout this chapter (problematic integration, illness narratives, multiple goals, speech act). All of these approaches to intervention position the messages of the patient and family as central in cuing nurse clinicians about the most effective communication practice.

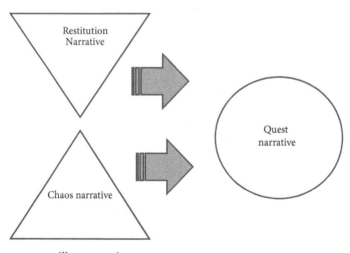

FIGURE 7.3 Illness narratives

To remain focused on the goal of intervening to improve patient/family understanding, the quest narrative tenets can serve as a driving force in implementing plans of care to address these needs:

1. Is there some acknowledgment of a change in health and life?
   - If there is not, it is up to the clinician to acknowledge these changes.
2. Are there discussions about a turning point in the illness trajectory and its impact on the quality-of-life domains?
   - If not, it is up to the clinician to facilitate recognition and hopefully discussion about turning points.
3. Can the patient/family describe their place in the illness journey?
   - If not, or if description does not account for or acknowledge change and loss, it is up to the clinician to contribute her description of the illness journey as well.

Relating to patients and families by letting them lead in conversational importance is a productive way to intervene. The connection between people and their conversation is a powerful thing. This second set of intervention recommendations reminds the clinician to practice narrative nursing. The patient/family will determine what news is bad, how the story will end, what a shift in perspective will bring to the situation, and so on. Use the acceptability chart in Table 7.6 that identifies three primary areas of understanding and practical approaches for intervention.

Table 7.6 Increasing Understanding

Increasing Understanding/ Understanding	Practical Interventions to Apply
Adaptive Communication	• If a patient or family revolt, or become highly agitated, give them time and space.
	• If a patient/family cannot digest the reality of a diagnosis, recurrence, turning point, give them some time and try again with a new tactic.
Diffusion of Topic	• Do not force a piece of information to be central to the conversation if the patient/family stray from it to other concerns.
	• Follow the primary need of the patient/family—they have a better idea of what it is than anyone.
	• Suspend the need to achieve your goals and work. More time invested in relating will save time as end of life approaches.
Team Based and Family Interactions	• Use human resources available on your team.
	• Employ the complicated dynamics in the family to serve needs of the patient.

Used with permission from: Wittenberg-Lyles, Goldsmith, Sanchez-Reilly, & Ragan (2008). Communicating a terminal prognosis in a palliative care setting: Deficiencies in current communication training protocols. *Social Science & Medicine, 66,* 2356–2365.

EVALUATE

The use of diaries in the clinical setting is rare and is typically assigned to clinical trial tasking. As such, "diaries" are often highly sanitized of narrative and essentially serve as a schedule of events and results. The first evaluation recommendation does enlist a diary. However, in this particular evaluative effort, a daily account of a patient's progress would be written in everyday language by nursing staff. This account might even include simple drawings or photographs in some cases. The diary would be given to the patient/family after discharge from the unit and would include a simple questionnaire with an area for comments about the diary as helpful and representative of the experience they shared with their nurses.

In a previous study that analyzed this evaluative tool, the results showed that half of the diaries in the sample had been reread more than 10 times by family members/patients. Nearly 70% of the questionnaire topics were graded as very positive or positive (Bäckman & Walther, 2001).

The limitations to such evaluations include time, money, and resources. But even on a small scale, this can be a rich tool for study. A more feasible evaluative method is to follow a case with a chart review and identify the conversations that took place, with whom and when. Observe the presence or absence of communication charting. Describe and then determine if communicative practice is central enough to be considered chartable at the institution doing the evaluating.

CHAPTER SUMMARY

This chapter presents relating as one dominant strategy to advance patient and family understanding. The surface of the spoken word is peeled back to consider what the action or force of language might include. A complex architecture of goals is always at play, no matter who is doing the speaking. Because the true motives and goals of a speaker are rarely fully understood or realized, the recommendation in this chapter is to attend to the relationship goal always in order to facilitate the instrumental goals of nursing. Throughout this section of the book, authors provide an opportunity to examine the phenomenon of patient/family acceptance of an illness status, as well as understanding patient/family perspectives on adjusting to new information unfolding throughout a serious or terminal illness.

Talking and communicating in a way that is radically adaptive assume that the clinician cannot know the reaction or perspective of the patient/family without first receiving it. Narrative nursing creates the opportunity to learn about dissonance between desired outcomes and realities of illness. The idea of problematic integration addresses this dissonance directly. Recognizing these particular challenges can move a patient/family toward the quest narrative and away from the experience of chaos or denial—both of which exacerbate feelings of dissonance.

Also explored in this chapter is a study of speech acts and multiple goals. Both of these tool sets help clinicians reveal the difficulties and stumbling blocks that patients and families face as they work to acknowledge their changing health and identity.

REFERENCES

Austin, J. L. (1962). *How to Do Things With Words.* Oxford, UK: Oxford University Press.

Babrow, A. S. (1992). Communication and problematic integration: Understanding diverging probability and value, ambivalence, and impossibility. *Communication Theory, 2,* 95–130.

Babrow, A. S., & Mattson, M. (2003). Theorizing about health communication. In T. Thompson, A. Dorsey, K. Miller, & R. A. Parrot (Eds.), *Handbook of Health Communication* (pp. 35–62). Mahwah, NJ: Lawrence Erlbaum.

Back, K, & Harnish, R. (1979). *Linguistic Communication and Speech Acts.* Cambridge, MA: MIT Press.

Bäckman, C., & Walther, S. (2001). Use of a personal diary written on the ICU during critical illness. *Intensive Care Medicine, 27,* 426–429. doi: 10.1007/s001340000692.

Brataas, H. V., & Thorsnes, S. L. (2009). Cancer nurses narrating after conversations with cancer outpatients: How do nurses' roles and patients' perspectives appear in the nurses' narratives? *Scandinavian Journal of Caring Sciences, 23,* 767–774. doi:10.1111/j.1471–6712.2008.00679.x

Butler, J. (1997). *Excitable Speech: A Politics of the Performative.* New York: Routledge.

Clark, H. (1979). Responding to indirect speech acts. *Cognitive Psychology, 11,* 430–477.

Costello, J. (2009). Last words, last connections: How augmentative communication can support children facing end of life. *The ASHA Leader,* December 15, pp. 8–11.

Eggly, S., Penner, L., Albrecht, T., Cline, R., Foster, T., Naughton, M., et al. (2006). Discussing bad news in the outpatient oncology clinic: Rethinking current communication guidelines. *Journal of Clinical Oncology, 24,* 716–719.

Ferrell, B., Dow, K. H., & Grant, M. (1995). Measurement of the quality of life in cancer survivors. *Quality of Life Research, 4,* 523–531.

Frank, A. (1995). *The Wounded Storyteller.* Chicago: University of Chicago Press.

Hines, S. C., Babrow, A. S., Badzek, L., & Moss, A. (2001). From coping with life to coping with death: Problematic integration for the seriously ill elderly. *Health Communication, 13*(3), 327–342.

McGurk, M. (2006). *A Lion in the House: Five Families. Six Years. True Stories From the War on Cancer.* Wilmington, OH: Orange Frazier Press.

Searle, J. (1969). *Speech Acts: An Essay in the Philosophy of Language.* Cambridge, UK: Cambridge University Press.

Sharf, B., & Vanderford, M. L. (2003). Illness narratives and the social construction of health. In T. Thompson, A. Dorsey, K. Miller, & R. Parrot (Eds.), *Handbook of Health Communication* (pp. 9–34). Mahwah, NJ: Lawrence Erlbaum.

Sharf, B. F., Stelljes, L. A., & Gordon, H. S. (2005). "A little bitty spot and I'm a big man": Patients' perspectives on refusing diagnosis or treatment for lung cancer. *Psycho-Oncology, 14*(8), 636–646. doi: 10.1002/pon.885

Step, M., & Ray, E. (2011). Patient perceptions of oncologist-patient communication about prognosis: Changes from initial diagnosis to cancer recurrence. *Health Communication, 26*(1), 48–58. doi: 931971302 [pii] 10.1080/10410236.2011.527621

The, A. (2004). *Palliative Care and Communication.* Philadelphia: Open University Press.

Tracy, K., & Coupland, N. (1990). Multiple goals in discourse: An overview of issues. *Journal of Language and Social Psychology, 9,* 1–13.

Wittenberg-Lyles, E., Goldsmith, J., Sanchez-Reilly, S., & Ragan S. (2008). Communicating a terminal prognosis in a palliative care setting: Deficiencies in current communication training protocols. *Social Science & Medicine, 66,* 2356–2365. doi: 10.1016/j.sociscimed.2008.01.042

Additional Resources

Brataas, H. V., Thornes, S. L., & Hargie, O. (2010). Themes and goals in cancer outpatient–cancer nurse consultations. *European Journal of Cancer Care, 19,* 184–191.

Dysvik, E., Soomerseth, R., & Jacobsen, F. F. (2011). Living a meaningful life with chronic pain from a nursing perspective: Narrative approach to a case story. *International Journal of Nursing Practice, 1,* 36–42.

Egerod, I., & Bagger, C. (2010). Patients' experience of intensive care diaries—A focus group study. *Intensive and Critical Care Nursing, 26,* 278–287.

Repass, M., & Matusitz, J. (2010). Problematic integration theory: Implications of supportive communication for breast cancer patients. *Health Care for Women International, 31,* 402–420.

Smith, B., & Sparkes, A. C. (2007). Changing bodies, changing narratives and the consequences of tellability: A case study of becoming disabled through sport. *Sociology of Health and Illness, 30,* 217–236.

Additional References for Quest Narrative

Andrews, M., Squire, C., & Tamboukou, M. (2008). *Doing Narrative Research.* Los Angeles: Sage.

Frank, A. W. (1991). *At the Will of the Body: Reflections on Illness.* New York: Houghton Mifflin Company.

Frank, A. W. (1995). *The Wounded Storyteller: Body, Illness, and Ethics.* Chicago: University of Chicago Press.

Gubrium, J. F., & Holstein, J. A., (2009). *Analyzing Narrative Reality.* Thousand Oaks, CA: Sage.

Harter, L. M., Japp, P. M., & Beck, C. (Eds.). (2005). *Narratives, Health, and Healing: Communication Theory, Research, and Practice.* Mahway, NJ: Lawrence Erlbaum Associates.

Holloway, I., & Wheeler, S. (2002). *Qualitative Research in Nursing* (2nd ed.). Malden, MA: Blackwell Publishing.

Website: http://www.arthurwfrank.com/publications

Additional References for Problematic Integration Theory

Babrow, A. S. (1992). Communication and problematic integration: Understanding diverging probability and value, ambiguity, ambivalence, and impossibility. *Communication Theory, 2,* 95–130.

Babrow, A. S. (2001). Uncertainty, value, communication, and problematic integration. *Journal of Communication, 51,* 553–574.

Babrow, A.S., & Mattson, M. (2003). Theorizing about health communication. In T. Thompson, A. Dorsey, K. Miller, & R. A. Parrot (Eds.), *Handbook of Health Communication* (pp. 35–62). Mahway, NJ: Lawrence Erlbaum.

Hines, S. C., Babrow, A. S., Badzek, L., & Moss, A. (2001). From coping with life to coping with death: Problematic integration for the seriously ill elderly. *Health Communication, 13*, 327–342.

Parrott, R., Silk, K., Weiner, J., Condit, C., Harris, T., & Bernhardt, J. (2004). Deriving lay models of uncertainty about genes' role in illness causation to guide communication about human genetics. *Journal of Communication, 54*, 105–122.

Additional References for Speech Act Theory and Multiple Goals Theory

Ragan, S. (1990). Verbal play and multiple goals in the gynecological exam interaction. *Journal of Language and Social Psychology, 9*, 67–84.

Searle, J. (1969). *Speech Acts: An Essay in the Philosophy of Language.* Cambridge, UK: Cambridge University Press.

Tracy, K. (1984). The effect of multiple goals on conversational relevance and topic shift. *Communication Monographs, 51*, 274–287.

Tracy, K. (1995). Action-implicative discourse analysis. *Journal of Language and Social Psychology, 14*, 195–216.

DISCUSSION QUESTIONS

1. How can problematic integration theory be used to conduct a communication research project in nursing?
2. What is the nurse's role in the cultivation of a quest narrative?
3. What are the implications of the term "acceptability" in serious and terminal illness?
4. How does narrative nursing adapt to the conversation and topic diffusion of a patient/family?
5. What is the impact of indirect speech acts produced by your team members?
6. How can nurses prioritize their relationship tasks with patients and families when they are so pressed for time, energy, and resources?
7. What are some ways to navigate the pressure of time if patient and family topic diffusion defies the health decisions needed to best care for a patient?
8. Consider a challenge faced in practice that involves acceptability. What is a strategy that prioritizes the narrative of the patient or family?

TEACHING RESOURCES AND MATERIALS

Exercise #1: Problematic Integration in Families

Apply problematic integration to the following family statements about serious illness. Please consider 1) which of the four forms of problematic integration is described (divergence, ambiguity, ambivalence, and impossibility), and 2) what conversational approach might be useful with this patient/family member to support them. The first case is about a pediatric patient's younger brother. In the second case, a caregiver daughter describes her mother's new diagnosis.

Passage One:
When there is an illness like that, the worst thing you can do is not talk about it. Your kids are left to draw their own conclusions, and it scares the hell out of them. We never talked about it in my family. Never. When you are young, you want to know what's going on, but nobody would tell us. We were just left out a lot. You never did get that sense that "Everything is okay." It was always pins and needles. It's one thing to think it, but to have an adult say, "Everything is okay right now, this is what's going on... " that calming factor never did come in. You're a kid. Your mind wanders. You worry about things. Your own health is jeopardized, if you're focused on him (brother) and you don't pay attention to yourself.

Used with permission from: McGurk, M. (2006). *A Lion in the House: Five Families. Six Years. True Stories from the War on Cancer.* Wilmington, OH: Orange Frazier Press. Chapter One, Justin Ashcraft, p. 15.

Passage Two:
My mother was diagnosed in February 2009 with an unknown primary. She had a malignant pericardial effusion and almost died. When she was diagnosed she was told she had a few months to live and make her final arrangements. Her oncologist gave her no hope.

My mom was devastated by the news initially. We decided she should have a second diagnosis. The second diagnosis confirmed the original diagnosis.

Even though my mom was devastated by this she decided she would fight. My mom is a very strong woman and has never complained about any medical problems at all.

The oncologist believed that chemotherapy would only be a palliative measure and that she would not go into remission and that she would not be cured. I contacted Dr. XXXX who verified her chemo treatments were right on track.

My mom has surprised everyone!!! In June of 2009 the oncologist told her she was in remission and she has been in remission now for 9 months. I believe her oncologist is even amazed at her being in remission.

I have heard many, many sad stories about ACUP diagnosis. However, I have also heard some very good stories about people living for many years with an ACUP diagnosis. I believe my mother will be one of those good stories.

Excerpted from a caregiver posting on the ACUPS group on www2.acor.org. March 20, 2010.

Exercise #2: Quest Narrative

The quest narrative is an illness story that acknowledges significant changes in life, rather than a narrative that clings to the promise of reverting back to the way things were before a devastating illness. Using the quotes below, answer the questions about where this patient or family member might be in their quest and then identify what a nurse clinician might be able to do in conversation to address one or more of these reauthoring opportunities. Nurses can work on these quotes individually and then discuss them in small groups to increase the production of communication intervention ideas.

- "I feel I needed to talk and maybe cry a little and needed his [husband] shoulder to do so with. But was denied, this hurt me and again I felt isolated. Now that is all behind me. Everyone acts as though nothing ever happened. I still feel the need to speak about it but feel I have no one to talk to about it. I am not the same person."—Lung cancer patient in remission

Table 7.7 Quest Indicators

Does this patient acknowledge significant changes in health?	Yes/No	How is this revealed in words?	Relating to the patient in the quest narrative
Has this patient experienced a turning point in his or her illness experience?	Yes/No	How is this revealed in words?	Relating to the patient in the quest narrative
Does this patient indicate a shift in identity?	Yes/No	How is this revealed in words?	Relating to the patient in the quest narrative

- "My mother flat out told me she would not talk about anything about the cancer. She is too scared.... It is awful ... She told me to grow up and I had to make my own decisions and take responsibility for my treatment and she wouldn't discuss my cancer with me."—Breast cancer patient

Table 7.8 Quest Indicators

Does this patient acknowledge significant changes in health?	Yes/No	How is this revealed in their words?	Relating to the patient in the quest narrative
Has this patient experienced a turning point in his or her illness experience?	Yes/No	How is this revealed in their words?	Relating to the patient in the quest narrative
Does this patient indicate a shift in identity?	Yes/No	How is this revealed in their words?	Relating to the patient in the quest narrative

Exercise #3: Adapting to the Patient

All patients/families communicate uniquely. Often, the nursing task of communicating changes in disease/function can be accompanied by a clear display from the patient/family that the news is not being processed for what it is. In this exercise, there are two scenarios presented in which a nurse is communicating information (task goals) and this communication requires radical adaptivity based on the acceptability of the patient. For the following interactions:

1. Cast the roles of the nurse and the patient and "perform" them.
2. Examine the dialogue in discussion form.
3. What seems to be the primary challenge for the nurse/patient in processing information?
4. Identify what the nurse is expressing directly and indirectly.
5. Identify what action the patient/family is expressing directly and indirectly.
6. What recommendations can be made about an improvement in radical adaptivity for nurse communication in each interaction?

Interaction One:

> NURSE: From now on your cancer will be with you. It is a kind of cancer that has no cure at this point.
> PATIENT: Well, they haven't actually said that.
> NURSE: It is not curable. [Silence]. But it is a slow cancer. And what we are really most concerned about is your pain. Are you in pain?
> PATIENT: No. I'm fine.
> NURSE: Have you heard of hospice?
> PATIENT: Yes, it's for your dying days.
> NURSE: Well, actually it's for people with advanced disease. You have an advanced disease.
> PATIENT: God, you are an optimist. I have been totally fine.
> [silence]

PATIENT: But I want to go home. A couple of days in hospice might be okay, but then I want to go home.

Interaction Two:

NURSE: What did the doctor tell you about the tumor?

PATIENT: Similar comments from this doc. It seems I am going to come out of this.

NURSE: It is hard to realize that your tumor is not going to go away.

PATIENT: During the last operation they put a chemo disk in my brain to reduce the size of the tumor.

NURSE: But, the tumor itself will not go away. So we need to figure out how we can help you be the most comfortable and pain free.

[patient stirs in bed, mumbling, showing distress]

NURSE: What do you think about what I am saying?

PATIENT: If you can monitor the tumor …

NURSE: Right. Yes. To make sure you are not in pain or distress.

PATIENT: The treatment I am receiving now, whatever prognosis you all make up … but I don't know one way or the other the best treatment now.

NURSE: We will take care of you. Treat you. We especially want to address your headaches. We just cannot cure you and make it go away.

Used with permission from: Wittenberg-Lyles, Goldsmith, Sanchez-Reilly, & Ragan (2008). Communicating a terminal prognosis in a palliative care setting: Deficiencies in current communication training protocols. *Social Science & Medicine, 66,* 2356–2365.

Exercise #4: Mining the Goals

The multiple goals theory described in this chapter reminds clinicians and all health professionals that in any interaction, each participant is likely pursuing more than one thing. It is also probable that the goals of one person might be in conflict with the goals of another. For just a moment, change the context of the multiple goals scene from nursing to *romance!* This also requires that readers think now about the relational tasks that are at work in all interactions.

Think about a dating situation between a young woman named Jill, and her college friend, and now romantic partner, Kendall. For just over 2 weeks, the two of them have been "dating," and their relationship has progressed quickly from classmates and lunch buddies to two partners in a passionate romance. After a fun evening including a picnic and long walk in the park, Kendall brings Jill to her dorm. He bids her good night and they share a long kiss. As they conclude the evening, Kendall lingers, taking Jill's hands. With intentioned seriousness he says to Jill, "I love you." Jill, not feeling this same level of connection is stymied and embarrassed about the appropriate response. She is shocked that Kendall could produce this claim after such a short time in this new phase of their relationship. Conversationally, it is clearly her turn to speak. She takes a deep breath and produces, "Thank you."

Jill and Kendall had conflicting relational goals. This is a pretty stark example that is made clear by the speech exchanged at the close of their date. The relational goal differences are not always so clearly evidenced and in the clinical setting can become lost or overshadowed by the instrumental goals/tasks that need to be completed. Now that multiple goals as a theory is refreshed, the frame is changed back from romance to the nursing context. The following story is told by the young mother of a 2-year-old boy born at 24 weeks. Abe and his family have faced the threat of his death countless times in the 2 years of his life. His health is compromised by breathing, digestive, and developmental difficulties.

> Abe had gone in for a test to check the level of his acid reflux and see if he had sustained any damage to his esophagus. The procedure was a routine one. He would be mildly sedated, a probe would be inserted down his throat, and we would stay in the hospital for 24 hours while it recorded every incident of reflux.... When I went to meet Abe in the recovery room after the probe was inserted, I found him terrified, hyperventilating, and vomiting profusely. The nurse taking care of him had just started him on a heavy dose of morphine and oxygen through a nasal cannula because "he couldn't calm down." I took him, spoke to him softly to explain what was going on, and rocked him until he settled. When I questioned the nurse about what had occurred, it immediately became clear to me that in treating Abe in recovery, she had not taken into account that he has significant visual impairment. While she was pulling off medical tape, adjusting an IV, and moving him around, he felt attacked on all fronts because he did not know what was happening to him. If the nurse had taken a few extra minutes to consider the patient as a whole person—not just as someone there for a ph probe—she would have noted that he is legally blind. It was on his chart, and anyone spending time with him can quickly tell that he does not see very much at all. Speaking with the family would have helped, too; the nurse could have asked how to approach Abe so that he wouldn't be scared and could have given the necessary treatment in a way that would be less frightening and ultimately less invasive for him. We could have avoided the morphine, the supplementary oxygen, and, most importantly, an experience that terrorized my 2-year-old.

Read the story of Abe and the nurse in a small group. Discuss the following questions together:

· Is the nurse at fault in this story?
· Does the family member expect too much? Are her goal expectations unreasonable?
· What goals take priority for the nurse? Are they the right goals in this situation?
· Can the task and the relational goals be separated in this story?

COMPREHENSIVE EXERCISES FOR CHAPTER MATERIAL

TALKING ABOUT TALK OR SILENCE

In this exercise, people can work together in dyads or larger numbers. Because the case study is so simple, this is a good icebreaker for this chapter and quickly gets people to share ideas. First, individuals should read this case silently; then, they can join together to share their reactions and ideas for 5–10 minutes.

> You come into a room to perform an intake interview with a patient new to this care center. As you open the door to the room, you see a woman in her early 40s, alone. She has been crying, and now tears begin to flow uncontrollably. She is unable to speak and her body shakes from sobbing. What do you do?

REFLECTING ON MEMORABLE SPEECH ACTS

This brief journaling exercise is a good engagement for students new to the idea of speech acts and multiple goals. It also uses their own life experience as primary material for working through the ideas of indirect speech acts and considering the interaction between task and relational goals.

Step One – The student recalls a *memorable* speech act delivered in the following contexts/by the following people:
- A teacher (that the student knew in a student/teacher relationship)
- A spouse or parent (of the student)
- A clinician (when the student sought help as a patient or caregiver)

Step Two – The student divides a piece of paper into three sections and in each section writes one of the three memorable utterances delivered by the teacher/spouse or parent/clinician.

Table 7.9 The Meaning of a Message

Teacher	*Spouse*	*Clinician*
You are not honors material.	Where did you learn to cook?	Let me show you a picture of normal.

Step Three – For each of the three utterances, the student should identify what the *indirect speech act(s)* were that he or she understood based on the utterance. A direct act unpacks the contents of what someone does in saying something. An indirect act presents plausible additional actions exerted through the spoken word—many of which are not controllable by the speaker. This is a useful journaling project because the student will know the context of the memory and the relationship dynamic shared or absent with the speaker described.

Step Four – For each of the three utterances, the students should identify what they believed to be the goals of the speaker. What were their task goals? What were their relational goals?

Step Five – For each of the three utterances, the student should identify what made this utterance memorable for him or her.

This small speech analysis should give students some insight into the complicated world of spoken communication and also the complicating variables that relational goals impose on speech in a given context.

EXPLORING IDEAS FOR A RESPONSE

The practice of communicating with patients and families is a major portion of the work performed by nurses. This exercise is most useful if performed with one or two partners. The patient/family quotes below require some action from the nurse. Consider together the most effective way to relate and adapt to your conversational partner as you engage them. Partners are helpful in considering the various contextual impacts that might contribute to different response options.

To facilitate this exercise in relationship to the speech acts discussed previously in this chapter, a simple chart will identify the four major areas of action expressed in our everyday talk. Consult this chart as you identify and reflect upon the patient/family utterance, and the response ideas for the nurse in the interaction; it might be helpful. Move through the patient/family quotes and discuss each one. Discussions from one interaction will likely inform the others (see Table. 7.10).

Table 7.10 Speech Acts

Constatives:	Affirming, alleging, announcing, answering, attributing, claiming, classifying, concurring, confirming, conjecturing, denying, disagreeing, disclosing, identifying, informing, insisting, predicting, ranking, reporting, stating, stipulating
Directives:	Advising, alleging, asking, begging, dismissing, excusing, forbidding, instructing, ordering, permitting, requesting, requiring, suggesting, urging, warning
Commissives:	Agreeing, guaranteeing, inviting, offering, promising, swearing, volunteering
Acknowledgments:	Apologizing, condoling, congratulating, greeting, thanking, accepting

Example One

The husband of a patient says to the nurse as he enters the room, "I touched her and her arm was cold, and I touched her face and it was cold. Do you think she's alright?"

Please write your response ideas.

Example Two

A family and patient have just been admitted to the oncology floor. An exploratory surgery revealed metastatic cancer. The family and patient are totally disoriented and have no oncologist. The sister of the patient appeals to the RN: "Can't someone just tell us what this is and how we deal with it? We don't even have a doctor yet."

Please write your response ideas.

Example Three

A dialysis patient has gone to her NP as she is spiking a fever. Early in the appointment, the patient says to the NP, "I don't know why I am going through all of this."

Example Four

A palliative care nurse meets with a family in critical care. The patient is in her 30s and has late-stage Huntington's disease and sepsis and is experiencing general organ failure. The patient's husband says to the nurse, "She is going to shake this thing. We've just gotta stay positive as a family."

Please write your response ideas.

Example Five

A pediatric oncology nurse stops in to deliver medication to Tim, a 4-year-old who is receiving a blood transfusion so that he can continue his chemotherapy in order to begin radiation in 2 weeks. Despite his grave situation, Tim is cheery upon seeing his nurse. Tim's mother says to the nurse, "I wish his erstwhile father would get here and relieve me for once."

Please write your response ideas.

ADDITIONAL SUPPLEMENTAL MATERIALS

Potential clinician barriers that will interfere with relating (understanding what is spoken by patient/family):

Table 7.11 Barriers to Relating

- Clinician lacking awareness of changes in a patient case
- Clinician unwilling to engage or discuss with patient/family
- Time constraints
- Lack of continuity in patient care over a period of time
- Relational tasking is not part of measurable nursing practice.

(continued)

Table 7.11 (*continued*)

- Personal preference not to engage in relating
- Lack of interprofessional cooperation/communication

- Last words and last connections at the end of life for children require the extraordinary support of speech language therapists (SLTs). The nurse can identify patients and families in need of this specialized support early on and contribute to an SLP in preparation for their work (voice banking, vocabulary selection, communication device development) with a patient and family. Supporting children's autonomy, their questions and literacy, and their own narratives about the illness experience will increase patient and family quality of life.

1. SLP inclusion in pediatric care services provided as early as possible will support a child's changing communication potential and his/her continuity of care.
2. Engage the family and patient in the idea of an SLP and establish this support as normative.
3. Encourage self-expression of patient.
4. Create opportunities in the day when SLP therapy would be most effective.

Concepts adapted from Costello, J. (2009). Last words, last connections: How augmentative communication can support children facing end of life. *The ASHA Leader*, December 15, pp. 8–11.

FILMS HIGHLIGHTING PATIENT/FAMILY NARRATIVE

Aronson, I. (1997). *Tell Them You're Fine*. Canada: Fanlight. http://www.fanlight.com/catalog/films/235_ttyf.php

- Three young people with cancer confront the day-to-day realities of coping with the impact of the disease, with therapy, and with the attitudes of family, friends, and coworkers.

Bognar, S., & Reichert, J. (2006). *A Lion in the House*. USA: Independent Lens. http://www.lioninthehouse.com

- Five families struggle with the ups and downs of cancer treatment over the course of 6 years.

Curtis, D., & National Film Board of Canada. (2003). *Bearing Witness: Jocelyn Morton*. Canada: Fanlight. http://onf-nfb.gc.ca/eng/collection/film/?id=51157

- Follows sculptor Jocelyn Morton over the course of her last 4 months, as she copes with her impending death from cancer

New England Cable News. (1997). *Look for Me Here: 299 Days in the Life of Nora Lenihan.* Canada: Fanlight. http://www.fanlight.com/catalog/films/244_lfmh.php

- When she learns that her cancer has recurred and metastasized, 40-year-old Nora chooses to forego radical treatment and face death with hospice care at home. Focusing on the comfort provided by her caregivers, family, and support network of family, friends, and coworkers, this portrait chronicles the year from that decision to her death.

Rabow, M., Goodman, S., & Folkman, S. (2008). *The Caregivers.* Open Eye Pictures, California. http://openeyepictures.com/thecaregivers

Rabow, M., Goodman, S., & Folkman, S. (2008). *The Caregivers Project Film Discussion Guide.* UCSF Osher Center for Integrative Medicine. http://www.osher.ucsf.edu/patient-care/self-care-resources/caregivers/

- The Caregivers Project teamed with Open Eye Pictures, an award-winning, non-profit production company to create *The Caregivers,* an educational film about caregiving for loved ones with an aggressive form of brain cancer. The film follows patients, their family caregivers, and physicians-in-training to reveal the complexities of caregiving, patient–doctor–caregiver communications, and the health care system.

Watson-Burgess, H., & National Film Board of Canada. (2005). *At My Mother's Breast.* Canada: Fanlight. http://www.fanlight.com/catalog/films/435_ammb.php

- The filmmaker's mother, grandmother, and great grandmother all had breast cancer. So have two of her three aunts. The result of this work is a portrait of strong women in one family system who find unity and peace while facing a terrifying and tragic genetic legacy.

8

TEAM

Mrs. Lindsey is a 52-year-old woman diagnosed with late-stage breast can-
cer. She has three teenage daughters, all in high school. Three months prior to
her diagnosis, Mrs. Lindsey's husband moved out of the house after disclosing
that he had been having an affair with a coworker. Their divorce is in process.
Mrs. Lindsey's mother and older sister both died from breast cancer over the
last 10 years.

Mrs. Lindsey had attempted to remain as functional as possible, but she has
been rapidly declining, including recent brain metastasis. Her daughters have
tried to care for her, but she has fallen several times while the daughters are at
school. Hospice has now been initiated, and the team social worker has con-
ducted an initial assessment, which she has presented to the team. She reports
that the ex-husband had offered to move back into the home and support his
ex-wife and their daughters. There are strong opinions expressed by the team
members. The chaplain, John, expresses his belief that Mr. Lindsey is genuinely
remorseful and that having him in the home would be very positive. A few of the
hospice nurses express their dislike for the ex-husband ("that jerk") and believe
that it would be an insult to Mrs. Lindsey.

Over the next few weeks, Mrs. Lindsey continues to decline, and she does
reluctantly agree to have Mr. Lindsey move back in, only because of her con-
cern for her daughters. At the next team meeting, the chaplain reports that he
is very disappointed in his colleagues, as he has observed the nursing assistant
and primary nurse being very hostile toward Mr. Lindsey. The social worker
reports that she believes Mrs. Lindsey has forgiven Mr. Lindsey and would like
help in communicating her feelings to her daughters and ex-husband so she can
die peacefully.

Difficult cases such as the Lindsey family can make communicating with colleagues
challenging. Conflict can arise when team members are protective of their area of
expertise and specialized contribution to the team, or because team members simply
disagree about how best to assist patients and families. Commitment to collaboration,
role-modeling collaboration, and creating a sense of community are necessary skills
for nurses working in teams (Huston, 2008). The focus of this chapter is team communication and being able to communicate effectively with colleagues, even when

disagreement is prevalent. This chapter will detail the main principles of interdisciplinary collaboration, feature team meetings as a place to resolve conflict, and identify common team communication problems that can lead to an ineffective decision-making process called groupthink.

INTERDISCIPLINARY TEAMS

In an **interdisciplinary team**, clinicians work from different orientations while at the same time engaging in joint work. Team members representing varying disciplines within the biopsychosocial model (traditionally, physicians, nurses, social workers, volunteers, and chaplains) are represented on the hospice/palliative care team to produce family-focused care (Connor, Egan, Kwilosz, Larson, & Reese, 2002). Team members need to collaborate, integrate specialized knowledge into a comprehensive plan of care, and translate discipline-specific jargon for each other (D'Amour, Ferrada-Videla, San Martin Rodriguez, & Beaulieu, 2005). Each team member holds expertise, and leadership is influenced by the needs of the patient, family, and sometimes the team (Youngwerth & Twaddle, 2011). Ideally, under this holistic interdisciplinary approach patients and families are provided with care plans that have been assessed by experts in different disciplines (Dyeson, 2005). The holistic nature of hospice and palliative care necessitates that team members achieve interdisciplinary collaboration. Collaboration is an evolving practice that takes focused communication work (D'Amour et al., 2005).

INTERDISCIPLINARY COLLABORATION

Interdisciplinary Collaboration is a dynamic communication process that relies on sharing resources, mutual dependence between team members, and sharing and respecting positions of power afforded by credibility or expertise (D'Amour et al., 2005). Despite discipline-specific expertise, team members share the same task and relational communication responsibilities discussed in Chapter 2. Task communication on the team includes educating each other about successes and failures on the job and/or appropriate communication strategies for specific patients and family members. Meanwhile, relational communication consists of providing support to team members and sharing workplace stress.

The **model of interdisciplinary collaboration** best represents the theoretical framework for the interdisciplinary approach to care (Bronstein, 2003). This model includes a combination of multidisciplinary theory of collaboration, services integration, role theory, and ecological systems theory (Bronstein, 2003). Based on the model, interdisciplinary collaboration consists of: (1) interdependence and flexibility, (2) newly created professional activities, (3) collective ownership of goals, and (4) reflection on process. Table 8.1 illustrates an interdisciplinary collaboration observation form.

Interdependence and flexibility are characterized by interaction among team members in order to accomplish goals. For each patient/family plan of care, team members take on varying roles and responsibilities. Team members are dependent

Table 8.1 Interdisciplinary Collaboration Observation Form

Date: _____

Observation	Comments
Team Member Flexibility (team members assume duties outside of their area of expertise to accomplish team goals) ☐ Discussed communicating with outside staff (other physicians, hospices, nursing home) ☐ Discussed speaking with patient ☐ Discussed speaking with caregiver ☐ *No* discussion of outside communication	
Newly Created Activities (a clinical task that wasn't previously identified as a need but has now been identified as a result of team communication) ☐ Staff education took place (teaching one another) ☐ Identification of tasks to be done (e.g., "I will call," "Can you go out … ") ☐ *No* newly created activities generated	
Collective ownership of goals (the team engages in a shared problem solving around a problem) ☐ Discussed problem(s) with informal caregivers, other health care professionals ☐ Shared frustration about job/plan of care ☐ Discussed safety issues ☐ *No* discussion of these issues	
Reflective process ☐ Procedural issues discussed ☐ Death reviewed, if applicable ☐ Workplace stress was shared and discussed. ☐ *No* discussion of these issues	
Please check if the following issues were discussed: ☐ Pain management ☐ Spiritual background/needs ☐ Psychological suffering ☐ Social impact (isolation, loneliness) ☐ *No* discussion of these issues	
Were there any interruptions (cell phone, pagers)? ☐ YES ☐ NO	

Adapted from the following works:

Bronstein, L. R. (2003). A model for interdisciplinary collaboration. *Social Work, 48*(3), 297–306.

Wittenberg-Lyles, E., & Oliver, D. P. (2007). The power of interdisciplinary collaboration in hospice. *Progress in Palliative Care, 15*(1), 6–12.

Wittenberg-Lyles, E. M., Parker Oliver, D., Demiris, G., & Regehr, K. (2010). Interdisciplinary collaboration in hospice team meetings. *Journal of Interprofessional Care, 24*(3), 264–273.

upon each other for information that determines their role within a patient's plan of care; each case requires team member flexibility in order to achieve care outcomes. When spiritual needs are requested from a nurse, the nurse is able to manage spiritual communication. Similarly, when a chaplain is asked opinions about pain medication use, she is able to reinforce pain education and dispel myths regarding addiction or tolerance. Interdisciplinary team members are united by **psychospiritual care**, the underlying care required to meet the needs of patients'/families' personal labor with terminal illness that often brings psychological suffering and spiritual realities (Grey, 1996). Psychospiritual care is complex and ambiguous and cannot be attended to best by any one core team member.

Box 8.1

"A doctor came in and gave him an explanation that they couldn't do any more chemo [chemotherapy] on him.... The patient didn't hear it, just didn't hear it ... because I was the chaplain I said pretty much the same thing as the doctor said, but I think because I was just a normal person ... he could hear me." —Palliative Care Chaplain

(Goldsmith, Wittenberg-Lyles, Rodriguez, & Sanchez-Reilly, 2010).

When information is shared among team members, **newly created tasks and responsibilities** emerge and collaborative activities maximize each individual's expertise. Because team members are interdependent, sharing information with each other leads to new tasks. Although each team member provides a special service, the team must labor together to serve the patient and family (Grey, 1996). This can mean "doing the job no one wants to do" on behalf of the team (O'Brien, Martin, Heyworth, & Meyer, 2009). Collaboration requires team members to be accessible to other team members—allowing ease and frequency of contact—so that team members can develop mutual respect and trust (Petri, 2010).

Collaboration is produced through a **collective ownership of goals** as team members have a shared responsibility for producing quality holistic care. Team members are joined together by the experience of patients and families, collectively engaging in the voice of the Lifeworld about disease and illness (see Chapter 4 for further discussion) (Goldsmith, Wittenberg-Lyles, Rodriguez, & Sanchez-Reilly, 2010). In hospice and palliative care, team members share the same view that the patient and caregiver are an integral part of the team (D'Amour et al., 2005; Goldsmith et al., 2010). While each discipline has its own goal of care, team members have a shared common purpose (Katzenbach & Smith, 1993). Hospice/palliative care team members consistently describe themselves as having high spiritual well-being, the ability to self-actualize, and making a conscious effort to integrate spiritual beliefs into their everyday work (Clark et al., 2007). Finally, team members can become aware of the process of collaboration by engaging in a **reflective process**. By reviewing team processes, such as plans of care, discharges, or a patient's death, team members can evaluate their own collaborative process. Unfortunately, research has shown that this is the lowest ranked aspect of collaboration among hospice and other health care teams (Tubbs-Cooley et al., 2011; Wittenberg-Lyles, Parker Oliver, Demiris, & Regehr, 2010) (see Box 8.2).

Box 8.2 Example of Collaboration

Collaboration is a dynamic, fluid process that transpires in daily palliative care work. In addition to team collaboration, nurses must also collaborate with other clinicians outside of hospice/palliative care. A typical patient visit to an Alzheimer's Assisted Living Facility by Lance, an RN at a local hospice, characterizes collaboration:

> Upon arriving at the facility Lance is greeted at the door by Cindy, the Resident Director, who immediately wants a private meeting. She pulls Lance into her private office to discuss her dissatisfaction with hospice personnel. Even though Lance has never met Cindy before, he is recognized as part of hospice staff and is *interdependently* related to the hospice team and agency. He must be *flexible* to answer all of her questions related to the patient's care as well as the agency's policies regarding patient care.
>
> Cindy reports that the hospice medical director and licensed vocational nurse (LVN) were there for a patient visit 2 days ago. During the visit, Sally, the unit charge nurse, asked the hospice medical director if he would speak to the patient's daughter and tell her that the patient was declining. Sally felt that this would help the daughter develop realistic expectations for care in the assisted living facility. According to Cindy, the hospice LVN called the patient's daughter later that day and told her that Sally asked the hospice medical director to give her a "reality check." Consequently, the daughter called the assisted living facility, asked for Sally, and "chewed her out and chewed out all the staff."
>
> Upon hearing this, Lance was very apologetic about the circumstances. Cindy reiterated that the hospice LVN and Sally are on the same team, and the LVN "went behind our backs and got us in trouble." Lance acknowledges that the LVN's communication was completely unprofessional and agrees that they are all united by the *collective goal* of providing quality health care to this patient and comforting his daughter. Cindy made it very clear to Lance that the hospice LVN was no longer welcome at the facility, explaining: "If my charge nurse was inappropriate, then it was your medical director's responsibility to correct her."
>
> This impromptu meeting with Sally *creates a new responsibility* for Lance, who must now contact the hospice medical director as well as the hospice LVN to report on this meeting and then contact administration to change the LVN assignment for this patient. Finally, Sally was asked to join this meeting; together the three of them *reflected on what had transpired* and then established a shared communication plan to convey to the patient's daughter.

Interdisciplinary team (IDT) meetings are routinely held in hospice and palliative care to enable team members to practice interdisciplinary collaboration. The IDT meeting facilitates communication that produces an interdisciplinary plan of care for each patient. During the IDT meeting, teams form a single care plan wherein team members share responsibilities and implement their part of the plan (Sabur, 2003). Informal exchange of information between team members also happens prior to and after meetings, in the hallways, over lunch, or in passing at the patient's home (Youngwerth & Twaddle, 2011). The example in Figure 8.1 demonstrates interdisciplinary collaboration in a team meeting format among a nurse (RN), medical director (MD), social worker (SW), and Chaplain (C).

This team meeting discussion involves all team members—each member provides information about the patient's plan of care, and the patient's family is addressed within this discussion. Elements of interdisciplinary collaboration emerge from the discussion among team members.

The collaborative process also includes conflict as part of interdisciplinary team communication. Disagreements among team members include varying opinions about difficult patients/families and misunderstandings/personality conflicts (Parker Oliver & Peck, 2006; Wittenberg-Lyles, Oliver, Demiris, Baldwin, & Regehr, 2008). After presenting a case report and summary to the team, nurses often provide their own impressions about the patient and caregiver (Wittenberg-Lyles, Gee, Oliver, & Demiris, 2009). Troubled patients/families are discussed at greater length, and "atrocity stories" are often relayed among team members to provide insight into patient/family living circumstances or difficult cases (Li & Arber, 2006; Wittenberg-Lyles, 2005). Atrocity stories are shared to recount the insensitive behavior of other clinical staff or patients/family members. Team members are not always able to agree on a plan of care, and a lack of understanding across disciplines can produce conflict as team members can struggle with overlapping roles (Connor et al., 2002). These conflicts as well as others can be managed during team meeting discussions if the team has a problem-solving procedure in place (Parker Oliver & Peck, 2006; Wittenberg-Lyles, 2005).

GROUPTHINK

Although the goal for an interdisciplinary palliative care team is to achieve high-performance group status, research shows that hospice and palliative care teams more commonly perform as working groups that do not always achieve collaboration (Baldwin, Wittenberg-Lyles, Parker Oliver, & Demiris, 2011; Bokhour, 2006; Demiris, Washington, Doorenbos, Parker Oliver, & Wittenberg-Lyles, 2008; Demiris, Washington, Parker Oliver, & Wittenberg-Lyles, 2008; Katzenbach & Smith, 1993; Wittenberg Lyles, 2005; Wittenberg-Lyles, Gee, Oliver, & Demiris, 2009; Wittenberg-Lyles, Parker Oliver, Demiris, Baldwin, & Regehr, 2009; Wittenberg-Lyles, Parker Oliver, Demiris, & Cunningham, 2011). In a **working group,** members interact regularly, share information, perspectives, and best practices, but there is no organizational policy for how the team is evaluated as a whole, nor is there an assessment of the productivity level of the team (Katzenbach & Smith, 1993). A study of hospice teams

RN: [Patient's name] is a 69 year old patient who resides at home. She has stage four ovarian cancer. Her daughter Velma provides care. Louise (Nurse Case Manager) said yesterday she saw her this week and she's in bed more. She's not getting up as often. And her pain seems to be pretty well controlled. It's hard to get ahold of them. Louise actually had to go back to their house for impromptu visits just because she can't get ahold of them. You can try their cell phones—they have those rechargeable cell phones.

MD: Could you agree to a time that the phone could be free so that you could call?

RN: I don't know. That's a good idea. One of the problems that I know that [chaplain] has run into is he can't get hold of anybody.

SW: We've made it known that we have questions and so I've called several times on several days for several weeks and nothing. I leave messages on the track phones or the phones aren't working.

> Collective ownership of goals – members of the team share common problem and attempt to problem solve.

RN: And then when they [other clinical staff] do leave messages, they will ask them well did you get my message? And they'll say they didn't. So I don't know if they're not checking their messages or if that part of their service isn't working. I don't know. The patient sometimes complains of having numbness in her feet, and that kind of makes it hard for her to walk. If she's up, it's usually always assisted with someone in the house. She does have a walker, but lately she's just been staying in bed most of the time. Her pain is well-controlled, she even has a decrease in the dizziness she was having there for awhile, but then, she's in bed all the time—she probably doesn't feel that dizzy, because she's not up as much.

SW: She needs a walker.

RN: She has a walker and she does use it, but lately the daughter has had to kind of get her up and kind of stand there and hands-on assist. I'd say the daughter, she takes good care of her—making sure that she has food to eat, and she gets her up, but what happens is, ... [weekend nurse] says that when she was out there this week, she's noticed that they're not getting her up to go into the living room where the TV is at.

> Interdependence and flexibility – SW suggests that the patient needs additional medical equipment

MD: I think the lack of moving and not getting to what she wants is a concern.

RN: Right. And just the fact that if she wants to get up, they need to be there for her.

C: Has anyone talked to her about a volunteer?

SW: I saw her on initial assessment and they are a real supportive family. There is just a lot of family visiting and the daughter's doing well enough despite the intrusion of a lot of people.

C: I've been able to get the Catholic Church to get over there to give her sacraments and prayer. She was very thankful for that but she said we could still come and visit.

> Newly created task – Chaplain identifies that a volunteer may be appropriate/needed

RN: The biggest issue with her is the fear of her daughter having to see her go through this, and I think you've [chaplain] probably talked to her about these things, and nothing else—death doesn't seem to be an issue for her when she talks to me. More so, it's that Velma is going to have to see her go through all this stuff. And Velma and I have talked about this this and she wouldn't want to have it any other way.

> Reflective process – Psychosocial elements of care are discussed by the team

C: I agree. I think Velma will be able to handle this.

SW: I'll try to get there Monday, if I can get a hold of them.

RN: I'll tell them you'll try to call – you'll try to call and talk to them Monday then.

FIGURE 8.1 Interdisciplinary collaboration

found that hospice agencies do evaluate teams, but little is known about what they are evaluating, whether or not the evaluation impacts or influences team processes, and whether or not anything is done with this information to improve team collaboration (Baldwin et al., 2011). Typically, team members are evaluated for individual performance rather than team performance.

Collaboration doesn't occur just because group members are placed in the same room (D'Amour et al., 2005). Interpersonal and communication conflicts are likely and can result in factions within the group and isolation of group members. Poor decisions can be made when group members ignore each other's conflicting opinions or if the group doesn't deal openly with disagreements. While meetings are a safe place for members to share, collaborate, and be collegial, they are also a venue for group communication that involves managing professional boundaries and practicing conflict resolution (Arber, 2007). Thus, we move now from interdisciplinary teams to looking at palliative care nursing from a group communication perspective.

Although group commitment is high (goals are shared and identified) among palliative care teams, research has found that group members in highly committed groups are more likely to prioritize group cohesion rather than critical evaluation of the group task (Youngwerth & Twaddle, 2011). In health care organizations, there is a stronger relationship between strategic consensus (e.g., agreement on a plan of care) and organizational commitment (how much an employee feels committed to the organization) rather than involvement and commitment (Carney, 2007). With organizational commitment more likely to predict consensus with group members, there is greater likelihood that members aren't as involved in the collaborative decision-making process (Carney, 2007). **Groupthink** can occur when "deeply involved" cohesive group members engage in a mode of thinking that centers on unanimity over the motivation to rationally assess various courses of action (Janis, 1982). In these groups, the focus of groupwork is on group cohesion and group relations rather than decision making; groupthink results in poor decision making and/or lack of collaboration.

Clinical palliative care work in the team environment requires nurses to be aware of the communicative elements that can lead to groupthink. Group cohesion may be the result of the group's inability to engage in effective group discussion and conflict resolution. Groupthink occurs when there is pressure on group members to agree not to disagree (Napier & Gershenfeld, 1999). This pressure emerges informally through the culture of the group. Group members embrace a decision even though they recognize it may not be the best decision. Disagreements among members are suppressed, giving way to the perception that conflict means more work for the group (Heinemann, Farrell, & Schmitt, 1994). When groupthink occurs, members are unable to consider all aspects of information and alternative solutions, and fail to understand the risk of failure (Heinemann et al., 1994) (see Box 8.3).

Box 8.3

"Contrary to the notion that teams waste time and energy arguing, those that avoid conflict actually doom themselves to revisiting issues again and again without resolution." (Lencioni, 2002, p. 202)

Group cohesion can be triggered by a perceived threat (Degnin, 2009). Sometimes difficult patients and/or family members can be perceived as a threat to the palliative care team. **Stereotyping** patients/or family members can lead to groupthink when team members categorize others outside of the group in ways that are considered unacceptable (Miller, 2009). Patients and family are considered "outsiders" to the palliative/hospice process when complex family dynamics require extensive time, a patient's eligibility for hospice is questionable, the team perceives that family decision making is dependent upon financial gain, the team perceives problems with the safety and compliance of pain medication at home, or the patient/family demands care services inconsistent with hospice benefits. Stereotyping patients and families results in "tunnel vision," and group members are unable to consider alternatives to the plan of care (Degnin, 2009).

A heavy emphasis on biomedical information sharing and reporting within the group can also result in **self-censorship** and contribute to perceived group cohesion. Self-censorship occurs when group members elect not to share their opinion to counter a prevailing thought in the group (Miller, 2009). Prior research on hospice interdisciplinary team meetings has found that team members do not contribute equally, shared information is primarily biomedical, there is limited structured team member support, and psychosocial information sharing is limited (Wittenberg Lyles, 2005; Wittenberg-Lyles, Gee, et al., 2009; Wittenberg-Lyles, Parker Oliver, et al., 2009; Wittenberg-Lyles et al., 2011). A typical case-reporting format among hospice/palliative care teams includes: the date the patient was admitted, a complete diagnosis, medical history of the patient, current medications, whether there is a do-not-resuscitate order and/or a health care proxy for the patient, and an assessment of pain management (Wittenberg-Lyles, 2005). Social workers and chaplains who do not have a specific role in case report formats typically do not share their opinions in patient care discussions. Consequently, all team members are not treated equally and psychosocial information is considered secondary. The desire to fit in with the team and cooperating to impress a workplace superior contribute to self-censorship and groupthink (Halpern, 2009).

The following example demonstrates how a team meeting discussion can be impacted by groupthink attitudes (Box 8.4):

Box 8.4 Team Meeting Discussions

RN-1: He's declining, he's very weak, he staggers and he's fallen once. He is confused a lot of the time. He's had chest pain. Sunday he had chest pain that required three nitros, some oral morphine, and then two more nitros to relieve the pain. Daughter is very understanding. She provides excellent care and support to him. She's real sweet.

RN-2: Is the daughter in the home?

RN-1: Yeah, they live together. First she took care of her mother, now she's taking care of him. She told me yesterday she is a breast cancer survivor and now had uterine cancer. Now her father's dying. She had gotten obese during all

---

(continued)

Box 8.4 (*continued*)

of this. She's lost almost seventy pounds with Weight Watchers® and said she feels better now than she's felt in many, many years. I guess with all her health issues she started gaining a lot of weight. Health issues and caregiving issues, she gained lots and lots of weight, so she's looking really good and she's feeling really good about herself, and providing really good care for him and, and he seems to be accepting everything. I asked him if there's anything I could do and he said, "Well, if you could make me about 25 years younger I'd be fine."

R-2: Is he the one that has the girlfriend that comes there?

RN-1: No, that's a different patient.

RN-1: Okay. Chaplain, the social worker, everybody?

(Nods of agreement)

RN: He's starting MSIR, and maybe [medication]. You might check the chart. I can't remember if it was there prior to. I think we started [medication] also.

While the discussion of this patient's plan of care did include information about pain, pain medication, and the caregiver, the only member of the hospice team to contribute to this discussion was the hospice nurse case manager. The remaining team members, specifically the medical director, social worker, and chaplain, decided not to share information. Self-censorship occurred when these team members nodded in agreement and allowed the discussion about this patient's plan of care to end. In hospice, nurses often find themselves responsible for presenting patient cases, and it is important to recognize when groupthink is occurring and work to create an environment where everyone can contribute knowledge and expertise.

In addition to group cohesion, the structure of hospice and hospital systems can contribute to the propensity for groupthink to occur in hospice and palliative care (Degnin, 2009). **Structural characteristics** are the direct result of the organizational process that contributes to the development and maintenance of interdisciplinary teams. Structural constraints that influence group cohesion and the ability to collaborate include manageable caseloads, an organizational culture that supports and encourages interdisciplinary collaboration, administrative support, professional autonomy, and the time and space for collaboration to occur (Bronstein, 2003; Youngwerth & Twaddle, 2011). Structural constraints produce **direct pressure on dissenters**, an inherent force that pressures group members to behave and think in similar ways (Miller, 2009). When caseloads become unmanageable, there are concerns about time, and/or group members do not have solid information-sharing procedures in place, the effectiveness of communication in IDT meetings can be decreased by challenges to information flow, including access to and recording of information, documentation of services, obtaining information from absent team members, data redundancy, and updating of recorded information (Demiris, Washington, Doorenbos, et al., 2008; Demiris, Washington, Parker Oliver, et al., 2008). As such, the ability to engage in collaboration is influenced by organizational policies and procedures of the hospital unit or hospice agency (Tubbs-Cooley et al., 2011).

Finally, the **situational context** of group members can lead to groupthink. The situational context is the temporary condition of the team resulting from recent events. These factors include high stress coming from outside of the group (e.g., institutionalized care facility staff, primary care/attending physicians, health care policy), low self-esteem among group members (e.g., suffering compassion fatigue, recent high frequency of patient deaths), and trouble making group decisions and talking openly about moral dilemmas. To cope with situational factors, group members fail to engage in collaborative problem solving and instead commit to decisions and do not change them. Nurses must work to reevaluate decisions about plans of care as the patient's status changes often and new care options become available.

Other factors influence the conflict management process among members (Miller, 2009). **Personal factors** such as gender and cultural (racial, ethnic) differences, personality differences, or the way an individual approaches conflict (avoids or confronts) can determine whether or not members engage in conflict management. **Relational factors** include issues of power that arise between members when there are differences in age, educational training, years of experience, or hierarchical positioning in the team/group structure.

DEVELOPING CLINICAL PRACTICE SKILLS

This chapter reviews team communication in palliative nursing, explaining the interdisciplinary collaboration process, interdisciplinary team meetings, and the propensity for groupthink among palliative care team members. Team-building skills are an essential nurse leader competency, and we offer the following clinical tools to assist in teamwork and communication with colleagues (Huston, 2008). Consistent with other chapters, these tools are summarized according to each step of nursing practice.

Assessment

The team environment needs to be assessed for infrastructure that enables interdisciplinary collaboration and for any signs that groupthink behavior may be the norm.

Take into consideration the following elements that influence the team's ability to develop interdisciplinary care plans (Bronstein, 2003) (Box 8.5):

Box 8.5

➢ Professional Roles
  o Is there a defined hierarchy within the team structure? How is this communicated?
  o Do all team members sit at the table, or are some team members sitting outside of the group?

(continued)

Box 8.5 (*continued*)

   o Are team members knowledgeable about each other's roles, responsibilities, background/training?
➤ Personal Characteristics
   o What similarities/differences do team members have with each other?
   o What gender/cultural differences exist within the team?
   o In what ways do team members approach conflict (avoid, confront)?
➤ Structural Characteristics
   o Is there a place for team meetings that allows everyone to sit together equally? Is there an agenda? Is an agenda prepared in advance, and is the patient's medical chart ready and accessible?
   o Does an administrator sit in on these team meetings?
   o How long do team meetings last? How many people are present?
   o Are organizational policies/housekeeping conducted as part of the team meeting?
➤ History of Collaboration
   o How long has the team been together?
   o What conflicts have occurred in the past?
   o How often are on-call staff or per diem staff included in team meetings?

If the right infrastructure is in place, team members have a greater likelihood of achieving collaboration.

In the opening case study of this chapter we can assume that this team engages in interdisciplinary collaboration and effective decision-making. The team meeting is a safe environment that allows all team members to share equally. First, the social worker provides an initial assessment to the team, suggesting that she has a regular speaking role in the team meeting. Second, team members feel comfortable and do share strong opinions with each other. The nurses, social worker, and chaplain all contribute to the discussion of Mrs. Lindsey's care plan. There does not appear to be any direct pressure on dissenters within this group, as John (chaplain) feels comfortable speaking up in opposition to the rest of the team. Reflect on your own team meetings using the checklist in Box 8.6.

Box 8.6 Checklist

✓ CHECKLIST

Are your team meetings boring?
Do they have an environment where back-channel politics and personal attacks thrive?
Are controversial topics ignored?

(*continued*)

Box 8.6 (*continued*)

Does the team fail to tap into all the opinions and perspectives of team members?
Does the team waste time and energy with interpersonal risk management?

If the answer was yes to any of these questions, the team may be prone to groupthink behavior and interdisciplinary collaboration may be at risk. Here are some telltale signs that groupthink behavior may exist:

BEWARE of GROUPTHINK!

➢ Directive, overpowering leader
➢ Isolation from others who are not associated with the team (non–team members)
➢ Lack of critical discussions
➢ Loyalty to the group (when loyalty prevails over critical thinking!)
➢ Lack of norms for procedures

Used with permission from: Lencioni, P. (2002). *The Five Dysfunctions of a Team: A Leadership Fable.* San Francisco: Jossey-Bass. 204.

Plan

Team-based palliative care requires that all team members engage in the planning process.

Although Mrs. Lindsey's hospice team was able to effectively engage in collaboration with one another, the collaborative process resulted in conflict. Conflict during group discussions is important and reflects quality decision making. John, the chaplain, did not allow the rest of the team to stereotype Mr. Lindsey as a "jerk." Rather, he highlighted the benefits of Mr. Lindsey's involvement. John's role during this case discussion reflects the team's ability to consider alternative courses of action and avoid groupthink behavior. Other tips for avoiding groupthink are included in Box 8.7.

Box 8.7 Tips for Avoiding Groupthink

➢ Discuss the problem and draw out different perspectives.
➢ Clarify the patient's goal of care.
➢ Make a list of criteria for the decision.
➢ Use a voting technique to ensure all opinions are considered.
➢ Ask probing questions.

Adapted from: Whyman, W., & Ginnett, R. (2005). A question of leadership: What can leaders do to avoid groupthink? *Leadership in Action, 25*(2), 12.

For patient/family cases that are particularly troublesome, we recommend appointing a team member to serve as devil's advocate to help the team consider all options and enhance their ability to engage in creative problem solving. Rotating opening case summary presentations during team meetings from among the core disciplines may also serve this very purpose.

Intervene

Good patient care is predicated upon effective, unified teams led by a directive leader assigned within the system (Degnin, 2009). Nurses often serve as team leaders during palliative care team meetings, and this role can influence group communication patterns. To help the team achieve collaboration, nurses need to use interpersonal relationship skills to help team members establish mutual respect and trust as well as facilitate conflict resolution (Petri, 2010). For members of Mrs. Lindsey's team, conflict emerges from the team's inability to establish a collective goal for her case. Collaborative problem solving is impeded when team members do not have the same sense of the "problem." During Mrs. Lindsey's care planning, some team members prioritized the loss of the marriage and betrayal as key factors that should influence decision making. On the other hand, John recognized that the immediate need for the care plan was a primary caregiver. Handling difficult conversations, before, after, or during team meetings, can result in further conflict and segregation of team members—however, when handled appropriately with the right message structure these discussions can transition into moments that foster team membership (Figure 8.2, Boxes 8.8 and 8.9).

Box 8.8 Communication Skills and Overcoming Conflict

The following communication skills are critical to learn and practice on teams:
- ✓ Actively Listen: Rephrase the issue and repeat the statement.
- ✓ Define the Problem. Emphasize the areas of agreement and frame the area of disagreement.
- ✓ Open Questions. Ask questions that encourage discussion and permit disagreement. "Can you tell me more about it?" "What else do we need to consider?"
- ✓ Clarify Responses. Help others recognize members' attitudes and feelings.
- ✓ Paraphrase and Reframe. Summarize discussion to ensure that the disagreement is understood. Explore group problem solving and encourage solutions that have not been considered before.

Tools to Overcome Conflict

- Attack the problem, not the person.
- Focus on what can be done, not on what can't be done.
- Encourage different points of view and honest dialogue.
- Express your feelings in a way that does not blame.

(continued)

Box 8.8 (*continued*)

- Accept ownership for your part of the problem.
- Listen to understand the other person's point of view before giving your own.
- Show respect for the other person's point of view.
- Solve the problem while building the relationship.

Used with permission from: Hyer, K. (C. Rader, Ed.). (1998). Module 20. *Interdisciplinary Collaboration for Elder Care.* Funded by John A. Hartford Foundation – Institute for Geriatric Nursing.

Evaluate

Agreeing on a problem-focused process and openness to share resources can lead to effective interdisciplinary collaboration (Petri, 2010), yet team members still need to reflect on these processes and evaluate their own communication. It's likely that most teams have never considered team goals outside of the organization's requirement that

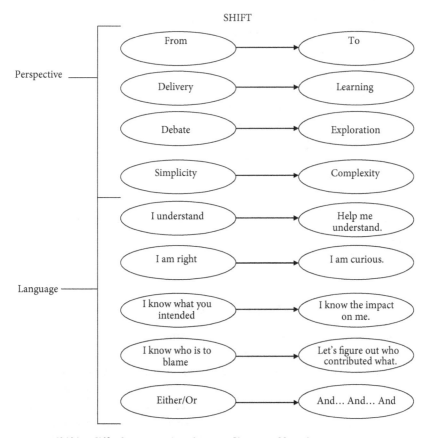

FIGURE 8.2 **Shifting difficult conversations from conflict toward learning**

a team meet regularly. Use the following list (Box 8.9) to establish a team goal, such as improving/addressing the safety of home patients, which can be accomplished through collaboration. When a team identifies a goal, team members create a measuring stick for evaluating their own practices. Setting goals is important. But it is also important to consider team communication processes that enable these goals to be met. When evaluating your own team, consider the communication practices that enable effective interdisciplinary collaboration. Table 8.1 is a form to use for team evaluation. This form can be used by an outside evaluator, such as a nursing or medical student who is observing your team during a hospice/palliative care rotation. Students are excellent observers as they are not familiar with informal group dynamics, such as group rules. The form becomes a learning tool for the student as well as an assessment tool for team communication practices.

Box 8.9

✓ CHECKLIST

- Maintaining the functional status of the patient
- Decreasing loss in activities of daily living
- Reducing use of home health care services
- Decreasing rates of depression
- Decreasing prevalence and symptoms of delirium
- Improving caregiver health
- Improving medication adherence
- Preventing adverse drug reactions
- Decreasing hospital utilization
- Reducing hospital length of stay
- Delaying nursing home placement
- Decreasing nursing home admissions

Used with permission from: Youngwerth, J., & Twaddle, M. (2011). Cultures of interdisciplinary teams: How to foster good dynamics. *Journal of Palliative Medicine, 14*(5), 650–654.

CHAPTER SUMMARY

Alongside clinical knowledge in palliative care settings, nurses need team communication skills to establish a leadership role on the palliative care team. Team-building skills include encouraging other team members to actively contribute during team decision making, fostering opposing viewpoints when they arise in care planning, and evaluating team goals and communication processes. Representing the cornerstone of the COMFORT model, this chapter presented an overview of team communication, focusing on interdisciplinary collaboration and warning against communication processes that lead to groupthink. In truly collaborative teams, intellectual resources are utilized, coordination is maximized, professions gain recognition, and individual health care providers fulfill their potential within their professions (Pringle, Levitt, Horsburgh, Wilson, & Whittaker, 2000). To achieve this potential, palliative nurses need to remain approachable, be interpersonally skilled, and listen to their colleagues (O'Brien, et al., 2009). Chapter 9 departs from the COMFORT model to address the taxing work of palliative care communication, its impact within and outside of clinical settings, and to focus on self-care as a way of improving (and maintaining!) nursing communication skills.

REFERENCES

Adams, T. (2005). Vote red, vote green: A class exercise in groupthink dialectics. *The Florida Communication Journal, 333*(1), 15–22.

Arber, A. (2007). "Pain talk" in hospice and palliative care team meetings: An ethnography. *International Journal of Nursing Studies, 44*(6), 916–926. doi: S0020-7489(06)00112-X [pii]10.1016/j.ijnurstu.2006.04.002

Baldwin, P., Wittenberg-Lyles, E., Parker Oliver, D., & Demiris, G. (2011). An evaluation of interdisciplinary team training in hospice care. *Journal of Hospice and Palliative Nursing, 13*(3), 172–182.

Bokhour, B. G. (2006). Communication in interdisciplinary team meetings: What are we talking about? *Journal of Interprofessional Care, 20*(4), 349–363. doi: L29246M45313K354 [pii]10.1080/13561820600727205

Bronstein, L. R. (2003). A model for interdisciplinary collaboration. *Social Work, 48*(3), 297–306.

Carney, M. (2007). How commitment and involvement influence the development of strategic consensus in health care organizations: The multidisciplinary approach. *Journal of Nursing Management, 15*(6), 649–658. doi: JNM742 [pii]10.1111/j.1365-2834.2007.00742.x

Clark, L., Leedy, S., McDonald, L., Muller, B., Lamb, C., Mendez, T., et al. (2007). Spirituality and job satisfaction among hospice interdisciplinary team members. *Journal of Palliative Medicine, 10*(6), 1321–1328. doi: 10.1089/jpm.2007.0035

Connor, S. R., Egan, K. A., Kwilosz, D. M., Larson, D. G., & Reese, D. J. (2002). Interdisciplinary approaches to assisting with end-of-life care and decision making. *American Behavioral Scientist, 46*(3), 340–356.

D'Amour, D., Ferrada-Videla, M., San Martin Rodriguez, L., & Beaulieu, M. D. (2005). The conceptual basis for interprofessional collaboration: Core concepts and theoretical frameworks. *Journal of Interprofessional Care, 19*(Suppl. 1), 116–131. doi: N81WJW222JU44776 [pii]10.1080/13561820500082529

Degnin, F. D. (2009). Difficult patients, overmedication, and groupthink. *Journal of Clinical Ethics, 20*(1), 64–74.

Demiris, G., Washington, K., Doorenbos, A., Parker Oliver, D., & Wittenberg-Lyles, E. (2008). Use of the time interaction and performance theory to study hospice interdisciplinary team meetings. *Journal of Hospice & Palliative Nursing, 10*(6), 376–381.

Demiris, G., Washington, K., Parker Oliver, D., & Wittenberg-Lyles, E. (2008). A study of information flow in hospice interdisciplinary team meetings. *Journal of Interprofessional Care, 22*(6), 621–629.

Dyeson, T. B. (2005). The home health care team: What can we learn from the hospice experience? *Home Health Care Management & Practice, 17,* 125–127.

Eckstein, N. J. (2005). "Making a lion into a pussycat": Working with difficult group members. *Communication Teacher, 19*(4), 111–115.

Ellingson, L. L. (2003). Interdisciplinary health care teamwork in the clinic backstage. *Journal of Applied Communication Research, 31*(2), 93–117.

Goldsmith, J., Wittenberg-Lyles, E., Rodriguez, D., & Sanchez-Reilly, S. (2010). Interdisciplinary geriatric and palliative care team narratives: Collaboration practices and barriers. *Qualitative Health Research, 20*(1), 93–104. doi: 20/1/93 [pii]10.1177/1049732309355287

Grey, R. (1996). The psychospiritual care matrix: A new paradigm for hospice care giving. *American Journal of Hospice and Palliative Care, 13*(4), 19–25.

Halpern, J. (2009). Groupthink and caregivers' projections: Addressing barriers to empathy. *Journal of Clinical Ethics, 20*(1), 75–78.

Heinemann, G. D., Farrell, M. P., & Schmitt, M. H. (1994). Groupthink theory and research: Implications for decision-making in geriatric health care teams. *Educational Gerontology, 20*(1), 71–85.

Hyer, K. (C. Rader, Ed.). (1998). Module 20. *Interdisciplinary Collaboration for Elder Care.* John Hartford Foundation, Institute for Geriatric Nursing.

Huston, C. (2008). Preparing nurse leaders for 2020. *Journal of Nursing Management, 16*(8), 905–911. doi: JNM942 [pii]10.1111/j.1365-2834.2008.00942.x

Janis, I. L. (1982). *Groupthink.* Boston: Houghton Mifflin.

Katzenbach, J. R., & Smith, D. K. (1993). *The wisdom of teams: Creating the high-performance organization.* Boston: Harvard Business School Press.

Kurylo, A. (2010). Teaching the difference between compromise and collaboration through trial and error. *Communication Teacher, 24*(1), 25–29.

Lencioni, P. (2002). *The Five Dysfunctions of a Team: A Leadership Fable.* San Francisco: Jossey-Bass.

Li, S., & Arber, A. (2006). The construction of troubled and credible patients: A study of emotion talk in palliative care settings. *Qualitative Health Research, 16*(1), 27–46. doi: 16/1/27 [pii]10.1177/1049732305284022

McBride, M. C. (2006). "—ing" Project: Encouraging cohesion in small groups. *Communication Teacher, 20*(2), 53–56.

Miller, K. (2009). *Organizational Communication: Approaches and Processes* (5th ed). Boston: Wadsworth Cengage Learning.

Napier, R. W., & Gershenfeld, M. K. (1999). *Groups: Theory and Experience* (6th ed). Boston: Houghton Mifflin Company.

O'Brien, J. L., Martin, D. R., Heyworth, J. A., & Meyer, N. R. (2009). A phenomenological perspective on advanced practice nurse-physician collaboration within an interdisciplinary healthcare team. *Journal of American Academy of Nurse Practitioners, 21*(8), 444–453. doi: JAAN428 [pii]10.1111/j.1745-7599.2009.00428.x

Parker Oliver, D., & Peck, M. (2006). Inside the interdisciplinary team experiences of hospice social workers. *Journal of Social Work and End of Life & Palliative Care, 2*(3), 7–21.

Petri, L. (2010). Concept analysis of interdisciplinary collaboration. *Nursing Forum, 45*(2), 73–82. doi: NUF167 [pii]10.1111/j.1744-6198.2010.00167.x

Pringle, D., Levitt, C., Horsburgh, M. E., Wilson, R., & Whittaker, M. K. (2000). Interdisciplinary collaboration and primary health care reform. *Canadian Journal of Public Health, 91*(2), 85–88, 97.

Sabur, S. (2003). Measuring the success of the interdisciplinary team. *Hospice Palliative Insights, 4,* 47–49.

Siegler, E., Hyer, K., Fulmer, T., & Mezey, M. (1998). *Geriatric Interdisciplinary Team Training.* John A. Hartford Foundation.

Tubbs-Cooley, H. L., Santucci, G., Kang, T. I., Feinstein, J. A., Hexem, K. R., & Feudtner, C. (2011). Pediatric nurses' individual and group assessments of palliative, end-of-life, and bereavement care. *Journal of Palliative Medicine, 14*(5), 631–637. doi: 10.1089/jpm.2010.0409

Whyman, W., & Ginnett, R. (2005). A question of leadership: What can leaders do to avoid groupthink? *Leadership in Action, 25*(2), 12.

Wittenberg-Lyles, E., Oliver, D. P., Demiris, G., Baldwin, P., & Regehr, K. (2008). Communication dynamics in hospice teams: Understanding the role of the chaplain in interdisciplinary team collaboration. *Journal of Palliative Medicine, 11*(10), 1330–1335. doi: 10.1089/jpm.2008.0165

Wittenberg-Lyles, E., Parker Oliver, D., Demiris, G., Baldwin, P., & Regehr, K. (2009). Communication dynamics in hospice teams: Understanding the role of the chaplain in interdisciplinary team collaboration. *Journal of Palliative Medicine, 11*(10), 1330–1335.

Wittenberg-Lyles, E., Parker Oliver, D., Demiris, G., & Cunningham, C. (2011). Sharing atrocity stories in hospice: A study of niceness message strategies in interdisciplinary team meetings. *Progress in Palliative Care, 19*(4), 172–176.

Wittenberg-Lyles, E., Parker Oliver, D., Demiris, G., & Regehr, K. (2010). Interdisciplinary collaboration in hospice team meetings. *Journal of Interprofessional Care, 24*(3), 264–273. doi: 10.3109/13561820903163421

Wittenberg-Lyles, E. M. (2005). Information sharing in interdisciplinary team meetings: An evaluation of hospice goals. *Qualitative Health Research, 15*(10), 1377–1391. doi: 15/10/1377 [pii]10.1177/1049732305282857

Wittenberg-Lyles, E. M., Gee, G. C., Oliver, D. P., & Demiris, G. (2009). What patients and families don't hear: Backstage communication in hospice interdisciplinary team meetings. *Journal of Housing for the Elderly, 23*(1–2), 92–105. doi: 10.1080/02763890802665007

Youngwerth, J., & Twaddle, M. (2011). Cultures of interdisciplinaryt Teams: How to foster good dynamics. *Journal of Palliative Medicine, 14*(5), 650–654. doi: 10.1089/jpm.2010.0395

Additional References for Interdisciplinary Collaboration

Bokhour, B. G. (2006). Communication in interdisciplinary team meetings: What are we talking about? *Journal of Interprofessional Care, 20*(4), 349–363.

Bronstein, L. R. (2003). A model for interdisciplinary collaboration. *Social Work, 48,* 297–306.

Dawson, S. (2007). Interpersonal working: Communication, collaboration … perspiration! *International Journal of Palliative Nursing, 13*(10), 502–505.

Hearn, J., & Higginson, I. J. (1998). Do specialist palliative care teams improve outcomes for cancer patients? A systematic literature review. *Palliative Medicine, 12*(5), 317–332.

Horak, B. J., Hicks, K., Pellicciotti, S., & Duncan, A. (2006). Create cultural change and team building. *Nursing Management, 37,* 12–14.

Morin, D., Saint-Laurent, L., Bresse, M. P., Dallaire, C., & Fillion, L. (2007). The benefits of a palliative care network: A case study in Quebec, Canada. *International Journal of Palliative Nursing, 13*(4), 190–196.

Oliver, D. P., Wittenberg-Lyles, E. M., & Day, M. (2006). Variances in perceptions of interdisciplinary collaboration by hospice staff. *Journal of Palliative Care, 22*(4), 275–280.

Oliver, D. P., Wittenberg-Lyles, E. M., & Day, M. (2007). Measuring interdisciplinary perceptions of collaboration on hospice teams. *American Journal of Hospice & Palliative Care, 24*(1), 49–53.

Wittenberg Lyles, E., Oliver, D. P., Demiris, G., & Courtney, K. (2007). Assessing the nature and process of hospice interdisciplinary team meetings. *Journal of Hospice and Palliative Nursing, 9*(1), 17–21.

Wittenberg Lyles, E., & Parker Oliver, D. (2007). The power of interdisciplinary collaboration in hospice. *Progress in Palliative Care, 15*(1), 6–12.

Wittenberg-Lyles, E. M., Parker Oliver, D., Demiris, G., & Regehr, K. (2009). Exploring interpersonal communication in hospice interdisciplinary team meetings. *Journal of Gerontological Nursing, 35*(7), 38–45.

Wittenberg-Lyles, E. M., Parker Oliver, D., Demiris, G., & Regehr, K. (2010). Interdisciplinary collaboration in hospice team meetings. *Journal of Interprofessional Care, 24*(3), 264–273.

Additional References for Groupthink

Ahlfinger, N. R., & Esser, J. K. (2001). Testing the groupthink model: Effects of promotional leadership and conformity predisposition. *Social Behavior & Personality: An International Journal, 29*(1), 31–42.

Degnin, F. D. (2009). Difficult patients, overmedication, and groupthink. *The Journal of Clinical Ethics, 20*(1), 64–74.

Esser, J. K. (1998). Alive and well after 25 years: A review of groupthink research. *Organizational Behavior & Human Decision Processes, 73*(2–3), 116–141.

Halpern, J. (2009). Groupthink and caregivers' projections: Addressing barriers to empathy. *The Journal of Clinical Ethics, 20*(1), 75–78.

Heinemann, G. D., Farrell, M. P., & Schmitt, M. H. (1994). Groupthink theory and research: Implications for decision-making in geriatric health care teams. *Educational Gerontology, 20*(1), 71–85.

Janis, I. L. (1982). *Groupthink.* Boston: Houghton Mifflin.

Miller, K. (2009). *Organizational Communication: Approaches and Processes* (5th ed.). Boston: Wadsworth Cengage Learning.

Napier, R. W., & Gershenfeld, M. K. (1999). *Groups: Theory and Experience* (6th ed). Boston: Houghton Mifflin Company.

Schafer, M., and Crichlow, S. (1996) Antecedents of groupthink: A quantitative study. *Journal of Conflict Resolution, 40,* 415–435.

DISCUSSION QUESTIONS

1. What are the characteristics of an interdisciplinary team?
2. Provide an example of task and relational communication within a team.
3. What are the four elements of the model of interdisciplinary collaboration? Give an example for each one.
4. In what ways do nurses practice psychospiritual care?
5. What are the collective goals of a palliative care team?

6. For each aspect of the model of interdisciplinary collaboration, identify and explain how the nurse's role may impact or be impacted by other team members.
7.   In what ways are palliative care teams like a working group?
8. What are the three main elements of groups that lead to groupthink?
9. How are group members pressured to avoid conflict within the group?
10. Describe a time when you opted to self-censor your participation in a group. What circumstances or factors led to your decision?
11. Compare and contrast the two excerpts from interdisciplinary team meetings in this chapter. Identify the similarities and differences between the two discussions using key terms from this chapter.
12. Of the personal and relational factors that contribute to groupthink, which are most applicable to you? How will you work to overcome them?

TEACHING RESOURCES AND MATERIALS

EXERCISES FOR INTERDISCIPLINARY COLLABORATION
Exercise #1

First, have students write down three terms that they associate with interdisciplinary health care teams. Next, place students into small groups and have them share their terms. Then have all groups report to the class as a whole. Have a representative from each group write the group's terms on the board. Then, the instructor should task the class with narrowing the list of terms to three terms and should limit the task to no more than 5 minutes. The instructor should give no further instructions and allow the class to complete the task. Typically, one student emerges who leads the class in a quick discussion in which few students participate.

The instructor should then debrief the class by facilitating a discussion about the decision-making process. Specific questions can help the class reflect on decision making as a team: (1) Did everyone participate in the discussion? (2) Who emerged as the leader and why? (3) How were decisions made? After a class discussion, the instructor should poll the students by asking how satisfied they are with the terms that were identified. Students begin to realize that they either felt empowered by their participation or disempowered and silenced by their nonparticipation. Class discussion should now highlight reasons for compromise or collaboration. Instructors may choose to go around the room and solicit each student to explain his or her role in the decision-making process and reasons why he or she chose to either participate or remain the silent majority. Finally, the instructor discusses specific collaboration techniques and the benefits of them. For example:

1. Focused discussion toward a goal. This may be accomplished if one or more group members:
   - Determine the most important goals for the group
   - Keep discussion moving by limiting extraneous conversation
   - Are practical/realistic when making contributions to discussion
   - Keep interest of group members by recruiting participation from those less vocal
   - Are willing to take charge of the collaboration process
   - Are willing to let someone else take charge
   - Create rules to guide collaboration (e.g., one person speaks at a time)
   - Follow/enforce rules
2. Ensuring all options have been considered. This may be accomplished if one or more group members:
   - Explain/justify preferences for specific ideas rather than merely state them
   - Recruit advocates for the available options

- Require others to explain nonspecific justifications (e.g., "I just like that one.")
- Play devil's advocate before eliminating an option
- Allow silence so that those less vocal can have the opportunity to contribute
- Keep all group members involved
- Avoid relying on supposed democratic processes. For example, decisions made by majority rule may bypass more valid but less popular options.
- Consider options that are more unusual or "outside of the box"
- Consider even obvious options
- Consider unlikely or "wishful thinking" options

As a follow up to this assignment, instructors can provide students with a patient case study and ask them to collaborate on developing an appropriate plan of care. Following this exercise, students should discover that they are more satisfied with the experience when collaboration occurs instead of compromise.

Adapted from: Kurylo, A. (2010). Teaching the difference between compromise and collaboration through trial and error. *Communication Teacher, 24*(1), 25–29.

Exercise #2

Box 8.10 details the case for this exercise. The goal of the meeting you are about to join is to come up with an interdisciplinary care plan for Ms. J. Please decide your team roles and prepare an agenda for the meeting. Decide how you will conduct your team meeting. You should plan on 20 minutes for your team meeting.

Box 8.10

Debra J. is a 55-year-old woman, widowed, and living in a small rural town in the Central Valley. She has worked on an assembly line at a local manufacturing plant for the past 25 years. She drives to work in an old car.

Debra married at 15 and had her three children before age 20. She did not graduate from high school. Her husband died 5 years ago of a heart attack and left her a $70.00 monthly pension from his work on the railroad. She lives on her family's farm with her 85-year-old mother. Her children are all away from home. Her two eldest live out of state, and her youngest daughter lives in San Francisco

Medical History. BP = 150/80; Weight = 150 lbs.; Height = 5'5"

She has smoked one pack per day for 30 years, had her lower teeth extracted at age 40 with dentures made, and had three normal vaginal deliveries. She has two or three urinary tract infections per year. In addition to her work on the assembly line, she works long hours on the family farm. She is beginning to show signs and symptoms of degenerative joint disease in her hands and knees. She comes to the clinic today for a simple check-up.

Questions

- What team members need to be involved in this case?
- What are Ms. J's most important health issues, and who should be involved in managing these issues?
- Develop a management plan for Ms. J.

Use the following grid to assess the patient's situation from each need aspect (medical, emotional, etc.) and identify the impact of the problem on the patient's health and quality of life. Identify community or family resources that could be redirected to address the problem and outcomes or triggers to notify the team that the plan is or is not working. The care plan should identify what activities are expected but also which member of the team is responsible for initiation, follow-up, and reporting back to the team with the results.

Table 8.2 Overarching Team Goals:

Patient's: _____

Family's: _____

Team's: _____

Problem	Expected Outcome	Impact on Health and Quality of Life	Strengths/ Resources	Plan (What/ Who/When) ... Includes Getting More Information

Assess the actual functioning of the team—the team process and the efficiency of addressing clinical aspects or needs. The learners/participants should be able to develop the plan and set the priorities for the team plan of care, and be able to evaluate what to look for and when to determine if the plan was effective. The last step reinforces the team's responsibility for ongoing care management and joint accountability.

Considering the patient's medical, emotional, social, environmental, and economic needs, answer each of the following questions:

- What is the overarching goal? At least three perspectives need to be considered and reconciled: (a) the patient; (b) his/her family; and (c) the team.

- What are the patient's problems? Consider a wide range of possible foci: medical, emotional, social, environmental, and economic.
- What is the impact of each problem on the patient's health and quality of life?
- What strengths and resources does the patient have or can be mobilized to deal with each problem?
- What additional information is needed to adequately define the problem or its implications?
- What is the plan of care? What needs to be done? Who will do it? When will it happen?
- What priority should be assigned to each problem in either a linear order or categories of importance?
- How important is its effect on the overarching problem? What other factors might influence its relative priority?
- What outcomes should be expected for each problem? Express each in measurable terms. When would be an appropriate time to measure the outcomes?

Used with permission from: Siegler, E., Hyer, K., Fulmer, T., & Mezey, M. (1998). *Geriatric Interdisciplinary Team Training. Module 20. Interdisciplinary Collaboration for Elder Care.* Funded by John A. Hartford Foundation – Institute for Geriatric Nursing.

Exercise #3

To help students learn to develop creative communication strategies when dealing with complex or difficult team members, introduce the class to contrasting pictures of an animal, for example, an angry animal versus a sweet, cuddly animal. Pictures must be of the same animal type (e.g., dog, cat). Place students in small groups and ask them to brainstorm creative ways to transform the angry animal into the nice animal. Encourage them to be creative in their ideas and methods for taming the angry animal. You should allow the groups about 15 minutes to complete the brainstorming task.

Next, small groups should send a designated leader to the board to share their ideas with the rest of the class. Using the ideas on the board, the instructor should review the chapter material on groupthink. Analogies can be drawn from the class ideas to the deliberate steps that can be taken to work with difficult team members. First, instructors should begin by identifying behaviors that can build a supportive communication climate among team members (e.g., active listening, showing support, and expressing solidarity). Second, instructors should discuss varying personality types and group behaviors. For example, issues such as dominance and control can be contrasted with the need for understanding, inclusion, affection, self-esteem, and hesitancy to speak in a small-group format.

The class list of taming methods should be reviewed, and students should be encouraged to develop analogies to the interpersonal and small group behaviors (see example table below). For example, a common taming method is to feed the animal. The instructor then has students list communication strategies related to "feeding" a team member, such as spending more time with the individual and engaging in social and relationship building outside of the team format.

Ideas for taming an animal and corresponding communication strategies were taken from Eckstein (2005).

Table 8.3 Creative Team Communication Strategies

Taming Behaviors	Interpersonal and Small-Group-Building Behaviors
Praise it.	Confirming messages (recognition, endorsement)
	Supportive message behaviors ("You are doing a good job.")
	("I like the way you handled that.")
Speak gently.	Speak slowly, allowing for silence and clarity.
	Understanding defensive responses
	Assertive language
	Nonassertive language
	Using "I" language ("I have a hard time with … ")
	Confirming language
	Perception checking ("So what I hear you saying is … ")
	Self-disclosure ("It hurt my feelings"/"I took it personally")
	Recognizing others' existence, position, feelings
Feed it.	Spending more time on social and relational group building
	Bringing/sharing food with others
Pet it.	Affirming nonverbal cues (smiling, hugging)
	Eye contact while listening
	Shaking hands in greeting
	Understanding individual rules of touch
Approach slowly.	Listening to help
	Listening for feelings
	Reading body language
Neuter it/Spay it.	Understanding gender differences
	Win–win problem solving
	Conflict styles

Exercise #4

For instructors who wish to develop small group assignments in their course, this assignment may be done to establish small-group relationships. First, instruct small groups to spend time together engaging in at least four activities. A picture of all group members engaging in the activity together must be provided for evidence of the activity. For example, one of the activities may be to share a meal together. Second, instruct small groups to develop a set of communication rules for their small group. These rules will serve as a code of conduct for acceptable behaviors and group operating procedures. Some things to consider are:

- What should a member do if he or she cannot attend a meeting? What are acceptable reasons for absences, if anything?
- Who is going to organize the agenda for our meetings?
- What do we expect group members to do/have ready for meetings?
- How will we manage conflict?

Students should be given 2 weeks to complete their activities and provide the instructor with a written report that summarizes activities, provides pictures of the group's experiences, and details the group's set of communication rules. Ideally, groups should present their experiences and highlight what they learned about other group members by engaging in shared experiences.

Additional assignment: Instructors may wish to use the team's communication rules as a grading rubric for team assignments. The rules may also be used for peer evaluation should the instructor decide to include team member evaluation of other team members.

Adapted from: McBride, M. C. (2006). "—ing" Project: Encouraging cohesion in small groups. *Communication Teacher, 20*(2), 53–56.

Exercise #5

Ellingson (2003) provides extensive work on the backstage communication processes of interdisciplinary teams. Pair students or establish several small groups in the classroom. Provide students with a handout of the table below. Instruct students to review each verbal behavior by sharing their own examples and then discussing whether or not the communication enhances or decreases opportunities for interdisciplinary collaboration among team members.

Table 8.4 Characteristics of Team Communication

Verbal Behavior	Definition
Request for clarification	Questioning each other about information about the patient being discussed
Request for opinion	Questions that solicit opinions on issues such as patient/ caregiver affect, depression *or* to confirm their own opinion *or* initiate discussion about how team members can resolve problem
Offering of information	Information shared that would provide practical assistance to other team member's communication with patient

(continued)

Table 8.4 (*continued*)

Verbal Behavior	Definition
Offering of impressions	Descriptive statements that share positive or negative impressions and opinions about patients/caregivers
Request for reinforcement of a message	Asking team member to repeat information already mentioned to the patient.
Clinical progress	Asking team members which patients had been seen and by whom *or* stating when the patient had been seen.
Life talk—Patients	Sharing outside patient information such as life history/experiences
Life talk—Team members	Sharing outside personal information such as life experiences
Troubles talk	Complaining about scheduling, limited resources, behavior of outside clinic staff
Handling interruptions	Patient care related or personal and family concerns. Service interruptions—e.g., nurse listening to caregiver concerns, taking phone calls from caregivers for lengths of time
Formal reporting	Primarily diagnostic (such as patient name, age, diagnosis, medical history, primary care physician), "Yes" and "No" responses
Organizational Issues	Comments about health care system, such as billing, costs, insurance issues

Adapted from: Ellingson, L. L. (2003). Interdisciplinary health care teamwork in the clinic backstage. *Journal of Applied Communication Research, 31*, 93–117.

COMMUNICATION ROLE REVERSAL

Exercise #1

http://kilmanndiagnostics.com/taketki.html
The Thomas-Kilmann Conflict Mode Instrument (referred to as the TKI) is a tool that assesses a person's behavior during conflict. There is a charge for this instrument.

Exercise #2

See also:
Adams, T. (2005). Vote red, vote green: A class exercise in groupthink dialectics. *The Florida Communication Journal, 333*(1), 15–22.

9

COMMUNICATING SELF-CARE NEEDS

Nurses are in a uniquely vulnerable position in the practice of palliative care. Not only do they witness the suffering of patients and their families—and also the anxiety and grief of their fellow palliative care team members—but they also suffer their own pain and grief. They are both participant and observer in what is arguably life's most stressful crisis: the transition from life to death. An inseparable relationship often exists between the suffering person and the professional who provides care while witnessing that suffering, as each party is vulnerable to the other (Ferrell & Coyle, 2008). Thus, nurses frequently must step back and ask the question: "Whose suffering am I experiencing?" (p. 87). Particularly when patients face discouraging diagnoses, nurses must strive to find that delicate balance in continuing to care for the patient while also acknowledging the patient's and family's—as well as their own—fears.

In their book on the nature of suffering and the goals of nursing, Ferrell & Coyle (2008) note that all nurses encounter suffering on a daily basis; yet, palliative care, hospice, and oncology nurses are particularly vulnerable to patient suffering. The relief of suffering is central to oncology nursing: " … working with cancer patients means 'being there' for people in their most private moments of suffering and responding to the heights and depths of their responses to this suffering" (Cohen & Sarter, 1992, p. 1485).

Much of the suffering nurses must face is caused not only by their stress from witnessing the suffering of others but also by the stress of witnessing (and occasionally being forced to deliver) medically futile care (Ferrell and Coyle, 2008). Nurses across care settings have identified "aggressive care" and "aggressive care denying palliative care" as the most common sources of their distress in caring for critically ill and dying patients and their families (Ferrell, 2006). Conflicts and feelings of moral distress related to futile care occur between patients and their families, between patients/families and their medical teams, or even within the medical team itself. This experience of distress is linked to **burnout**—nurses' emotional exhaustion related to the frequency of incidents regarding care seen as futile or unbeneficial (Meltzer & Huckaby, 2004). Thus, there is much need for nurses to be able to self-reflect, engage peer support, and permit themselves to grieve in the face of the stress of witnessing these futile care incidents (Stairs, 2000). We close this volume by emphasizing the importance of self-care, encouraging nurses to be aware of their feelings and to communicate these feelings to others.

Just as the patient and family need to tell their story, to have it be heard by others as a way of making meaning out of what they experience and witness, nurses also need opportunities to share their experiences and emotions with others. It is essential that nurses be aware of and deal with their own grief and sense of loss when a patient receives a terminal prognosis or when a patient succumbs to disease (Baird, 2010; Ferrell & Coyle, 2008; Levine & Levine, 1999, as cited in Baird). For many nurses, there is often an inability to separate their professional and personal lives when loss is so prevalent (Ablett & Jones, 2007; Arnaert & Wainwright, 2009). Working conditions, inadequate preparation, lack of time to relax or grieve, and staff relationships contribute to workplace stress and necessitate communication and self-disclosure about the emotional labor of palliative care work (Barnes, 2001; McCloskey & Taggart, 2010). Commonly, nurses do not attend to self-care, and job stress emerges at home—impacting relationships and causing irritability, sleeplessness, and fatigue (McCloskey & Taggart, 2010).

When nurses are tired and overworked, they are unable to provide adequate care and to appreciate their role and relationships with patients and families. Inadequate self-care can lead to quicker emotional responses than normal, a tendency to overreact with clinical team members and family, and anger. The call button becomes easier to ignore, emotions become easier to tuck away and hide with busy clinical work, and withdrawing from clinical team members, patients, and families becomes a routine coping mechanism that results in burnout (Blomberg & Sahlberg-Blom, 2007). Some nurses feel that the only remedy is to call in sick, feeling guilty that they want to avoid work and momentarily escape daily pressures from their job (McCloskey & Taggart, 2010), or even worse, to leave the field of palliative care or nursing.

SPECIFIC STRESSORS IN PALLIATIVE NURSING

Nurses experience stress when working with family caregivers, during challenging clinical situations, and as a result of service delivery issues in their care setting (Brazil, Kassalainen, Ploeg, & Marshall, 2010). Since the nurse is always available and easily accessed, patients and families expect nurses to have competent communication skills and be able to provide answers to all inquiries about patient care (Arnaert & Wainwright, 2009). Given such high demands, negative feelings can emerge from personal inadequacy if nurses are not able to provide enough information and/or control the patient's symptoms (Keidel, 2002). The intimacy of nursing care also creates opportunities for nurses to become attached to patients and family members, often because they are similar to loved ones in their own lives or because a particular situation resonates with them (Ablett & Jones, 2007). Nurses face difficult situations as they struggle to be close to patients and families yet distance themselves from too much emotional involvement (Blomberg & Sahlberg-Blom, 2007). As family caregivers become responsible for home hospice care, nurses witness caregiver burden and patient neglect or abuse; they thus struggle with the competency of caregivers to provide care (Brazil et al., 2010).

Challenging clinical situations also reveal personal and situational variables that add to the amount of stress experienced by palliative care nurses (Hulbert & Morrison, 2006).

While palliative nurses have an awareness of their own mortality and spirituality (Ablett & Jones, 2007), clinical situations can require nurses to enact decisions that do not reflect their own choices or beliefs. Nurses encounter challenges related to patient decision making, particularly when a nurse feels the patient is at risk, as well as disagreements over the appropriateness of treatment between the provider and family (Brazil et al., 2010). Some of the more uncomfortable circumstances include families who refute the patient's advance directives and insist that staff do "everything" to save the patient's life. Family complexities can involve working with ex-family members, dysfunctional family systems, and requests to conceal the type of care being offered (hospice/palliative) (Gentry, 2008). Nurses also struggle to impact care for patients when no family is present and little is known about the patient's life (Brazil et al., 2010).

Finally, nurses work in the dysfunction of hospital systems or hospice agencies that sustain a complex communication climate that leaves little to no time or energy for self-care. Nurses feel stress when workloads are high, as a result of shift work, or an effect of staff shortages (Ablett & Jones, 2007). Although continuing education training is regularly offered, stress can be high for nurses who learn a great deal from on-the-job training (Arnaert & Wainwright, 2009). The organizational structure that dictates service delivery routines can result in a lack of clear roles, professional boundaries that aren't clearly defined, and multiprofessional work that is difficult to accomplish (Gupta & Woodman, 2010). Table 9.1 provides suggestions for how to build a collaborative partnership among peers.

Burnout and compassion fatigue are typical responses to the stressors that palliative care nurses confront daily (Vachon & Huggard, 2010). Nurses experience emotional exhaustion, feelings of cynicism and detachment from the job (depersonalization), and a sense of ineffectiveness and the lack of personal accomplishment (Maslach, 2003; Maslach & Leiter, 2008; Maslach, Schaufeli, & Leiter, 2001). Symptoms of burnout can be found at the physical, psychological, occupational, and social levels. **Compassion fatigue**—the physical and spiritual exhaustion that comes from compassionate caregiving, particularly in futile care—manifests in symptoms closely related to those of posttraumatic stress disorder; in contrast to burnout, however, nurses with compassion fatigue can still care and be involved.

Because of the occupational hazards of burnout and compassion fatigue, Vachon and Huggard (2010) stress the importance of self-care for oncology and palliative care

Table 9.1 Ways to Build a Collabortive Partnership

- Work collaboratively by making suggestions to others
- Share information with others
- Continually teach others (nurses and informal caregivers) about hospice/palliative care
- Adopt a nonjudgmental approach (don't be pushy!)

Used with permission from: Arnaert, A., and Wainwright, M. (2009). Providing care and sharing expertise: Reflections of nurse-specialists in palliative home care. *Palliative and Supportive Care*, 7(3), 357–364.

nurses. Vachon (2008) notes that as oncology nurses educate cancer patients about the importance of wellness strategies, they should take their own advice and integrate wellness changes in their own lives. Puchalski (2008) suggests that the practice of compassionate presence (see also Chapter 4) lessens the likelihood of burnout and compassion fatigue—if health care professionals are trained to be compassionate, burnout is likely to be diminished.

REALIZING THE NEED FOR SELF-CARE

Nurses can help prevent caregiver burnout and compassion fatigue by knowing their own physical and emotional limits, realizing the need for self-care, and acknowledging

Table 9.2 Self-Care Planning

Physical Stress—Solutions
    Stretching neck and shoulders
    Practice deep breathing
    Use audio recordings to assist with relaxation
    Exercise—walkingListening to music

Emotional/cognitive
    Explore "helper grief" by expressing feelings through talk, paint, music, dance, art, writing.
    Time alone, to meditate, pray
    Develop a daily release ritual
    Seek comfort (bath tub, pets, praying, etc.)

Relational
    Set and maintain relational boundaries
    Identify your own needs
    Ask for what you need
    Set healthy limits with others

Spiritual
    Get in touch with nature
    Pray
    Meditate
    Read sacred or inspirational material
    Participate in holy sacraments
    Interact with children

RED FLAGS FOR NOT HAVING LIMITS:
    Giving out your home phone or personal cell phone number
    Extended visits
    Thinking about the patient/family after work
    Extending professional relationship to a personal relationship
    Sharing more personal information than usual

Used with permission from: Jones, S. H. (2005). A self-care plan for hospice workers. *American Journal of Hospice & Palliative Medicine, 22*(2), 125–128.

Table 9.3 Actions Often Connected with Stress

Physical
    Excessive tension
    Becoming accident prone
    Teeth grinding
    Restlessness
Mental
    Forgetfulness
    Poor concentration
    Confusion
    "Spacing out"
Emotional
    Pronounced mood swings
    Frequent irritability
    Crying spells
    Lashing out
Spiritual
    Chronic cynicism
    Needing to "prove" oneself
    Apathy
    Loss of direction in life

Used with permission from: Davidhizar, R., & Shearer, R. (1996). Using humor to cope with stress in home care. *Home Healthcare Nurse, 14*(10), 825–830.

their own feelings about dying and death (Sherman, 2004). Puchalski and McSkimming (2006) described interventions to promote healing environments in hospitals. Such interventions focused on the spirituality of health care professionals and included brown bag lunches and workshops on spiritual care as well as mindfulness meditation and mindfulness-based stress reduction (mindfulness is discussed briefly in the next paragraphs and more fully in Chapter 4). See Table 9.2 for self-care planning tips.

Because of the emphasis of mindfulness on self-care, compassion, and healing, it is seen as a relevant intervention in promoting nurses' attempts to care for themselves in their stressful environments. Mindfulness-based stress reduction in particular is a helpful self-care strategy for nurses (Mackenzie, Poulin, and Seidman-Carlson, 2006). One way to achieve the deep personal and interpersonal understanding and sensitivity required of nurses is by practicing the tenets of mindfulness such as awareness of the moment, nonjudging acceptance, patience, and kindness (Henry & Henry, 2003; Mackenzie, Poulin, and Seidman-Carlson, 2006). As noted earlier, nurses are faced with even greater stress and burnout due to an increasingly complex health care system and sicker patients. Indicators of stress are summarized in Table 9.3. Several studies have demonstrated reduced stress, increased coping, and improved empathy in health care providers after they have completed a mindfulness-based stress reduction program (Beddoe & Murphy, 2004; Galantino, Baime, Maguire, Szapary, & Farrar, 2005).

Bruce and Davies (2005) in particular found that staff and volunteers at a Zen hospice who practiced mindfulness meditation reported more empathy and attentiveness to their patients, such that it was easier for them to discuss death with their patients and to better cope with patients' imminent deaths. Mindfulness-based stress reduction for nurse stress and burnout has resulted in more relaxation and self-care and improvement in both work and family relationships (Cohen-Katz, Wiley, Capuano, Baker, & Shapiro, 2004, 2005a, 2005b).

Structured reflection—an insightful analysis of one's own experiences, thoughts, and feelings—is a component of communication said to occur at the **intrapersonal level** or within the person herself. The essential need for palliative care nurses' self-care involves knowing oneself thoroughly, understanding one's motivations, being aware of one's special talents and abilities but also of one's liabilities, and being able to put this self-knowledge to work in effective interactions with patients, families, and other members of the health care team. The attributes of mindfulness, presence, empathy, and deep listening, described in preceding chapters, are paramount to achieving this self-knowledge and must be nurtured by effective palliative care nurses. Developing such attributes also requires a keen awareness of one's thoughts, feelings, attitudes, beliefs, and values. By becoming more self-aware, nurses can help to better manage those stressors in their work environment that contribute to burnout, compassion fatigue, suffering, and grief.

One of the concepts most useful to self-care is **self-compassion**, the ability to feel compassion for oneself (Neff, 2003a, 2003b; Neff, Kirkpatrick, & Rude, 2007). Self-compassion as: "being open to and moved by one's own suffering, experiencing feelings of caring and kindness towards oneself, taking an understanding, nonjudgmental attitude toward one's inadequacies and failures, and recognizing that one's experience is part of the common human experience" (Neff, 2003a, pp. 85–102). Elements of self-compassion include common humanity (shared human experience), self-kindness (which is different from self-pity), and mindfulness (Neff, 2003a.) Self-compassion requires a fair, objective awareness of one's emotions; it includes the process of confronting rather than avoiding painful thoughts and emotions. Developing an awareness of and appreciation for self-compassion is helpful not only for palliative care nurses' self-care; self-compassion also may permit nurses to feel more compassionately toward their patients (Heffernan, Griffin, McNulty, & Fitzpatrick, 2010).

Ferrell and Coyle (2008) point out that nurses' spirituality may influence their responses to suffering in ways that are similar to how patients and families experience their own spirituality in facing terminal illness: "…nurses frequently struggle in an attempt to balance the patient and family's faith with their own and to balance personal and professional values" (p. 96). Yet in a study conducted by Ferrell, Virani, Grant, Coyne, & Uman (2000), nurses initially did not report their own spirituality as being linked to their experiences of suffering. Ferrell et al. (2000) believe that this suggests that nurses may have been trained to separate their own faith and personhood from their role as nurse—that their education may be one that separates mind, body, and spirit (teaching that is also damaging to patient care).

Sherman (2010) also advocates that palliative care nurses should engage in self-reflection and self-healing and should explore their own values and attitudes toward death. She further states that nurses have the potential to provide spiritual care to their patients, yet the ongoing care of the dying may drain their energy and uncover spiritual issues—thus, there is a need for spiritual growth and renewal as part of staff support. A study by Hunnibell, Reed, Quinn-Griffin, & Fitzpatrick (2008) found that hospice and palliative care and oncology nurses measured high on a scale for self-transcendence, which is the awareness of one's spiritual self, one's relationship to others and to a higher being, and finding meaning and purpose in life.

Self-compassion is also linked to **emotional intelligence** in nurses—the ability to recognize and to manage emotions. Emotional intelligence is useful in potentially enhancing patient care as well as maintaining nurses' emotional health while also preventing burnout (Davies, Jenkins, & Mabbett, 2010). Emotional intelligence creates self-awareness, allows nurses to control their emotions, enhances assessment, and promotes palliative care and leadership (Davies et al., 2010). The clinical setting of palliative care requires a high level of emotional intelligence in order to foster different coping strategies to prevent burnout. Informal team support can play a pivotal role in sustaining emotional intelligence in such a demanding clinical environment (Davies et al., 2010).

Borneman and Brown-Saltzman (2010) stress the need for self-care for dealing with grief, particularly since nurses are at great risk for turning away from feeling—most nurses receive little mentoring, debriefing, or counseling after their first death experience. Scant research has looked at the effect on nurses of cumulative losses and many years of witnessing suffering. As a result, Borneman and Brown-Saltzman (2010) recommend: "healthcare needs healing rituals for all its health-care professionals" (p. 682). They point out one example of such a healing ritual, a renewal program known as the "Circle of Caring" which is a self-care weekend retreat integrating spirituality, the arts, and community building.

In discussing palliative care nurses' inevitable loss, suffering, grief, and bereavement, Potter (2010) poses the need for nurses to self-assess: where am I (the nurse) on the journey toward healing? In conflict with traditional nurse training in which nurses are encouraged to maintain composure and not to express emotion, Potter advocates that "constructive self-disclosure of feelings by the nurse may role-model to others a healthy process of acknowledging and resolving the suffering of loss" (p. 208). Examining their own personal experiences with death helps nurses to better understand their fears and anxieties surrounding it. Potter (2010) believes that nurses must engage in self-care by: getting support from colleagues; ensuring time for self; maintaining healthy boundaries with patients/family; and tending to their physical emotional, and spiritual needs.

OPPORTUNITIES TO COMMUNICATE
SELF-CARE NEEDS

The team-based structure of palliative care can and should provide both informal and formal environments for nurses to discuss their feelings, emotions, worries, experiences, regrets, hopes, and anxieties related to workplace stress (Blomberg & Sahlberg-Blom, 2007; Wittenberg-Lyles, Oliver, Demiris, Baldwin, & Regehr, 2008). While clinical **frontstage communication** and activities include rounds and meetings with patients and families, nurses also engage in **backstage communication** and activities that occur in hallway conversations; before, during, and after team meetings; and over lunch (Ellingson, 2003; Lewin & Reeves, 2011). These encounters, both planned and unplanned in front and backstage, facilitate impression management between colleagues and either legitimate healthy changes in the workplace or simply perpetuate them (Lewin & Reeves, 2011; Wittenberg-Lyles, Parker Oliver, Demiris, & Cunningham, 2011). The nurse's station is a regular site for planned and unplanned backstage communication.

Communication between colleagues, away from families and patients, is where emotional work has the potential to occur. The team environment allows nurses to vent workplace stress, share difficult patient/family situations, seek and receive confirmation for care choices, and share emotions (Goldsmith, Wittenberg-Lyles, Rodriguez, & Sanchez-Reilly, 2010; Wittenberg-Lyles, 2005; Wittenberg-Lyles, Gee, Parker Oliver, & Demiris, 2009). Nurses naturally rely on other nurses to support care decisions, especially with regard to pain management (Arnaert & Wainwright, 2009). Ad hoc as well as planned backstage communication can and should allow nurses to work on overcoming problems with other staff members (Lewin & Reeves, 2011).

Team meetings that take place prior to or after patient rounds, or as part of interdisciplinary team structure, can be used to create an appropriate interpersonal climate for sharing and releasing the emotional burden of palliative care work. An **interpersonal climate** is the feeling or emotional mood that is created between people and can include defensive or supportive communication (Wood, 2004). **Supportive communication** can foster working relationships that contribute to self-care. The way we relay messages to one another can foster a supportive communication climate. To become more effective at contributing thoughts on clinical decisions, nurses should engage in language that describes instead of evaluates. Think about the difference between these two messages: (1) "You shouldn't have done that." (2) "You seem to have more to do today than usual." The first statement evaluates what someone else has done, while the second statement merely describes. The simple difference in these two messages is the outcome that results in a defensive or supportive communication climate. To create supportive climates, nurses need to remain open to other points of view and engage in open, honest, unpremeditated communication (Wood, 2004). Ideas for coping strategies can be found in Table 9.4.

Using "I statements" as discussed in Chapter 4 is one way nurses can convey their point of view while remaining open to hearing other opinions. For example, "The way I tend to see the issue is…" is much better than saying "I've already decided the best way to handle this patient is…" Team discussions should also be problem oriented and focus on solutions rather than blame. During clinical rounds and team meetings, nurses should express empathy with other team members and confirm that their thoughts and feelings are a concern to the entire team. Teams possess powerful

Table 9.4 Coping Strategies

- Do an honest self-assessment to objectively evaluate your work place
- Monitor the tendency to get overinvolved
- Ask yourself whose needs you're trying to meet
- Consciously avoid viewing yourself as the "savior" of the terminally ill patient
- See things from the family's perspective rather than feeling their emotions
- Feed your spiritual side, whatever that means to you
- Keep interested in and challenged by your patients' spiritual, emotional, and physical problems
- Set attainable goals for yourself, and reward yourself when you reach them
- Learn to say no and to ask for what you need
- Try to see each task as a challenge rather than a hassle
- Adapt your job rather than accepting it as handed to you
- Cultivate a supportive and enjoyable social network
- Share your distress and get support from friends, but do not discuss your work problems with everybody
- Talk over your concerns with a supportive hospice staff member
- Strive for balance in your family and professional life
- Combat stress by eating healthy and getting adequate sleep and exercise

Used with permission from: Keidel, G. C. (2002) Burnout and compassion fatigue among hospice caregivers. *American Journal of Hospice and Palliative Care, 19*(3), 204.

potential for reflective practice in order to improve their own self-care experience and sustainability as health care workers (Goldsmith et al., 2010).

Nurses should connect with other team members to form support groups, share stories and experiences, keep a journal, and recognize their positive, individual contributions to patient care (Sherman, 2010). **Offstage** is a third location that coworkers can experience away from their work place (Lewin & Reeves, 2011). Spending time in a new context with the people one experiences so much pressure and loss with can be a wonderful reframing and provide people access to new characteristics and skills possessed by their coworkers.

Even in the pressure-filled spaces of the workplace, creative experiences of decompression with teammates can be created. Carry-in meals for sharing, short yoga stretches before lunch, and relieving the busiest nurse on the floor are small opportunities to offer and experience self-care in the course of a busy day. "In caring for people with life-threatening and progressive illness, nurses must remain in tune with their own spiritual needs, healing themselves as well as others" (Sherman, 2010, p. 30).

FOCUSED SELF-REFLECTION

Once aware of the need for focused self-care, nurses can engage in focused reflection by journaling about their thoughts and feelings, seeking support from friends and colleagues, prioritizing celebrations such as birthdays and holidays, and engaging in other forms of distraction such as reading, exercise, or vacation (Anewalt, 2009). **Journaling** is a form of expressive writing that provides opportunity for reflection (Lauterbach & Hentz, 2005). Expressive writing exercises require participants to reflect on their deepest thoughts and feelings about an event or series of events (Sexton et al., 2009). Most nurses are exposed to journaling and reflective activities during undergraduate nursing education. Journaling can reveal interdisciplinary relationships and team processes and impact patient care and professional development (Makowsky et al., 2009). Clinician stories about palliative care reveal deep, intimate relationships with patients and families and spiritual strengthening, both fostering the strength to control emotions at the bedside and devotion and loyalty to special patients (Wittenberg-Lyles, Greene, & Sanchez-Reilly, 2007).

The ability to formulate a good story, in which both successes and losses are recognized to create meaning and understanding, can also yield several health benefits (Graybeal, Sexton, & Pennebaker, 2002). Writing has biological effects, including enhanced immune systems, decreased medical health markers among individuals with chronic health problems, and reduction in physiological stress (Pennebaker, 2004). Additionally, research has shown that an individual's mood changes after writing (Pennebaker, 2004).

Importantly, self-care should be modeled and encouraged by nurse leaders and nurse managers. Managers can mediate communication between clinical staff and encourage a supportive communication climate. Early-career nurses need to learn to emphasize self-care alongside clinical work obligations, and managers should provide protected time for these nurses to incorporate self-care into their daily routine. Feeling balanced involves having self-awareness, active coping, feeling spiritually enriched, and setting boundaries between professional and personal life (Rose & Glass, 2009).

Ferrell & Coyle (2008) advocate that nurses' suffering needs to be addressed in education and research: "Schools of nursing and continuing education programs can teach the skills of listening, responding to anguish, hearing 'why' questions, and in fundamentally re-envisioning what it means to be a nurse—perhaps even helping us return to our roots" (Ferrell & Coyle, 2008, p. 106). They cite physician Rachel Naomi Remen's work on how serving patients sustains nurses as health care providers, even in the face of suffering and death: "our service serves us as well as others. That which uses us strengthens us. Over time, fixing and helping are draining, depleting. Over time we burn out. Service is renewing. When we serve, our work itself will sustain us" (Remen, 1996, p. 24).

CHAPTER SUMMARY

The uniquely stressful environment of nursing and of palliative care nursing in particular makes self-care imperative. In this chapter, we have identified how communication at both the intrapersonal and interpersonal levels can facilitate such care. Intrapersonally, nurses can learn to be aware of their feelings, behaviors, and values through such practices as self-reflection and journaling. In this way, both self-compassion and emotional intelligence can be fostered—both of which help to prevent burnout and compassion fatigue. Spiritual awareness can also enhance a nurse's ability to cope with the suffering and death inevitably experienced in the context of palliative care nursing. Interpersonally, nurses and palliative care teams need to practice supportive rather than defensive communication behaviors in an effort to ameliorate the stressors in their work environments. Backstage, frontstage, and offstage communication can be utilized both to make other members of the health care team aware of one's self-care needs and to seek help for resolving those needs.

REFERENCES

Ablett, J. R., & Jones, R. S. (2007). Resilience and well-being in palliative care staff: A qualitative study of hospice nurses' experience of work. *Psychooncology, 16*(8), 733–740. doi: 10.1002/pon.1130

Anewalt, P. (2009). Fired up or burned out? Understanding the importance of professional boundaries in home health care and hospice. *Home Healthcare Nurse, 27*(10), 590–597.

Arnaert, A., & Wainwright, M. (2009). Providing care and sharing expertise: Reflections of nurse-specialists in palliative home care. [Research Support, Non-U.S. Gov't]. *Palliative & Supportive Care, 7*(3), 357–364. doi: 10.1017/S1478951509990290

Baird, P. (2010). Spiritual care interventions. In B. R. Ferrell & N. Coyle (Eds.), *Palliative Nursing* (3rd ed., pp. 663–672). New York: Oxford University Press.

Barnes, K. (2001). Staff stress in the children's hospice: Causes, effects and coping strategies. [Review]. *International Journal of Palliative Nursing, 7*(5), 248–254.

Beddoe, A. E., & Murphy, S. O. (2004). Does mindfulness decrease stress and foster empathy among nursing students? *Journal of Nursing Education, 43*, 305–312.

Blomberg, K., & Sahlberg-Blom, E. (2007). Closeness and distance: A way of handling difficult situations in daily care. *Journal of Clinical Nursing, 16*(2), 244–254. doi: JCN1503 [pii]10.1111/j.1365-2702.2005.01503.x

Borneman, T., & Brown-Saltzman, K. (2010). Meaning in illness. In B. R. Ferrell & N. Coyle (Eds.), *Palliative Care Nursing* (3rd ed., pp. 673–683). New York: Oxford University Press.

Brazil, K., Kassalainen, S., Ploeg, J., & Marshall, D. (2010). Moral distress experienced by health care professionals who provide home-based palliative care. *Social Science Medicine, 71*(9), 1687–1691. doi: S0277-9536(10)00600-3 [pii]10.1016/j.socscimed.2010.07.032

Bruce, A., & Davies, B., (2005). Mindfulness in hospice care: Practicing meditation-in-action. *Qualitative Health Research, 15*, 1329–1344.

Cohen, M. A. & Sarter, B. (1992). Love and work: Oncology nurses' view of the meaning of their work. *Oncology Nursing Forum, 19*, 1481–1486.

Cohen-Katz, J., Wiley, S. D., Capuano, T., Baker, D. M., & Shapiro, S. (2004). The effects of mindfulness-based stress reduction on nurse stress and burnout: A quantitative and qualitative study. *Holistic Nursing Practice, 18*(6), 302–308.

Cohen, Katz, J., Wiley, S. D., Capuano, T., Baker, D. M., & Shapiro, S. (2005a). The effects of mindfulness-based stress reduction on nurse stress and burnout, Part II: A quantitative and qualitative study. *Holistic Nursing Practice, 19*(1), 26–35.

Cohen-Katz, J., Wiley, S. D., Capuano, T., Baker, D. M., & Shapiro, S. (2005b). The effects of mindfulness-based stress reduction on nurse stress and burnout: A quantitative and qualitative study, Part III. *Holistic Nursing Practice, 19*(2), 78–86.

Coopman, S., & Wood, J. (2004). Student Companion for Wood's *Interpersonal Communication: Everyday Encounters* (p. 146, activity 7.1). Boston: Thomson Wadsworth.

Davidhizar, R., & Shearer, R. (1996). Using humor to cope with stress in home care. *Home Healthcare Nurse, 14*(10), 825–830

Davies, S., Jenkins, E., & Mabbett, G. (2010). Emotional intelligence: District nurses' lived experiences. *British Journal of Community Nursing, 15*(3), 141–146.

Ellingson, L. L. (2003). Interdisciplinary health care teamwork in the clinic backstage. *Journal of Applied Communication Research, 31*(2), 93–117.

Ferrell, B. R. (2006). Understanding the moral distress of nurses witnessing medically futile care. *Oncology Nursing Forum, 33,* 922–930.

Ferrell, B. R., & Coyle, N. (2008). *The Nature of Suffering and the Goals of Nursing.* New York: Oxford University Press.

Ferrell, B. R., Virani, R., Grant, M., Coyne, P., & Uman, G. (2000). Beyond the Supreme Court decision: Nursing perspectives on end-of-life care. *Oncology Nursing Forum, 27,* 445–455.

Galantino, M. L., Baime, M., Maguire, M., Szapary, P. O., & Farrar, J. T. (2005). Short communication: Association of psychological and physiological measures of stress in health-care professionals during an 8-week mindfulness meditation program: Mindfulness in practice. *Stress and Health, 21,* 255–261.

Gentry, J. (2008). "Don't tell her she's on hospice": Ethics and pastoral care for families who withhold medical information. *Journal of Pastoral Care & Counseling, 62*(5 Suppl.), 421–426.

Goldsmith, J., Wittenberg-Lyles, E., Rodriguez, D., & Sanchez-Reilly, S. (2010). Interdisciplinary geriatric and palliative care team narratives: Collaboration practices and barriers. *Social Science & Medicine, 20,* 93–104. doi: 10.1177/1049732309355287.

Graybeal, A., Sexton, J., & Pennebaker, J. W. (2002). The role of story-making in disclosure writing: The psychometrics of narrative. *Psychology and Health, 17*(5), 571–581.

Gupta, V., & Woodman, C. (2010). Managing stress in a palliative care team. *Paediatric Nursing, 22*(10), 14–18.

Halifax, J. (1999, October). *Being with dying. Contemplations on death and dying.* Presentation at the Art of Dying III Conference: Spiritual, Scientific and Practical Approaches to Living and Dying by the New York Open Center and Tibet House, New York.

Heffernan, M., Griffin, M. T. Q., McNulty, R., & Fitzpatrick, J. J. (2010). Self-compassion and emotional intelligence in nurses. *International Journal of Nursing Practice, 16,* 366–373.

Henry, J. D., & Henry, L. S. (2003). The self-caring nurse: Strategies for avoiding compassion fatigue and burnout. *Colorado Nurse, 103,* 29.

Hulbert, N. J., & Morrison, V. L. (2006). A preliminary study into stress in palliative care: Optimism, self-efficacy and social support. *Psychology, health & medicine, 11*(2), 246–254. doi: 10.1080/13548500500266664

Hunnibell, L., Reed, P., Quinn-Griffin, M., & Fitzpatrick, J. (2008). Self-transcendence and burnout in hospice and oncology nurses. *Journal of Hospice and Palliative Nursing, 10*(3), 172–179.

Johns, C. (1995). Framing learning through reflection within Carper's fundamental ways of knowing in nursing. *Journal of Advanced Nursing, 22,* 227.

Jones, S. H. (2005). A self-care plan for hospice workers. *American Journal of Hospice & Palliative Medicine, 22*(2), 125–128.

Keidel, G. C. (2002). Burnout and compassion fatigue among hospice caregivers. *American Journal of Hospice and Palliative Care, 19*(3), 200–205.

Lauterbach, S. S., & Hentz, P. B. (2005). Journaling to learn: A strategy in nursing education for developing the nurse as person and person as nurse. *International Journal for Human Caring, 9*(1), 29–35.

Levine, S., & Levine, O. (1999). *The Grief Process.* Boulder, CO: Sounds True.

Lewin, S., & Reeves, S. (2011). Enacting "team" and "teamwork": Using Goffman's theory of impression management to illuminate interprofessional practice on hospital wards. [Research Support, Non-U.S. Gov't]. *Social Science & Medicine, 72*(10), 1595–1602. doi: 10.1016/j.socscimed.2011.03.037

Mackenzie, C. S., Poulin, P. A., & Seidman-Carlson, R. (2006). A brief mindfulness-based stress reduction intervention for nurses and nurse aides. *Applied Nursing Research, 19,* 105–109.

Makowsky, M. J., Schindel, T. J., Rosenthal, M., Campbell, K., Tsuyuki, R. T., & Madill, H. M. (2009). Collaboration between pharmacists, physicians and nurse practitioners: A qualitative investigation of working relationships in the inpatient medical setting. *Journal of Interprofessional Care, 23*(2), 169–184. doi: 908923904 [pii]10.1080/13561820802602552

Maslach, C. (2003). Job burnout: New directions in research and intervention. *Current Directions in Psychological Science, 12,* 189–192.

Maslach, C., & Leiter, M. P. (2008). Early predictors of job burnout and engagement. *Journal of Applied Psychology, 93,* 498–512.

Maslach, C., Schaufeli, W. G., & Leiter, M. P. (2001). Job burnout. *Annual Review of Psychology, 52,* 397–422.

McCloskey, S., & Taggart, L. (2010). How much compassion have I left? An exploration of occupational stress among children's palliative care nurses. *International Journal of Palliative Nursing, 16*(5), 233–240.

Meltzer, L. S., & Huckabay, L. M. (2004). Critical care nurses' perceptions of futile care and its effect on burnout. *American Journal of Critical Care, 13,* 202–208.

Neff, K. D. (2003a). Self-compassion: An alternative conceptualization of a healthy attitude toward oneself. *Self & Identity, 2,* 85–102.

Neff, K. D. (2003b). Development and validation of a scale to measure self-compassion. *Self & Identity, 2,* 223–250.

Neff, K. D., Kirkpatrick, K., & Rude, S. S. (2007). Self-compassion and its link to adaptive psychological functioning. *Journal of Research in Personality, 41,* 139–154.

Pennebaker, J. W. (2004). *Writing to Heal: A Guided Journal for Recovering From Trauma and Emotional Upheaval.* Oakland, CA: New Harbinger Press.

Potter, M. (2009). Loss, suffering, grief & bereavement. In M. Matzo & D. W. Sherman, *Palliative Care Nursing: Quality Care to the End of Life* (p. 209). New York: Springer Publishing Company, Inc.

Potter, M. L. (2010). Loss, suffering, grief, and bereavement. In M. Matzo & D. W. Sherman (Eds.), *Palliative Care Nursing: Quality Care to the End of Life* (3rd ed., pp. 199–233). New York: Springer.

Puchalski, C. M. (2008, December). *Compassionate healthcare systems: Building resiliency and communities of support.* Presented at Spirituality and Healing in Medicine: The Resiliency Factor Boston. Harvard Medical School and Massachusetts General Hospital, Benson-Henry Institute for Mind Body Medicine, Boston.

Puchalski, C. M., & McSkimming, S. (2006). Creating healing environments. *Health Progress, May–June,* 30–35.

Remen, R. N. (1996). In the service of life. *Noetic Sciences Review, 37,* 24–26.

Rose, J., & Glass, N. (2009). An investigation of emotional wellbeing and its relationship to contemporary nursing practice. [Research Support, Non-U.S. Gov't]. *Collegian, 16*(4), 185–192.

Saakvitne, K., Pearlman, L., & and Staff of the Traumatic Stress Institute (1996). *Transforming the Pain: A Workbook on Vicarious Traumatization for Helping Professionals Who Work With Traumatized Clients.* New York: W.W. Norton.

Sexton, J., Pennebaker, J. W., Holzmueller, C., Wu, A. W., Berenholtz, S., Swoboda, S., et al. (2009). Care for the caregiver: Benefits of expressive writing for nurses in the United States. *Progress in Palliative Care, 17*(6), 307–312.

Sherman, D. W. (2004). Nurses' stress and burnout: How to care for yourself when caring for patients and their families experiencing life-threatening illness. *American Journal of Nursing, 104*(5), 48–57.

Sherman, D. W. (2010). Culture and spirituality as domains of quality palliative care. In Matzo, M., & Sherman, D. W. (Eds.), *Palliative Care Nursing: Quality Care to the End of Life* (3rd ed., pp. 3–38). New York: Springer.

Stairs, J. (2000). *Listening for the Soul: Pastoral Care and Spiritual Direction*. Minneapolis, MN: Augsburg Fortress Publishers.

Vachon, M. L. S. (2008). Meaning, spirituality, and wellness in cancer survivors. *Seminars in Oncology Nursing Issue Survivorship, 24*, 218–225.

Vachon, M. L. S., & Huggard, J. (2010). The experience of the nurse in end-of-life care in the 21st century: Mentoring the next generation. In B. R. Ferrell & N. Coyle (Eds.), *Palliative Care Nursing* (3rd ed., pp. 1131–1155). New York: Oxford University Press.

Wittenberg-Lyles, E. (2005). Information sharing in interdisciplinary team meetings: An evaluation of hospice goals. *Qualitative Health Research, 15*(10), 1377–1391. doi: 15/10/1377 [pii]10.1177/1049732305282857

Wittenberg-Lyles, E., Gee, G. C., Parker Oliver, D., & Demiris, G. (2009). What patients and families don't hear: Backstage communication in hospice interdisciplinary team meetings. *Journal of Housing for Elderly, 23*, 92–105.

Wittenberg-Lyles, E., Greene, K., & Sanchez-Reilly, S. (2007). The palliative power of story-telling: Using published narratives as a teaching tool in end-of-life care. *Journal of Hospice & Palliative Nursing, 9*(4), 198–205.

Wittenberg-Lyles, E., Oliver, D. P., Demiris, G., Baldwin, P., & Regehr, K. (2008). Communication dynamics in hospice teams: Understanding the role of the chaplain in interdisciplinary team collaboration. *Journal of Palliative Medicine, 11*(10), 1330–1335. doi: 10.1089/jpm.2008.0165

Wittenberg-Lyles, E., Parker Oliver, D., Demiris, G., & Cunningham, C. (2011). Sharing atrocity stories in hospice: A study of niceness message strategies in interdisciplinary team meetings. *Progress in Palliative Care, 19*(4), 172–176.

Wood, J. (2004). *Interpersonal communication: Everyday encounters* (4th ed.). Belmont, CA: Thomson Wadsworth.

Recommended Additional Reading:

Anewalt, P. (2009). Fired up or burned out? Understanding the importance of professional boundaries in home health care and hospice. *Home Healthcare Nurse, 27(10)*, 590–597.

Jasper, M. (2003). *Beginning Reflective Practice: Foundations in Nursing and Health Care*. Cheltenham, UK: Nelson Thornes.

Pennebaker, J. W. (1997). *Opening up: The Healing Power of Expressing Emotions*. New York: Guilford Press.

Pennebaker, J. W. (2004). *Writing to Heal: A Guided Journal for Recovering From Trauma and Emotional Upheaval*. Oakland, CA: New Harbinger Press.

DISCUSSION QUESTIONS

1. Identify factors in palliative care settings that make self-care of special importance for nursing.
2. What are strategies for nurses to better communicate their self-care needs?
3. What strategies can organizations initiate to create environments that support self-care of staff?

EDUCATOR RESOURCES AND MATERIALS

Activity 1

Identify three to five people or things that are important to you. When was the last time you called that person? When did you last spend quality time with that person? When was the last time you did that thing? How are you currently caring for yourself? What needs to change?

Activity 2

Make a list of the ways that you can tell that you are carrying too much loss. Think about how stress impacts your body (e.g., sleep/eating patterns), your attitude (e.g., moodiness, depression), and your behavior (e.g, irritability).

Activity 3

Devote one team meeting a month to reflective rounds. Ask team members to bring a journal and devote a half hour to a prompted reflective writing exercise (*Alternatively*, these exercises can be done individually). Options include:

1. Describe a time when you were angry. Identify the clinical team members involved, their reactions, how that made you feel, and what you did. Reflect on the chapter's discussion of supportive communication—what changes could you have made to your own communication to help foster support?
2. Identify the most supportive clinical team member on your team. Describe your interactions with this person. How does this person support your own clinical work? What is his or her most admirable communication quality? Write a statement that conveys how much he or she means to you (*Alternatively*, you could send them a note telling them!).
4. Describe your most memorable patient. Identify the significance of this patient in terms of communication (hint: you may need to use communication concepts talked about in previous chapters). Was a supportive communication climate in place? If so, identify aspects of the climate and provide examples. If not, how could things have been changed to improve the communication climate?
4. Sit yourself in your favorite spot at work. How do you feel? What are your thoughts? What are you thinking about? Slowly expand from your surroundings. What else is happening around you? Go beyond your field of vision to reflect on aspects of the workplace that detract from your favorite place at work.

5. Describe the most important thing in your life. Describe the second and third most important things. Then the fourth and fifth most important things. (This was taken from: http://www.davidrm.com/thejournal/tjresources-exercises. php#journaling.)

Activity 4

To foster a supportive communication climate, have interprofessional team members engage in a buddy system once a quarter. The buddy system consists of two different interdisciplinary team members engaging in clinical work alongside each other as compared with different visits. Team members should make note of new knowledge gained from the experience, particularly in learning about their colleague's contribution to the plan of care or assessment. After a patient/family interaction, colleagues should debrief about the plan of care and compare their perceptions and goals of the interaction.

Activity 5: Journaling

- What are the qualities/characteristics that you are proud to possess? What do your friends love about you? Can you identify how you developed these traits?
- Who are the three most influential people in your life? Are they positive influences? Why?
- Why did you enter the nursing profession? Why are you still here? What needs to happen to keep you here?
- Some days we wonder if we make a difference, and some days we are certain that we do. Write about a connection you made with a resident/patient/client when you *knew* that you were making a difference.

Used with permission from: Stephanie Staples at http://www.nursetogether.com/Lifestyle/Lifestyle-Article/itemId/1119/Stressed-Nurses-Try-Journaling-.aspx

Activity 6

For each emotion listed below, identify a situation with a patient, family, and other health care provider that warranted expression of that emotion.

Table 9.5 Identifying Emotions

Emotion	Patient	Family	Other Provider
Anxiety			
Disappointment			
Embarrassment			
Passion			
Happiness			

Elaborate on one of the situations you identified by detailing the prominent themes of the experience and describe what changes you could make to your own communication.

Adapted from Coopman, S., & Wood, J. (2004). Student Companion for Wood's *Interpersonal Communication: Everyday Encounters* (p. 146, activity 7.1). Englewood Cliffs, NJ: Thomson Wadsworth.

Activity 7

Use the structured reflection model below to focus your attention on feelings about your actions with patients and the insights you have gained from these experiences:

Model for Structured Reflection

Reflective cue:

- Bring the mind home.
- Focus on a description of an experience that seems significant in some way.
- What particular issues seem significant to pay attention to?
- How were others feeling and why did they feel that way?
- What was I trying to achieve and did I respond effectively?
- What were the consequences of my actions on the patient, others, and myself?
- What factors influence the way I was/am feeling, thinking, and responding to this situation (personal, organizational, professional, cultural)?
- What knowledge did or might have informed me?
- To what extent did I act for the best and in tune with my values?
- How does this situation connect with previous experiences?
- Given the situation again, how might I respond differently?
- What would be the consequences of responding in new ways for the patient, others, and myself?
- What factors might constrain me from responding in new ways?
- How do I *now* feel about this experience?
- Am I more able to support myself and others better as a consequence?
- What insights have I gained?
- Am I more able to realize my vision as a lived reality?

Adapted from: Johns, C. (1995). Framing learning through reflection within Carper's fundamental ways of knowing in nursing. *Journal of Advanced Nursing, 22*, 227.

Activity 8

Below are some self-reflective questions to assist nurses in self-understanding of their loss, suffering, death, grief, and bereavement:

- What experiences have you had with death? Describe your earliest memory of death. Was anything positive about it? Was anything negative about it? Have you experienced what you would call a "good death?" Have you experienced what you would describe as a "bad death?"

- Can you picture yourself helping someone who is dying? How? What do you have to offer that is special and unique?
- Relate what you believe happens when someone dies. What do you fear about death? What do you fear about your own death?
- Assume you have just received news that you have been diagnosed with a terminal illness. What would be the most difficult things for you to have to give up during this time?
- How do you feel about cultural attitudes or behaviors that may be different from your own?

Used with permission from: Potter, M. (2009). Loss, suffering, grief & bereavement. In M. Matzo & D. W. Sherman, *Palliative Care Nursing: Quality Care to the End of Life* (p. 209). New York: Springer Publishing Company, Inc.

Box 9.1

Repeat the following phrases to encourage self-reflection and self-healing:

- May I offer my care and presence unconditionally, knowing that it may be met with gratitude, indifference, anger, or anguish.
- May I offer love, knowing that I cannot control the course of life's suffering or death.
- May I remain in ease and let go of my expectations.
- May I view my own suffering with compassion just as I do the suffering of others.
- May I be aware that my suffering does not limit my good heart.
- May I forgive myself for things left undone.
- May I forgive all who have hurt me.
- May those whom I have hurt forgive me.
- May all beings and I live and die in peace.

Used with permission from: Halifax, J. (1999, October). *Being with dying. Contemplations on death and dying.* Presentation at the Art of Dying III Conference: Spiritual, Scientific and Practical Approaches to Living and Dying by the New York Open Center and Tibet House, New York. Roshi Joan is the founder of Upaya Zen Center (www.upaya.org).

Box 9.2

Self-Care Assessment

Take a moment to consider the frequency with which you do the following acts of self-care. Rate using the scale below:

4 = Often, 3 = Sometimes, 2 = Rarely, 1 = Are you kidding? It never even crossed my mind!

(continued)

Box 9.2 (*Continued*)

Physical Self-Care

__ Eat regularly (no skipping meals).

__ Eat healthfully.

__ Exercise at least 30 minutes five times a week.

__ Sleep 7–9 hours per night.

__ Schedule regular preventive health care appointments.

__ Take time off when ill.

__ Get massages or other body work.

__ Do enjoyable physical work.

Psychological Self-Care

__ Read a good novel or other non-work-related literature.

__ Write in a journal.

__ Develop or maintain a hobby.

__ Make time for self-reflection.

__ Seek the services of a counselor or therapist.

__ Spend time outdoors.

__ Say "no" to extra responsibilities when stressed.

__ Allow the gift of receiving (instead of just giving).

Emotional Self-Care

__ Stay in contact with important people.

__ Spend time with the people whose company is most comfortable.

__ Practice supportive self-talk; speak kindly in internal thoughts.

__ Allow both tears and laughter to erupt spontaneously.

__ Play with children and animals.

__ Identify comforting activities and seek them out.

__ "Brag" to a trusted friend or family member; be proud of accomplishments.

__ Express anger in a constructive way.

Spiritual Self-Care

__ Make time for regular prayer, meditation, and reflection.

__ Seek community among friends, neighbors, or other gatherings.

__ Cherish optimism and hope.

__ Contribute to or participate in meaningful activities of choice.

__ Be open to inspiration.

__ Use ritual to celebrate milestones and to memorialize loved ones.

__ Be aware of the nontangibles of life.

__ Listen to or create music.

(*continued*)

Box 9.2 (*Continued*)

Workplace Self-Care

__ Take time to eat lunch.

__ Make time to address both the physical and emotional needs of residents.

__ Take time to chat and laugh with coworkers.

__ Seek regular supervision and mentoring.

__ Set limits with residents, families, and colleagues.

__ Find a project or task that is exciting and rewarding in which to be involved.

__ Decrease time spent comparing work performance with others.

__ Seek a support group—even if it is only one other person.

Results

To compute your score, add all sections together and compare to the following ranges:

121–160 You're a self-care guru! Share the wisdom with everyone around you.

81–120 You're on the right track. Get creative in the areas of least scoring.

41–80 Uh-oh. There's some work to do. Hunker down and focus on yourself.

f 40 Are you still reading this? You're about to self-destruct. Call 911!

Adapted from Saakvitne, K., Pearlman, L., & and Staff of the Traumatic Stress Institute (1996). *Transforming the Pain: A Workbook on Vicarious Traumatization for Helping Professionals Who Work With Traumatized Clients.* New York: W.W. Norton.

INDEX

273